Ex Líbrís

A SURVEY OF
SYMBOLIC LOGIC

BY

C. I. LEWIS

DOVER PUBLICATIONS, INC.
NEW YORK

Published in the United Kingdom by Constable and Company, Ltd., 10 Orange Street, London WC 2.

This Dover edition, first published in 1960, is a corrected republication of the original work with the omission of chapters V and VI. These chapters were omitted for the reasons stated in the author's Preface to Dover Edition. This work was originally published by the University of California Press in 1918.

Standard Book Number: 486-60643-0
Library of Congress Catalog Card Number: 60-51510

Manufactured in the United States of America
Dover Publications, Inc.
180 Varick Street
New York, N.Y. 10014

TABLE OF CONTENTS

PREFACE TO DOVER EDITION vii

PREFACE TO FIRST EDITION ix

CHAPTER I. THE DEVELOPMENT OF SYMBOLIC LOGIC.   1

    SECTION I. The Scope of Symbolic Logic. Symbolic Logic
and Logistic. Summary Account of their
Development 1

    SECTION II. Leibniz 5

    SECTION III. From Leibniz to De Morgan and Boole 18

    SECTION IV. De Morgan 37

    SECTION V. Boole 51

    SECTION VI. Jevons 72

    SECTION VII. Peirce 79

    SECTION VIII. Developments since Peirce 107

CHAPTER II. THE CLASSIC, OR BOOLE–SCHRÖDER AL-
GEBRA OF LOGIC 118

    SECTION I. General Character of the Algebra. The Postulates
and their Interpretation 118

    SECTION II. Elementary Theorems 122

    SECTION III. General Properties of Functions 132

    SECTION IV. Fundamental Laws of the Theory of Equations ... 144

    SECTION V. Fundamental Laws of the Theory of Inequations. 166

    SECTION VI. Note on the Inverse Operations, "Subtraction"
and "Division" 173

CHAPTER III. APPLICATIONS OF THE BOOLE–SCHRÖDER
ALGEBRA 175

    SECTION I. Diagrams for the Logical Relations of Classes 175

    SECTION II. The Application to Classes 184

    SECTION III. The Application to Propositions 213

    SECTION IV. The Application to Relations 219

CHAPTER IV. SYSTEMS BASED ON MATERIAL IMPLI-
CATION 222

    SECTION I. The Two-Valued Algebra 222

SECTION II.   The Calculus of Propositional Functions. Functions of One Variable...................... 232

SECTION III.   Propositional Functions of Two or More Variables. 246

SECTION IV.   Derivation of the Logic of Classes from the Calculus of Propositional Functions................ 260

SECTION V.   The Logic of Relations....................... 269

SECTION VI.   The Logic of *Principia Mathematica*............. 279

APPENDIX. TWO FRAGMENTS FROM LEIBNIZ 291

BIBLIOGRAPHY 307

INDEX 325

PREFACE TO DOVER EDITION

The original edition of *A Survey of Symbolic Logic* was published by the University of California Press in 1918, as one of the series of volumes brought out by the university on the occasion of its Semi-Centennial Celebration. At that time, a book on this subject could hardly be expected to attain any wide circulation, and the appropriately small edition was exhausted some time in the 1920s.

Soon after publication of the book, Dr. E. L. Post of Columbia University pointed out an error with respect to one postulate of my system of Strict Implication, as contained in Chapter V. Notice of this error, together with the necessary correction, was printed in the *Journal of Philosophy, Psychology, and Scientific Method* (vol. XVII, p. 300) in 1920.

I soon became dissatisfied also with another postulate of this system as amended (now called S3), believing that certain consequences of this assumption are not in accord with the logical facts of what is strictly deducible from what.

In *Symbolic Logic*, which Cooper Harold Langford and I joined in publishing in 1932, both these shortcomings of Strict Implication, as presented in the *Survey*, were eliminated. I wish the System S2, as developed in *Symbolic Logic*, Chapter V and Appendices II and III, to be regarded as the definitive form of Strict Implication. *Symbolic Logic* also received the great benefit of the chapters contributed by Professor Langford.

In accepting the offer of Dover Publications, Inc., to reprint the *Survey*, I have, in view of the considerations mentioned above, stipulated that Chapter V be omitted. I have also suggested the omission of Chapter VI, thinking that whatever the reasons for continued interest in the book, it will not be the content of this concluding chapter, devoted to general considerations, which accounts for it.

The remaining chapters (I—IV, here reproduced) complete that task which the title of the book connotes: an outline of the earlier history of the subject, the classic Algebra of Logic founded by Boole and given its definitive form by Schröder, the interpretations and applications of it, and the connection between it and later developed systems of symbolic logic, currently familiar.

C. I. LEWIS.

MENLO PARK, CALIFORNIA, April, 1960.

PREFACE TO FIRST EDITION

The student who has completed some elementary study of symbolic logic and wishes to pursue the subject further finds himself in a discouraging situation. He has, perhaps, mastered the contents of Venn's *Symbolic Logic* or Couturat's admirable little book, *The Algebra of Logic*, or the chapters concerning this subject in Whitehead's *Universal Algebra*. If he read German with sufficient ease, he may have made some excursions into Schröder's *Vorlesungen über die Algebra der Logik*. These all concern the classic, or Boole-Schröder algebra, and his knowledge of symbolic logic is probably confined to that system. His further interest leads him almost inevitably to Peano's *Formulaire de Mathématiques*, *Principia Mathematica* of Whitehead and Russell, and the increasingly numerous shorter studies of the same sort. And with only elementary knowledge of a single kind of development of a small branch of the subject, he must attack these most difficult and technical of treatises, in a new notation, developed by methods which are entirely novel to him, and bristling with logico-metaphysical difficulties. If he is bewildered and searches for some means of further preparation, he finds nothing to bridge the gap. Schröder's work would be of most assistance here, but this was written some twenty-five years ago; the most valuable studies are of later date, and radically new methods have been introduced.

What such a student most needs is a comprehensive survey of the subject—one which will familiarize him with more than the single system which he knows, and will indicate not only the content of other branches and the alternative methods of procedure, but also the *relation* of these to the Boole-Schröder algebra and to one another. The present book is an attempt to meet this need, by bringing within the compass of a single volume, and reducing to a common notation (so far as possible), the most important developments of symbolic logic. If, in addition to this, some of the requirements of a "handbook" are here fulfilled, so much the better.

But this survey does not pretend to be encyclopedic. A gossipy recital of results achieved, or a superficial account of methods, is of no more use in symbolic logic than in any other mathematical discipline. What is presented must be treated in sufficient detail to afford the possibility of real insight and grasp. This aim has required careful selection of material.

The historical summary in Chapter I attempts to follow the main thread of development, and no reference, or only passing mention, is given to those studies which seem not to have affected materially the methods of later researches. In the remainder of the book, the selection has been governed by the same purpose. Those topics comprehension of which seems most essential, have been treated at some length, while matters less fundamental have been set forth in outline only, or omitted altogether. My own contribution to symbolic logic, presented in Chapter V, has not earned the right to inclusion here; in this, I plead guilty to partiality. The discussion of controversial topics has been avoided whenever possible and, for the rest, limited to the simpler issues involved. Consequently, the reader must not suppose that any sufficient consideration of these questions is here given, though such statements as are made will be, I hope, accurate. Particularly in the last chapter, on "Symbolic Logic, Logistic, and Mathematical Method", it is not possible to give anything like an adequate account of the facts. That would require a volume at least the size of this one. Rather, I have tried to set forth the most important and critical considerations—somewhat arbitrarily and dogmatically, since there is not space for argument—and to provide such a map of this difficult territory as will aid the student in his further explorations.

Proofs and solutions in Chapters II, III, and IV have been given very fully. Proof is of the essence of logistic, and it is my observation that students—even those with a fair knowledge of mathematics—seldom command the technique of rigorous demonstration. In any case, this explicitness can do no harm, since no one need read a proof which he already understands.

I am indebted to many friends and colleagues for valuable assistance in preparing this book for publication: to Professor W. A. Merrill for emendations of my translation of Leibniz, to Professor J. H. McDonald and Dr. B. A. Bernstein for important suggestions and the correction of certain errors in Chapter II, to Mr. J. C. Rowell, University Librarian, for assistance in securing a number of rare volumes, and to the officers of the University Press for their patient helpfulness in meeting the technical difficulties of printing such a book. Mr. Shirley Quimby has read the whole book in manuscript, eliminated many mistakes, and verified most of the proofs.

But most of all, I am indebted to my friend and teacher, Josiah Royce, who first aroused my interest in this subject, and who never failed to give me encouragement and wise counsel. Much that is best in this book is due to him.   C. I. Lewis.

Berkeley, July 10, 1917.

A SURVEY OF
SYMBOLIC LOGIC

CHAPTER I

THE DEVELOPMENT OF SYMBOLIC LOGIC

I. The Scope of Symbolic Logic. Symbolic Logic and Logistic. Summary Account of Their Development

The subject with which we are concerned has been variously referred to as "symbolic logic", "logistic", "algebra of logic", "calculus of logic", "mathematical logic", "algorithmic logic", and probably by other names. And none of these is satisfactory. We have chosen "symbolic logic" because it is the most commonly used in England and in this country, and because its signification is pretty well understood. Its inaccuracy is obvious: logic of whatever sort uses symbols. We are concerned only with that logic which uses symbols in certain specific ways—those ways which are exhibited generally in mathematical procedures. In particular, logic to be called "symbolic" must make use of symbols for the logical *relations*, and must so connect various relations that they admit of "transformations" and "operations", according to principles which are capable of exact statement.

If we must give some definition, we shall hazard the following: Symbolic Logic is the development of the most general principles of rational procedure, in ideographic symbols, and in a form which exhibits the connection of these principles one with another. Principles which belong exclusively to some one type of rational procedure—*e. g.* to dealing with number and quantity—are hereby excluded, and generality is designated as one of the marks of symbolic logic.

Such general principles are likewise the subject matter of logic in any form. To be sure, traditional logic has never taken possession of more than a small portion of the field which belongs to it. The modes of Aristotle are unnecessarily restricted. As we shall have occasion to point out, the reasons for the syllogistic form are psychological, not logical: the syllogism, made up of the smallest number of propositions (three), each with the smallest number of terms (two), by which any generality of reasoning can be attained, represents the limitations of human attention, not logical necessity. To regard the syllogism as indispensable, or as reasoning *par excellence*, is the apotheosis of stupidity. And the procedures of symbolic logic, not being thus arbitrarily restricted, may seem to mark a difference of subject matter between it and the traditional logic. But any such difference is accidental, not essential, and the really distinguishing mark of symbolic logic is the approximation to a certain *form*, regarded as ideal. There are all degrees of such approximation; hence the difficulty of drawing any hard and fast line between symbolic and other logic.

But more important than the making of any such sharp distinction is the comprehension of that ideal of form upon which it is supposed to depend. The most convenient method which the human mind has so far devised for exhibiting principles of exact procedure is the one which we call, in general terms, mathematical. The important characteristics of this form are: (1) the use of ideograms instead of the phonograms of ordinary language; (2) the deductive method—which may here be taken to mean simply that the greater portion of the subject matter is derived from a relatively few principles by operations which are "exact": and (3) the use of variables having a definite range of significance.

Ideograms have two important advantages over phonograms. In the first place, they are more compact, + than "plus", 3 than "three", etc. This is no inconsiderable gain, since it makes possible the presentation of a formula in small enough compass so that the eye may apprehend it at a glance and the image of it (in visual or other terms) may be retained for reference with a minimum of effort. None but a very thoughtless person, or one without experience of the sciences, can fail to understand the enormous advantage of such brevity. In the second place, an ideographic notation is superior to any other in precision. Many ideas which are quite simply expressible in mathematical symbols can only with the greatest difficulty be rendered in ordinary language. Without ideograms, even arithmetic would be difficult, and higher branches impossible.

The deductive method, by which a considerable array of facts is summarized in a few principles from which they can be derived, is much more than the mere application of deductive logic to the subject matter in question. It both requires and facilitates such an analysis of the whole body of facts as will most precisely exhibit their relations to one another. In fact, any other value of the deductive form is largely or wholly fictitious.

The presentation of the subject matter of logic in this mathematical form constitutes what we mean by symbolic logic. Hence the essential characteristics of our subject are the following: (1) Its subject matter is the subject matter of logic in any form—that is, the principles of rational or reflective procedure in general, as contrasted with principles which belong exclusively to some particular branch of such procedure.   (2) Its medium is an ideographic symbolism, in which each separate character represents a relatively simple and entirely explicit concept.   And, ideally, all non-ideographic symbolism or language is excluded.   (3) Amongst the ideograms, some will represent variables (the "terms" of the system) having a definite range of significance.   Although it is non-essential, in any system so far developed the variables will represent "individuals", or classes, or relations, or propositions, or "propositional functions", or they will represent ambiguously some two or more of these.   (4) Any system of symbolic logic will be developed deductively—that is, the whole body of its theorems will be derived from a relatively few principles, stated in symbols, by operations which are, or at least can be, precisely formulated.

We have been at some pains to make as clear as possible the nature of symbolic logic, because its distinction from "ordinary" logic, on the one hand, and, on the other, from *any* mathematical discipline in a sufficiently abstract form, is none too definite.   It will be further valuable to comment briefly on some of the alternative designations for the subject which have been mentioned.

"Logistic" would not have served our purpose, because "logistic" is commonly used to denote symbolic logic together with the application of its methods to other symbolic procedures.   Logistic may be defined as *the science which deals with types of order as such.*   It is not so much a subject as a method.   Although most logistic is either founded upon or makes large use of the principles of symbolic logic, still a science of order in general does not necessarily presuppose, or begin with, symbolic logic. Since the relations of symbolic logic, logistic, and mathematics are to be the topic of the last chapter, we may postpone any further discussion of that matter here.   We have mentioned it only to make clear the meaning which "logistic" is to have in the pages which follow.   It comprehends symbolic logic and the application of such methods as symbolic logic exemplifies to other exact procedures.   Its subject matter is not confined to logic.

"Algebra of logic" is hardly appropriate as the general name for our subject, because there are several quite distinct algebras of logic, and because symbolic logic includes systems which are not true algebras at all. "The algebra of logic" usually means that system the foundations of which were laid by Leibniz, and after him independently by Boole, and which was completed by Schröder. We shall refer to this system as the "Boole-Schröder Algebra ".

"Calculus" is a more general term than "algebra". By a "calculus" will be meant, not the whole subject, but any single system of assumptions and their consequences.

The program both for symbolic logic and for logistic, in anything like a clear form, was first sketched by Leibniz, though the ideal of logistic seems to have been present as far back as Plato's *Republic*.[1] Leibniz left fragmentary developments of symbolic logic, and some attempts at logistic which are prophetic but otherwise without value. After Leibniz, the two interests somewhat diverge. Contributions to symbolic logic were made by Ploucquet, Lambert, Castillon and others on the continent. This type of research interested Sir William Hamilton and, though his own contribution was slight and not essentially novel, his papers were, to some extent at least, responsible for the renewal of investigations in this field which took place in England about 1845 and produced the work of De Morgan and Boole. Boole seems to have been ignorant of the work of his continental predecessors, which is probably fortunate, since his own beginning has proved so much more fruitful. Boole is, in fact, the second founder of the subject, and all later work goes back to his. The main line of this development runs through Jevons, C. S. Peirce, and MacColl to Schröder whose *Vorlesungen über die Algebra der Logik* (Vol. I, 1890) marks the perfection of Boole's algebra and the logical completion of that mode of procedure.

In the meantime, interest in logistic persisted on the continent and was fostered by the growing tendency to abstractness and rigor in mathematics and by the hope for more general methods. Hamilton's quaternions and the *Ausdehnungslehre* of Grassmann, which was recognized as a continuation of the work begun by Leibniz, contributed to this end, as did also the precise logical analyses of the nature of number by Cantor and Dedekind. Also, the elimination from "modern geometry" of all methods of proof dependent upon "intuitions of space" or "construction" brought that subject within the scope of logistic treatment, and in 1889 Peano provided such a treatment in *I Principii di Geometria*. Frege's works, from the *Begriffsschrift* of 1879 to the *Grundgesetze der Arithmetik* (Vol. I, 1893; Vol. II, 1903) provide a comprehensive development of arithmetic by the logistic method.

[1] See the criticisms of contemporary mathematics and the program for the dialectic or philosophic development of mathematics in Bk. VI, Step. 510–11 and *Philebus*, Step. 56–57.

In 1894, Peano and his collaborators began the publication of the *Formulaire de Mathématiques*, in which all branches of mathematics were to be presented in the universal language of logistic. In this work, symbolic logic and logistic are once more brought together, since the logic presented in the early sections provides, in a way, the method by which the other branches of mathematics are developed. The *Formulaire* is a monumental production. But its mathematical interests are as much encyclopedic as logistic, and not all the possibilities of the method are utilized or made clear. It remained for Whitehead and Russell, in *Principia Mathematica*, to exhibit the perfect union of symbolic logic and the logistic method in mathematics. The publication of this work undoubtedly marks an epoch in the history of the subject. The tendencies marked in the development of the algebra of logic from Boole to Schröder, in the development of the algebra of relatives from De Morgan to Schröder, and in the foundations for number theory of Cantor and Dedekind and Frege, are all brought together here.[2] Further researches will most likely be based upon the formulations of *Principia Mathematica*.

We must now turn back and trace in more detail the development of symbolic logic.[3] A *history* of the subject will not be attempted, if by history is meant the report of facts for their own sake. Rather, we are interested in the cumulative process by which those results which most interest us today have come to be. Many researches of intrinsic value, but lying outside the main line of that development, will of necessity be neglected. Reference to these, so far as we are acquainted with them, will be found in the bibliography.[4]

II. Leibniz

The history of symbolic logic and logistic properly begins with Leibniz.[5] In the *New Essays on the Human Understanding*, Philalethes is made to say:[6] "I begin to form for myself a wholly different idea of logic from that which I formerly had. I regarded it as a scholar's diversion, but I now see that, in the way you understand it, it is like a universal mathe-

[2] Perhaps we should add "and the modern development of abstract geometry, as by Hilbert, Pieri, and others", but the volume of *Principia* which is to treat of geometry has not yet appeared.

[3] The remainder of this chapter is not essential to an understanding of the rest of the book. But after Chapter I, historical notes and references are generally omitted.

[4] Pp. 307

[5] Leibniz regards Raymond Lully, Athanasius Kircher, John Wilkins, and George Dalgarno (see Bibliography) as his predecessors in this field. But their writings contain little which is directly to the point.

[6] Bk. IV, Chap. XVII, § 9.

matics." As this passage suggests, Leibniz correctly foresaw the general character which logistic was to have and the problems it would set itself to solve. But though he caught the large outlines of the subject and actually delimited the field of work, he failed of any clear understanding of the difficulties to be met, and he contributed comparatively little to the successful working out of details. Perhaps this is characteristic of the man. But another explanation, or partial explanation, is possible. Leibniz expected that the whole of science would shortly be reformed by the application of this method. This was a task clearly beyond the powers of any one man, who could, at most, offer only the initial stimulus and general plan. And so, throughout his life, he besought the assistance of learned societies and titled patrons, to the end that this epoch-making reform might be instituted, and never addressed himself very seriously to the more limited tasks which he might have accomplished unaided.[7] Hence his studies in this field are scattered through the manuscripts, many of them still unedited, and out of five hundred or more pages, the systematic results attained might be presented in one-tenth the space.[8]

Leibniz's conception of the task to be accomplished altered somewhat during his life, but two features characterize all the projects which he entertained: (1) a universal medium ("universal language" or "rational language" or "universal characteristic") for the expression of science; and (2) a calculus of reasoning (or "universal calculus") designed to display the most universal relations of scientific concepts and to afford some systematic abridgment of the labor of rational investigation in all fields, much as mathematical formulae abridge the labor of dealing with quantity and number. "The true method should furnish us with an Ariadne's thread, that is to say, with a certain sensible and palpable medium, which will guide the mind as do the lines drawn in geometry and the formulae for operations which are laid down for the learner in arithmetic."[9]

This universal medium is to be an ideographic language, each single character of which will represent a simple concept. It will differ from existing ideographic languages, such as Chinese, through using a combina-

---

[7] The editor's introduction to "Scientia Generalis. Characteristica" in Gerhardt's *Philosophischen Schriften von Leibniz* (Berlin, 1890), VII, gives an excellent account of Leibniz's correspondence upon this topic, together with other material of historic interest. (Work hereafter cited as *G. Phil.*)

[8] See Gerhardt, *op. cit.* especially IV and VII. But Couturat, *La logique de Leibniz* (1901), gives a survey which will prove more profitable to the general reader than any study of the sources.

[9] Letter to Galois, 1677, *G. Phil.*, VII, 21.

tion of symbols, or some similar device, for a compound idea, instead of having a multiplicity of characters corresponding to the variety of things. So that while Chinese can hardly be learned in a lifetime, the universal characteristic may be mastered in a few weeks.[10] The fundamental characters of the universal language will be few in number, and will represent the "*alphabet of human thought*": "The fruit of many analyses will be the catalogue of ideas which are simple or not far from simple."[11] With this catalogue of primitive ideas—this alphabet of human thought—the whole of science is to be reconstructed in such wise that its real logical organization will be reflected in its symbolism.

In spite of fantastic expression and some hyperbole, we recognize here the program of logistic. If the reconstruction of all science is a project too ambitious, still we should maintain the ideal possibility and the desirability of such a reconstruction of *exact* science in general. And the ideographic language finds its realization in Peano's *Formulaire*, in *Principia Mathematica*, and in all successful applications of the logistic method.

Leibniz stresses the importance of such a language for the more rapid and orderly progress of science and of human thought in general. The least effect of it ". . . will be the universality and communication of different nations. Its true use will be to paint not the word . . . but the thought, and to speak to the understanding rather than to the eyes. . . . Lacking such guides, the mind can make no long journey without losing its way . . . : with such a medium, we could reason in metaphysics and in ethics very much as we do in geometry and in analytics, because the characters would fix our ideas, which are otherwise too vague and fleeting in such matters in which the imagination cannot help us unless it be by the aid of characters."[12] The lack of such a universal medium prevents coöperation. "The human race, considered in its relation to the sciences which serve our welfare, seems to me comparable to a troop which marches in confusion in the darkness, without a leader, without order, without any word or other signs for the regulation of their march and the recognition of one another. Instead of joining hands to guide ourselves and make sure of the road, we run hither and yon and interfere with one another."[13]

The "alphabet of human thought" is more visionary. The possibility of constructing the whole of a complex science from a few primitive con-

[10] Letter to the Duke of Hanover, 1679 (?), *G. Phil.*, vii, 24–25.
[11] *G. Phil.*, vii, 84.
[12] *G. Phil.*, vii, 21.
[13] *G. Phil.*, vii, 157.

cepts is, indeed, real—*vide* the few primitives of *Principia Mathematica*.
But we should today recognize a certain arbitrariness in the selection of
these, though an arbitrariness limited by the nature of the subject.   The
secret of Leibniz's faith that these primitive concepts are fixed in the nature
of things will be found in his conception of knowledge and of proof.   He
believes that all predicates are contained in the (intension of the) subject
and may be discovered by analysis.   Similarly, all truths which are not
absolutely primitive and self-evident admit of reduction by analysis into
such absolutely first truths.   And finally, only one real definition of a
thing—"real" as opposed to "nominal"—is possible;[14] that is, the result
of the correct analysis of any concept is unambiguously predetermined in
the concept itself.

The construction, from such primitives, of the complex concepts of
the various sciences, Leibniz speaks of as "synthesis" or "invention",
and he is concerned about the "*art of invention*".   But while the result of
analysis is always determined, and only one analysis is finally correct,
synthesis, like inverse processes generally, has no such predetermined
character.   In spite of the frequent mention of the subject, the only important suggestions for this art have to do with the provision of a suitable
medium and of a calculus of reasoning.   To be sure there are such obvious
counsels as to proceed from the simple to the complex, and in the early
essay, *De Arte Combinatoria*, there are studies of the possible permutations
and combinations or "syntheses" of fundamental concepts, but the author
later regarded this study as of little value.   And in *Initia et Specimina
Scientiæ novæ Generalis,* he says that the utmost which we can hope to
accomplish at present, toward the general art of invention, is a perfectly
orderly and finished reconstruction of existing science in terms of the
absolute primitives which analysis reveals.[15]   After two hundred years,
we are still without any general method by which logistic may be used in
fields as yet unexplored, and we have no confidence in any absolute primitives for such investigation.

The calculus of reasoning, or universal calculus, is to be the instrument
for the development and manipulation of systems in the universal language,
and it is to get its complete generality from the fact that all science will be
expressed in the ideographic symbols of that universal medium.   The
calculus will consist of the general principles of operating with such ideo-

---

[14] See *G. Phil.*, VII, 194, footnote.

[15] *G. Phil.*, VII, 84.

graphic symbols: "All our reasoning is nothing but the relating and substituting of characters, whether these characters be words or marks or images."[16]   Thus while the *characteristica universalis* is the project of the logistic treatment of science in general, the universal calculus is the precursor of symbolic logic.

The plan for this universal calculus changed considerably with the development of Leibniz's thought, but he speaks of it always as a mathematical procedure, and always as more general than existing mathematical methods.[17]   The earliest form suggested for it is one in which the simple concepts are to be represented by numbers, and the operations are to be merely those of arithmetical multiplication, division, and factoring.   When, later, he abandons this plan of procedure, he speaks of a general calculus which will be concerned with what we should nowadays describe as "types of order"—with combinations which are absolute or relative, symmetrical or unsymmetrical, and so on.[18]   His latest studies toward such a calculus form the earliest presentation of what we now call the "algebra of logic". But it is doubtful if Leibniz ever thought of the universal calculus as restricted to our algebra of logic: we can only say that it was intended to be the science of mathematical and deductive form in general (it is doubtful whether induction was included), and such as to make possible the application of the analytic method of mathematics to all subjects of which scientific knowledge is possible.

Of the various studies to this end our chief interest will be in the early essay, *De Arte Combinatoria*,[19] and in the fragments which attempt to develop an algebra of logic.[20]

Leibniz wrote *De Arte Combinatoria* when he was, in his own words, *vix egressus ex Ephebis*, and before he had any considerable knowledge of mathematics.   It was published, he tells us, without his knowledge or consent.   The intention of the work, as indicated by its title, is to serve the general art of rational invention, as the author conceived it.   As has been mentioned, it seems that this end is to be accomplished by a complete analysis of concepts of the topic under investigation and a general survey of the possibilities of their combination.   A large portion of the essay is concerned with the calculation of the possible forms of this and that type

[16] *G. Phil.*, VII, 31.

[17] See *New Essays on the Human Understanding*, Bk. IV, Chap. XVII, §§ 9–13.

[18] See *G. Phil.*, VII, 31, 198 *ff.*, and 204.

[19] *G. Phil.*, IV, 35–104.   Also Gerhardt, *Leibnizens mathematische Schriften* (1859), V, 1–79.

[20] *Scientia Generalis.   Characteristica*, XV–XX, *G. Phil.*, VII.

of logical construct: the various dyadic, triadic, etc., complexes which can be formed with a given number of elements; of the moods and figures of the syllogism; of the possible predicates of a given subject (the complexity of the subject as a concept being itself the key to the predicates which can be analyzed out of it); of the number of propositions from a given number of subjects, given number of predicate relations, and given number of *quaestiones*; [21] of the variations of order with a given number of terms, and so on. In fact so much space is occupied with the computation of permutations and combinations that some of his contemporaries failed to discover any more important meaning of the essay, and it is most frequently referred to simply as a contribution to combinatorial analysis.[22]

Beyond this the significance of the essay lies in the attempt to devise a symbolism which will preserve the relation of analyzable concepts to their primitive constituents. The particular device selected for this purpose—representation of concepts by numbers—is unfortunate, but the attempt itself is of interest. Leibniz makes application of this method to geometry and suggests it for other sciences.[23] In the geometrical illustration, the concepts are divided into classes. Class 1 consists of concepts or terms regarded as elementary and not further analyzable, each of which is given a number. Thereafter, the number is the symbol of that concept. Class 2 consists of concepts analyzable into (definable in terms of) those of Class 1. By the use of a fractional notation, both the class to which a concept belongs and its place in that class can be indicated at once. The denominator indicates the number of the class and the numerator is the number of the concept in that class. Thus the concept numbered 7 in Class 2 is represented by 7/2. Class 3 consists of concepts definable in terms of those in Class 1 and Class 2, and so on. By this method, the complete analysis of any concept is supposed to be indicated by its numerical symbol.[24]

---

[21] Leibniz tells us that he takes this problem from the *Ars Magna* of Raymond Lully. See *G. Phil.*, v, 62.

[22] See letter to Tschirnhaus, 1678, Gerhardt, *Math.*, iv, 451–63. Cf. Cantor, *Geschichte d. Math.*, iii, 39 *ff.*

[23] See the Synopsis, *G. Phil.*, iv, 30–31.

[24] See Couturat, *op. cit.*, appended Note vi, p. 554 *ff.*

The concepts are arranged as follows (*G. Phil.*, iv, 70–72):

"Classis I; 1. Punctum, 2. Spatium, 3. intervallum, 4. adsitum seu contiguum, 5. dissitum seu distans, 6. Terminus seu quae distant, 7. Insitum, 8. inclusum (v.g. centrum est insitum circulo, inclusum peripheriae), 9. Pars, 10. Totum, 11. idem, 12. diversum, 13. unum, 14. Numerus, *etc. etc.* [There are twenty-seven numbered concepts in this class.]

"Classis II; 1. *Quantitas* est 14 τῶν 9 (15). [Numbers enclosed in parentheses have their usual arithmetical significance, except that (15) signifies 'an indefinite number'.] 2. *Includens* est 6.10. III. 1. *Intervallum* est 2.3.10. 2. Aequale A τῆς 11.½. 3. *Continuum* est A ad B, si τοῦ A ἡ 9 est 4 et 7 τῷ B.; *etc. etc.*"

In point of fact, the analysis (apart from any merely geometrical defects) falls far short of being complete. Leibniz uses not only the inflected Greek article to indicate various relations of concepts but also modal inflections indicated by *et, si, quod, quam faciunt*, etc.

In later years Leibniz never mentions this work without apologizing for it, yet he always insists that its main intention is sound. This method of assuming primitive ideas which are arbitrarily symbolized, of introducing other concepts by definition in terms of these primitives and, at the same time, substituting a single symbol for the complex of defining symbols— this is, in fact, the method of logistic in general. Modern logistic differs from this attempt of Leibniz most notably in two respects: (1) modern logistic would insist that the *relations* whereby two or more concepts are united in a definition should be analyzed precisely as the substantives are analyzed; (2) while Leibniz regards his set of primitive concepts as the necessary result of any proper analysis, modern logistic would look upon them as arbitrarily chosen. Leibniz's later work looks toward the elimination of this first difference, but the second represents a conviction from which he never departed.

At a much later date come various studies (not in Gerhardt), which attempt a more systematic use of number and of mathematical operations in logic.[25] Simple and primitive concepts, Leibniz now proposes, should be symbolized by *prime* numbers, and the combination of two concepts (the qualification of one term by another) is to be represented by their product. Thus if 3 represent "rational" and 7 "animal", "man" will be 21. No prime number will enter more than once into a given combination—a rational rational animal, or a rational animal animal, is simply a rational animal. Thus logical synthesis is represented by arithmetical multiplication: logical analysis by resolution into prime factors. The analysis of "man", 21, would be accomplished by finding its prime factors, "rational", 3, and "animal", 7. In accordance with Leibniz's conviction that all knowledge is analytic and all valid predicates are contained in the subject, the proposition "All S is P" will be true if the number which represents the concept S is divisible by that which represents P. Accordingly the

[25] Dated April, 1679. Couturat (*op. cit.*, p. 326, footnote) gives the titles of these as follows: "*Elementa Characteristicae Universalis* (Collected manuscripts of Leibniz in the Hanover Library, PHIL., v, 8 b); *Calculi universalis Elementa* (PHIL., v, 8 c); *Calculi universalis investigationes* (PHIL., v, 8 d); *Modus examinandi consequentias per numeros* (PHIL., v, 8 e); *Regulae ex quibus de bonitate consequentiarum formisque et modis syllogismorum categoricum judicari potest per numeros* (PHIL., v, 8 f)." These fragments, with many others, are contained in Couturat's *Opuscules et fragments inédits de Leibniz*.

universal affirmative proposition may be symbolized by $S/P = y$ or $S = Py$ (where y is a whole number). By the plan of this notation, Py will represent some species whose "difference", within the genus P, is y. Similarly Sx will represent a species of S. Hence the particular affirmative, "Some S is P," may be symbolized by $Sx = Py$, or $S/P = y/x$. Thus the universal is a special case of the particular, and the particular will always be true when the universal is true.

There are several objections to this scheme. In the first place, it presumes that any part of a class is a species within the class as genus. This is far-fetched, but perhaps theoretically defensible on the ground that any part which can be specified by the use of language may be treated as a logical species. A worse defect lies in the fact that $Sx = Py$ will *always* be true. For a given S and P, we can always find x and y which will satisfy the equation $Sx = Py$. If no other choice avails, let $x = P$, or some multiple of P, and $y = S$, or some multiple of S. "Angel-man" = "man-angel" although no men are angels. "Spineless man" = "rational invertebrate", but it is false that some men are invertebrates. A third difficulty arises because of the existential import of the particular— a difficulty which later drew Leibniz's attention. If the particular affirmative is true, then for some x and y, $Sx = Py$. The universal negative should, then, be $Sx \neq Py$. And since the universal affirmative is $S = Py$, the particular negative should be $S \neq Py$. But this symbolism would be practically unworkable because the inequations would have to be verified for all values of x and y. Also, as we have noted, the equality $Sx = Py$ will always hold and $Sx \neq Py$, where x and y are arbitrary, will never be true.

Such difficulties led Leibniz to complicate his symbolism still further, introducing negative numbers and finally using a pair of numbers, one positive and one negative, for each concept. But this scheme also breaks down, and the attempt to represent concepts by numbers is thereafter abandoned.

Of more importance to symbolic logic are the later fragments included in the plans for an encyclopedia which should collect and arrange all known science as the proper foundation for future work.[26] Leibniz cherished the

<hr/>

[26] *G. Phil.*, VII, XVI–XX. Of these, XVI, without title, states rules for inference in terms of inclusion and exclusion; *Difficultates quaedam logicae* treats of subalternation and conversion and of the symbolic expression for various types of propositions; XVIII, *Specimen Calculi universalis* with its addenda and marginal notes, gives the general principles of procedure for the universal calculus; XIX, with the title *Non inelegans specimen*

notion that this should be developed in terms of the universal characteristic. In these fragments, the relations of equivalence, inclusion, and qualification of one concept by another, or combination, are defined and used. These relations are always considered *in intension* when it is a question of applying the calculus to formal logic. "Equivalence" is the equivalence of *concepts*, not simply of two classes which have the same members; "for A to include B or B to be included in A is to affirm the predicate B universally of the subject A".[27] However, Leibniz evidently considers the calculus to have many applications, and he thinks out the relations and illustrates them frequently in terms of extensional diagrams, in which A, B, etc., are represented by segments of a right line. Although he preferred to treat logical relations in intension, he frequently states that relations of intension are easily transformed into relations of extension. If A is included in B in intension, B is included in A in extension; and a calculus may be interpreted indifferently as representing relations of concepts in intension or relations of individuals and classes in extension. Also, the inclusion relation may be interpreted as the relation of an antecedent proposition to a consequent proposition. The hypothesis A includes its consequence B, just as the subject A includes the predicate B.[28] This accords with his frequently expressed conviction that all demonstration is analysis. Thus these studies are by no means to be confined to the logic of intension. As one title suggests, they are studies *demonstrandi in abstractis*.

demonstrandi in abstractis struck out, and xx, without title, are deductive developments of theorems of symbolic logic, entirely comparable with later treatises.

The place of symbolic logic in Leibniz's plans for the Encyclopedia is sufficiently indicated by the various outlines which he has left. In one of these (*G. Phil.*, vii, 49), divisions 1–6 are of an introductory nature, after which come:

"7. De scientiarum instauratione, ubi de Systematibus et Repertoriis, et de Encyclopaedia demonstrativa codenda.

"8. Elementa veritatis aeternae, et de arte demonstrandi in omnibus disciplinis ut in Mathesi.

"9. De novo quodam Calculo generali, cujus ope tollantur omnes disputationes inter eos qui in ipsum consenserit; est Cabala sapientum.

"10. De Arte Inveniendi.

"11. De Synthesi seu Arte combinatoria.

"12. De Analysi.

"13. De Combinatoria speciali, seu scientia formarum, sive qualitatum in genere (de Characterismis) sive de simili et dissimili.

"14. De Analysi speciali seu scientia quantitatum in genere seu de magno et parvo.

"15. De Mathesi generali ex duabus praecedentibus composita."

Then various branches of mathematics, astronomy, physics, biological science, medicine, psychology, political science, economics, military science, jurisprudence, and natural theology, in the order named.

[27] *G. Phil.*, vii, 208.

[28] "Generales Inquisitiones" (1686): see Couturat, *Opuscules etc.*, pp. 356–99.

It is a frequent remark upon Leibniz's contributions to logic that he failed to accomplish this or that, or erred in some respect, because he chose the point of view of intension instead of that of extension. The facts are these: Leibniz too hastily presumed a complete, or very close, analogy between the various logical relations. It is a part of his significance for us that he sought such high generalizations and believed in their validity. He preferred the point of view of intension, or connotation, partly from habit and partly from rationalistic inclination. As a consequence, wherever there is a discrepancy between the intensional and extensional points of view, he is likely to overlook it, and to follow the former. This led him into some difficulties which he might have avoided by an opposite inclination and choice of example, but it also led him to make some distinctions the importance of which has since been overlooked and to avoid certain difficulties into which his commentators have fallen.[29]

In *Difficultates quaedam logicae*, Leibniz shows that at last he recognizes the difficulty in connecting the universal and the corresponding particular. He sees also that this difficulty is connected with the disparity between the intensional point of view and the existential import of particular propositions. In the course of this essay he formulates the symbolism for the four propositions in two different ways. The first formulation is:[30]

Univ. aff.; All A is B: $AB = A$, or A non-B does not exist.

Part. neg.; Some A is not B; $AB \neq A$, or A non-B exists.

Univ. neg.; No A is B; AB does not exist.

Part. aff.; Some A is B; AB exists.

$AB = A$ and $AB \neq A$ may be interpreted as relations of intension or of extension indifferently. If all men are mortal, the intension of "mortal man" is the same as the intension of "man", and likewise the class of mortal men is identical in extent with the class of men. The statements concerning existence are obviously to be understood in extension only. The interpretation here put upon the propositions is identically that of contemporary symbolic logic. With these expressions, Leibniz infers the subaltern and the converse of the subaltern, from a given universal, by

[29] For example, it led him to distinguish the merely non-existent from the absurd, or impossible, and the necessarily true from the contingent. See *G. Phil.*, vii, 231, footnote; and "Specimen certitudinis seu de conditionibus," Dutens, *Leibnitii Opera*, iv, Part iii, pp. 92 *ff.*, also Couturat, *La Logique de Leibniz*, p. 348, footnote, and p. 353, footnote.

[30] *G. Phil.*, vii, 212.

means of the *hypothesis* that the subject, A, exists.   Later in the essay, he gives another set of expressions for the four propositions: [31]

All A is B: $AB = A$.

Some A is not B: $AB \neq A$.

No A is B: AB does not exist, or $AB \neq AB$ Ens.

Some A is B: AB exists, or $AB = AB$ Ens.

In the last two of these, AB before the sign of equality represents the *possible* AB's or the AB "in the region of ideas"; "AB Ens" represents existing AB's, or actual members of the class AB.   (Read AB Ens, "AB which exists".) $AB = AB$ Ens thus represents the fact that the class AB has members; $AB \neq AB$ Ens, that the class AB has no members.   A logical species of the genus A, "some A", may be represented by YA; YA Ens will represent existing members of that species, or "some existing A".   Leibniz correctly reasons that if $AB = A$ (All A is B), $YAB = YA$ (Some A is B); but if $AB \neq A$, it does not follow that $YAB \neq YA$, for if $Y = B$, $YAB = YA$.   Again, if $AB \neq AB$ Ens (No A is B), $YAB \neq YAB$ Ens (It is false that some A is B); but if $AB = AB$ Ens (Some A is B), $YAB = YAB$ Ens does not follow, because Y could assume values incompatible with A and B.   For example, some men are wise, but it does not follow that foolish men are foolish wise persons, because "foolish" is incompatible with "wise".[32]   The distinction here between AB, a logical division of A or of B, and AB Ens, existing AB's, is ingenious.   This is our author's most successful treatment of the relations of extension and intension, and of the particular to the universal.

In *Specimen calculi universalis*, the "principles of the calculus" are announced as follows: [33]

1) "Whatever is concluded in terms of certain variable letters may be concluded in terms of any other letters which satisfy the same conditions; for example, since it is true that [all] ab is a, it will also be true that [all] bc is b and that [all] bcd is bc. . . .

2) "Transposing letters in terms changes nothing; for example ab coincides with ba, 'animal rational' with 'rational animal'.

3) "Repetition of a letter in the same term is useless. . . .

4) "One proposition can be made from any number by joining all the subjects in one subject and all the predicates in one predicate: Thus, a is b and c is d and e is f, become ace is bdf. . . .

---

[31] *G. Phil.*, VII, 213–14.
[32] *G. Phil.*, VII, 215: the illustration is mine.
[33] *G. Phil.*, VII, 224–25.

5) "From any proposition whose predicate is composed of more than one term, more than one proposition can be made; each derived proposition having the subject the same as the given proposition but in place of the given predicate some part of the given predicate. If [all] *a* is *bcd*, then [all] *a* is *b* and [all] *a* is *c* and [all] *a* is *d*."[34]

If we add to the number of these, two principles which are announced under the head of "self-evident propositions"—(1) *a* is included in *a*; and (2) *ab* is included in *a*—we have here the most important of the fundamental principles of symbolic logic. Principle 1 is usually qualified by some doctrine of the "universe of discourse" or of "range of significance", but some form of it is indispensable to algorithms in general. The law numbered 2 above is what we now call the "principle of permutation"; 3, the "principle of tautology"; 4, the "principle of composition"; 5, the "principle of division". And the two "self-evident propositions" are often included in sets of postulates for the algebra of logic.

There remain for consideration the two fragments which are given in translation in our Appendix, XIX and XX of *Scientia Generalis: Characteristica*. The first of these, with the title *Non inelegans specimen demonstrandi in abstractis*, stricken out in the manuscript, is rather the more interesting. Here the relation previously symbolized by *AB* or *ab* is represented by $A + B$. And $A + B = L$ signifies that *A* is contained or included in (*est in*) *B*. A scholium attached to the definition of this inclusion relation distinguishes it from the part-whole relation. Comparison of this and other passages shows that Leibniz uses the inclusion relation to cover (1) the relation of a member of the class to the class itself; (2) the relation of a species, or subclass, to its genus—a relation in extension; (3) the relation of a genus to one of its species—a relation of intension. The first of these is our ε-relation; (2) is the inclusion relation of the algebra of logic; and (3) is the analogous relation of intension. Throughout both these fragments, it is clear that Leibniz thinks out his theorems in terms of extensional diagrams, in which classes or concepts are represented by segments of a line, and only incidentally in terms of the intension of concepts.

The different interpretations of the symbols must be carefully distinguished. If *A* is "rational" and *B* is "animal", and *A* and *B* are taken in intension, then $A + B$ will represent "rational animal". But if *A* and *B* are classes taken in extension, then $A + B$ is the class made up of those things which are either *A* or *B* (or both). Thus the inclusion relation,

---

[34] 4. and 5. are stated without qualification because this study is confined to the properties of universal affirmative propositions. 4. is true also for universal negatives.

$A + B = L$, may be interpreted either in intension or in extension as "A is in L". This is a little confusing to us, because we should nowadays invert the inclusion relation when we pass from intension to extension; instead of this, Leibniz changes the meaning of $A + B$ from "both A and B" (in intension) to "either A or B" (in extension). If A is "rational", B "animal", and L "man", then $A + B = L$ is true in intension, "rational animal" = "man" or "rational" is contained in "man". If A, B, and L are classes of points, or segments of a line, then $A + B = L$ will mean that L is the class of points comprising the points in A and the points in B (any points common to A and B counted only once), or the segment made up of segments A and B.

The relation $A + B$ does not require that A and B should be mutually exclusive. If L is a line, A and B may be overlapping segments; and, in intension, A and B may be overlapping concepts, such as "triangle" and "equilateral", each of which contains the component "figure".

Leibniz also introduces the relation $L - A$, which he calls *detractio*. $L - A = N$ signifies that L contains A and that if A be taken from L the remainder is N. The relations $[+]$ and $[-]$ are not true inverses: if $A + B = L$, it does not follow that $L - A = B$, because A and B may be overlapping (in Leibniz's terms, *communicantia*). If $L - A = N$, A and N must be mutually exclusive (*incommunicantia*). Hence if $A + B = L$ and A and B have a common part, M, $L - A = B - M$. (If the reader will take a line, L, in which A and B are overlapping segments, this will be clear.) This makes the relation of *detractio* somewhat confusing. In extension, $L - A$ may be interpreted "L which is not A". In intension, it is more difficult. Leibniz offers the example: "man" − "rational" = "brute", and calls our attention to the fact that "man" − "rational" is *not* "non-rational man" or "man" + "non-rational".[35] In intension, the relation seems to indicate an abstraction, not a negative qualification. But there are difficulties, due to the overlapping of concepts. Say that "man" + "woodworking" = "carpenter" and "man" + "white-skinned"

[35] *G. Phil.*, VII, 231, footnote. Couturat in commenting on this (*op. cit.*, pp. 377–78) says:

"Ailleurs Leibniz essaie de préciser cette opposition en disant:

'$A - A$ est *Nihilum*. Sed A non-A est *Absurdum*.' "Mais il oublie que le néant (non-Ens) n'est pas autre chose que ce qu'il appelle l'absurde ou l'impossible, c'est-à-dire le contradictoire."

It may be that Couturat, not Leibniz, is confused on this point. Non-existence may be contingent, as opposed to the *necessary* non-existence of the absurd. And the result of abstracting A from the concept A seems to leave merely non-Ens, not absurdity.

= "Caucasian". Then "Caucasian" + "carpenter" = "man" + "white-skinned" + "woodworking". Hence ("Caucasian" + "carpenter") − "carpenter" = "white-skinned", because the common constituent "man" has been abstracted in abstracting "carpenter". That is, the abstraction of "carpenter" from "Caucasian carpenter" leaves, not "Caucasian" but only that part of the concept "Caucasian" which is wholly absent in "carpenter". We cannot here say "white-skinned *man*" because "man" is abstracted, nor "white-skinned *animal*" because "animal" is contained in "man": we can only say "white-skinned" as a pure abstraction. Such abstraction is difficult to carry out and of very little use as an instrument of logical analysis. Leibniz's illustration is scribbled in the margin of the manuscript, and it seems clear that at this point he was not thinking out his theorems in terms of intensions.

Fragment XX differs from XIX in that it lacks the relation symbolized by [−]. This is a gain rather than a loss, both because of the difficulty of interpretation and because [+] and [−] are not true inverses. Also XX is more carefully developed: more of the simple theorems are proved, and more illustrations are given. Otherwise the definitions, relations, and methods of proof are the same. In both fragments the fundamental operation by which theorems are proved is the substitution of equivalent expressions.

If the successors of Leibniz had retained the breadth of view which characterizes his studies and aimed to symbolize relations of a like generality, these fragments might well have proved sufficient foundation for a satisfactory calculus of logic.

III. FROM LEIBNIZ TO DE MORGAN AND BOOLE

After Leibniz, various attempts were made to develop a calculus of logic. Segner, Jacques Bernoulli, Ploucquet, Tönnies, Lambert, Holland, Castillon, and others, all made studies toward this end. Of these, the most important are those of Ploucquet, Lambert and Castillon, while one of Holland's is of particular interest because it intends to be a calculus in extension. But this attempt was not quite a success, and the net result of the others is to illustrate the fact that a consistent calculus of logical relations in intension is either most difficult or quite impossible.

Of Segner's work and Ploucquet's we can give no account, since no copies of these writings are available.[36] Venn makes it clear that Plouc-

---

[36] There seem to be no copies of Ploucquet's books in this country, and attempts to secure them from the continent have so far failed.

quet's calculus was a calculus of intension and that it involved the quantification of the predicate.

Lambert[37] wrote voluminously on the subject of logic, but his most important contribution to symbolic procedure is contained in the *Sechs Versuche einer Zeichenkunst in der Vernunftlehre*.[38] These essays are not separate studies, made from different beginnings; later essays presuppose those which precede and refer to their theorems; and yet the development is not entirely continuous. Material given briefly in one will be found set forth more at length in another. And discussion of more general problems of the theory of knowledge and of scientific method are sometimes introduced. But the important results can be presented as a continuous development which follows in general the order of the essays.

Lambert gives the following list of his symbols:

The symbol of equality (*Gleichgültigkeit*)	=
addition (*Zusetzung*)	+
abstraction (*Absonderung*)	−
opposition (*des Gegentheils*)	×
universality	>
particularity	<
copula	∼
given concepts (*Begriffe*)	*a, b, c, d*, etc.
undetermined concepts	*n, m, l*, etc.
unknowns	*x, y, z*.
the genus	γ
the difference	δ

The calculus is developed entirely from the point of view of intension: the letters represent concepts, not classes, [+] indicates the union of two concepts to form a third, [−] represents the withdrawal or abstraction of some part of the connotation of a concept, while the product of *a* and *b* represents the common part of the two concepts. γ and δ qualify any term "multiplied" into them. Thus $a\gamma$ represents the genus of *a*, $a\delta$ the difference of *a*. Much use is made of the well-known law of formal logic that the concept (of a given species) equals the genus plus the difference.

(1) $$a\gamma + a\delta = a(\gamma + \delta) = a$$

---

[37] Johann Heinrich Lambert (1728–77), German physicist, mathematician, and astronomer. He is remembered chiefly for his development of the equation $x^n + px = q$ in an infinite series, and his proof, in 1761, of the irrationality of π.

[38] In *Logische und philosophische Abhandlungen;* ed. Joh. Bernoulli (Berlin, 1782), vol. I.

$a\gamma + a\delta$ is the definition or explanation (*Erklärung*) of a. As immediate consequences of (1), we have also

$$(2) \quad a\gamma = a - a\delta \qquad\qquad (3) \quad a\delta = a - a\gamma$$

Lambert takes it for granted that $[+]$ and $[-]$ are strictly inverse operations. We have already noted the difficulties of Leibniz on this point. If two concepts, a and b, have any part of their connotation in common, then $(a + b) - b$ will not be a but only that part of a which does not belong also to b. If "European" and "carpenter" have the common part "man", then ("European" + "carpenter") minus "carpenter" is not "European" but "European" minus "man". And $[+]$ and $[-]$ will not here be true inverses. But this difficulty may be supposed to disappear where the terms of the sum are the genus and difference of some concept, since genus anddifference may be supposed to be mutually exclusive. We shall return to this topic later.

More complex laws of genus and difference may be elicited from the fact that the genus of any given a is also a concept and can be "explained," as can also the difference of a.

$$(4) \qquad\qquad a = a(\gamma + \delta)^2 = a\gamma^2 + a\gamma\delta + a\delta\gamma + a\delta^2$$

Proof: $\quad a\gamma = a\gamma\gamma + a\gamma\delta \quad$ and $\quad a\delta = a\delta\gamma + a\delta\delta$

But $a = a\gamma + a\delta$. Hence Q.E.D.

That is to say: if one wish to define or explain a, one need not stop at giving its genus and difference, but may define the genus in terms of *its* genus and difference, and define the difference similarly. Thus a is equivalent to the genus of the genus of a plus the difference of the genus of a plus the genus of the difference of a plus the difference of the difference of a. This may be called a "higher" definition or "explanation" of a.

Obviously, this process of higher and higher "explanation" may be carried to any length; the result is what Lambert calls his "Newtonian formula". We shall best understand this if we take one more preliminary step. Suppose the explanation carried one degree further and the resulting terms arranged as follows:

$$a = a(\gamma^3 + \gamma\gamma\delta + \gamma\delta\delta + \delta^3)$$
$$+ \gamma\delta\gamma + \delta\gamma\delta$$
$$+ \delta\gamma\gamma + \delta\delta\gamma$$

The three possible arrangements of two γ's and one δ might be summarized by $3\gamma^2\delta$; the three arrangements of two δ's and one γ by $3\gamma\delta^2$. With this convention, the formula for an explanation carried to any degree, n, is:

$$(5) \quad a = a(\gamma^n + n\gamma^{n-1}\delta + \frac{n(n-1)}{2!}\gamma^{n-2}\delta^2 + \frac{n(n-1)(n-2)}{3!}\gamma^{n-3}\delta^3 + \ldots \text{ etc.}$$

This "Newtonian formula" is a rather pleasant mathematical conceit.

Two further interesting laws are given:

$$(6) \qquad a = a\delta + a\gamma\delta + a\gamma^2\delta + a\gamma^3\delta + \ldots \text{ etc.}$$

Proof: $\qquad\qquad a = a\gamma + a\delta$

But $\qquad\quad a\gamma = a\gamma^2 + a\gamma\delta$

and $\qquad\quad a\gamma^2 = a\gamma^3 + a\gamma^2\delta$

$\qquad\qquad\quad a\gamma^3 = a\gamma^4 + a\gamma^3\delta$, etc. etc.

$$(7) \qquad a = a\gamma + a\delta\gamma + a\delta^2\gamma + a\delta^3\gamma + \ldots \text{ etc.}$$

Proof: $\qquad\qquad a = a\gamma + a\delta$

But $\qquad\quad a\delta = a\delta\gamma + a\delta^2$

and $\qquad\quad a\delta^2 = a\delta^2\gamma + a\delta^3$

$\qquad\qquad\quad a\delta^3 = a\delta^3\gamma + a\delta^4$, etc. etc.

Just as the genus of a is represented by $a\gamma$, the genus of the genus of a by $a\gamma^2$, etc., so a species of which a is genus may be represented by $a\gamma^{-1}$, and a species of which a is genus of the genus by $a\gamma^{-2}$, etc. In general, as $a\gamma^n$ represents a genus above a, so a species below a may be represented by

$$a\gamma^{-n} \qquad \text{or} \qquad \frac{a}{\gamma^n}$$

Similarly any concept of which a is difference of the difference of the difference . . . etc., may be represented by

$$a\delta^{-n} \qquad \text{or} \qquad \frac{a}{\delta^n}$$

Also, just as $a = a(\gamma + \delta)^n$, where a is a concept and $a(\gamma + \delta)^n$ its "explanation", so $\dfrac{a}{(\gamma + \delta)^n} = a$, where $\dfrac{a}{(\gamma + \delta)^n}$ is the concept and a the "explanation" of it.

Certain cautions in the transformation of expressions, both with respect to "multiplication" and with respect to "division," need to be observed.[40]

[39] *Sechs Versuche*, p. 5.
[40] *Ibid.*, pp. 9–10.

The concept $a\gamma^2 + a\delta\gamma$ is very different from the concept $(a\gamma + a\delta)\gamma$, because

$$(8) \qquad (a\gamma + a\delta)\gamma = a(\gamma + \delta)\gamma = a\gamma(\gamma + \delta) = a\gamma$$

while $a\gamma^2 + a\delta\gamma$ is the genus of the genus of a plus the genus of the difference of a. Also $\dfrac{a}{\gamma}\,\gamma$ must be distinguished from $\dfrac{a\gamma}{\gamma}$. $\dfrac{a}{\gamma}\,\gamma$ is the genus of any species x of which a is the genus, i. e.,

$$(9) \qquad \frac{a}{\gamma}\,\gamma = a$$

But $a\gamma/\gamma$ is any species of which the genus of a is the genus, i. e., any species x such that a and x belong to the same genus.

We turn now to consideration of the relation of concepts which have a common part.

Similarity is identity of properties. Two concepts are similar if, and in so far as, they comprehend identical properties. In respect to the remaining properties, they are different.[41]

ab represents the common properties of a and b.

$a - ab$ represents the peculiar properties of a.

$a + b - ab - ab$ represents the peculiar properties of a together with the peculiar properties of b.

It is evident from this last that Lambert does not wish to recognize in his system the law $a + a = a$; else he need only have written $a + b - ab$.

If x and a are of the same genus, then

$$x\gamma = a\gamma \qquad \text{and} \qquad ax = a\gamma = x\gamma$$

If now we symbolize by $a\,|\,b$ that part of a which is different from b,[42] then

$$(10) \qquad a\,|\,b + b\,|\,a + ab + ab = a + b$$

Also

$$x - x\,|\,a = a\gamma, \qquad \text{or} \qquad x = a\gamma + x\,|\,a$$

$$ax = a\delta$$

$$a - ax = a\delta$$

$$a = ax + a\delta$$

$$ax = a - a\delta = a\gamma = x\gamma$$

---

[41] *Ibid.*, p. 10.

[42] Lambert sometimes uses $a \mid b$ for this, sometimes $a : b$.

And since

$$x = \frac{a\gamma}{\gamma}$$

$$ax + a\,|\,x = a \qquad\qquad ax + x\,|\,a = x$$

$$ax = a - a\,|\,x = x - x\,|\,a$$

$$a\,|\,x = a - ax \qquad\qquad x\,|\,a = x - ax$$

The fact that y is a property comprehended in x may be expressed by $y = xy$ or by $y + x\,|\,y = x$. The manner in which Lambert deduces the second of these expressions from the first is interesting.[43] If y is a property of x, then $y\,|\,x$ is null. But by (10),

$$2xy + x\,|\,y + y\,|\,x = x + y$$

Hence in this case, $\qquad 2xy + x\,|\,y = x + y$

And since $y = xy$, $\qquad\quad 2y + x\,|\,y = x + y$

Hence $\qquad\qquad\qquad y + x\,|\,y = x$

He has subtracted y from both sides, in the last step, and we observe that $2y - y = y$. This is rather characteristic of his procedure; it follows, throughout, arithmetical analogies which are quite invalid for logic.

With the complications of this calculus, the reader will probably be little concerned. There is no general type of procedure for elimination or solution. Formulae of solution for different types of equation are given. They are highly ingenious, often complicated, and of dubious application. It is difficult to judge of possible applications because in the whole course of the development, so far as outlined, there is not a single illustration of a solution which represents logical reasoning, and very few illustrations of any kind.

The shortcomings of this calculus are fairly obvious. There is too much reliance upon the analogy between the logical relations symbolized and their arithmetical analogues. Some of the operations are logically uninterpretable, as for example the use of numerical coefficients other than 0 and 1. These have a meaning in the "Newtonian formula", but $2y$ either has no meaning or requires a conventional treatment which is not given. And in any case, to subtract y from both sides of $2y = x + y$ and get $y = x$ represents no valid logical operation. Any adequate study of the properties of the relations employed is lacking. $x = a + b$ is transformed into $a = x - b$, regardless of the fact that a and b may have a common part and that

[43] *Sechs Versuche*, p. 12.

$x - b$ represents the abstraction of the *whole* of b from x. Suppose, for example, man = rational + animal. Then, by Lambert's procedure, we should have also rational = man − animal. Since Leibniz had pointed out this difficulty,—that addition and subtraction (with exactly these meanings) are not true inverses, it is the more inexcusable that Lambert should err in this.

There is a still deeper difficulty here. As Lambert himself remarks,[44] *no* two concepts are so completely dissimilar that they do not have a common part. One might say that the concept "thing" (Lambert's word) or "being" is common to every pair of concepts. This being the case, [+] and [−] are *never* really inverse operations. Hence the difficulty will not really disappear even in the case of $a\gamma$ and $a\delta$; and $a - a\gamma = a\delta$, $a - a\delta = a\gamma$ will not be strictly valid. In fact this consideration vitiates altogether the use of "subtraction" in a calculus based on intension. For the meaning of $a - b$ becomes wholly doubtful unless [−] be treated as a *wholly conventional* inverse of [+], and in that case it becomes wholly useless.

The method by which Lambert treats the traditional syllogism is only remotely connected with what precedes, and its value does not entirely depend upon the general validity of his calculus. He reconstructs the whole of Aristotelian logic by the quantification of the predicate.[45]

The proposition "All A is B" has two cases:

(1) $A = B$, the case in which it has a universal converse, the concept A is identical with the concept B.

(2) $A > B$, the case in which the converse is particular, the concept B comprehended in the concept A.

The particular affirmative similarly has two cases:

(1) $A < B$, the case in which the converse is a universal, the subject A comprehended within the predicate B.

(2) The case in which the converse is particular. In this case the subject A is comprehended within a subsumed species of the predicate and the predicate within a subsumed species of the subject. Lambert says this may be expressed by the pair:

$$mA > B \qquad \text{and} \qquad A < nB$$

Those who are more accustomed to logical relations in extension must not make the mistake here of supposing that $A > mA$, and $mA < A$. mA is a species of A, and in intension the genus is contained in the species,

---

[44] *Ibid.*, p. 12.
[45] *Ibid.*, pp. 93 *ff.*

not vice versa. Hence $mA > B$ does not give $A > B$, as one might expect at first glance. We see that Lambert here translates "Some A" by mA, a species comprehended in A, making the same assumption which occurs in Leibniz, that any subdivision or portion of a class is capable of being treated as some species comprehended under that class as its genus.

In a universal negative proposition—Lambert says—the subject and predicate each have peculiar properties by virtue of whose comprehension neither is contained in the other. But if the peculiar properties of the subject be taken away, then what remains is contained in the predicate; and if the peculiar properties of the predicate be taken away, then what remains is contained in the subject. Thus the universal negative is represented by the pair

$$\frac{A}{m} < B \quad \text{and} \quad A > \frac{B}{n}$$

The particular negative has two cases:

(1) When it has a universal affirmative converse, i. e., when some A is not B but all B is A. This is expressed by

$$A < B$$

(2) When it has not a universal affirmative converse. In this case a subsumed species of the subject is contained in the predicate, and a subsumed species of the predicate in the subject.

$$mA > B \quad \text{and} \quad A < nB$$

Either of the signs, $<$ and $>$, may be reversed by transposing the terms. And if $P < Q$, $Q > P$, then for some l, $P = lQ$. Also, "multiplication" and "division" are strict inverses. Hence we can transform these expressions as follows:

$A > B$ is equivalent to $A = mB$

$A < B \qquad\qquad\qquad n A = B$

$\left.\begin{array}{l} mA > B \\ A < nB \end{array}\right\} \qquad \left\{\begin{array}{l} mA = kB \\ lA = nB \end{array}\right\} \quad \text{or} \quad pA = qB$

$\left.\begin{array}{l} \dfrac{A}{m} < B \\[2mm] A > \dfrac{B}{n} \end{array}\right\} \qquad \left\{\begin{array}{l} \dfrac{A}{m} = \dfrac{B}{k} \\[2mm] \dfrac{A}{l} = \dfrac{B}{n} \end{array}\right\} \quad \text{or} \quad \dfrac{A}{p} = \dfrac{B}{q}$

It is evident from these transformations and from the propositional equivalents of the "inequalities" that the following is the full expression of these equations:

(1) $A = mB$: All A is B and some B is not A.

(2) $nA = B$: Some A is not B and all B is A.

(3) $mA = nB$: Some, but not all, A is B, and some, but not all, B is A.

(4) $\dfrac{A}{m} = \dfrac{B}{n}$: No A is B.

The first noticeable defect here is that $A/m = B/n$ is transformable into $nA = mB$ and (4) can mean nothing different from (3). Lambert has, in fact, only four different propositions, if he sticks to the laws of his calculus:

(1) $A = B$: All A is all B.

(2) $A = mB$: All A is some B.

(3) $nA = B$: Some A is all B.

(4) $mA = nB$: Some A is some B.

These are the four forms which become, in Hamilton's and De Morgan's treatises, the four forms of the affirmative. A little scrutiny will show that Lambert's treatment of negatives is a failure. For it to be consistent at all, it is necessary that "fractions" should not be transformed. But Lambert constantly makes such transformations, though he carefully refrains from doing so in the case of expressions like $A/m = B/n$ which are supposed to represent universal negatives. His method further requires that m and n should behave like positive coefficients which are always greater than 0 and such that $m \neq n$. This is unfortunate. It makes it impossible to represent a simple proposition without "entangling alliances". If he had taken a leaf from Leibniz's book and treated negative propositions as affirmatives with negative predicates, he might have anticipated the calculus of De Morgan.

In symbolizing syllogisms, Lambert always uses A for the major term, B for the middle term, and C for the minor. The perfectly general form of proposition is:

$$\frac{mA}{p} = \frac{nB}{q}$$

Hence the perfectly general syllogism will be: [46]

$$\text{Major} \qquad \frac{mA}{p} = \frac{nB}{q}$$

[46] Ibid., pp. 102–103.
[47] Ibid., p 107.

$$\text{Minor} \qquad \frac{\mu C}{\pi} = \frac{\nu B}{\rho}$$

$$\text{Conclusion} \quad \frac{\mu n}{\pi q} C = \frac{m\nu}{p\rho} A.$$

The indeterminates in the minor are always represented thus by Greek letters.

The conclusion is de ved from the premises as follows:

The major premise gives $B = \dfrac{mq}{np} A.$

The minor gives $B = \dfrac{\mu\rho}{\pi\nu} C.$

Hence $\dfrac{mq}{np} A = \dfrac{\mu\rho}{\pi\nu} C.$

and therefore $\dfrac{\mu n}{\pi q} C = \dfrac{m\nu}{p\rho} A.$

The above being the general form of the syllogism, Lambert's scheme of moods in the first figure is the following: it coincides with the traditional classification only so far as indicated by the use of the traditional names:

I. Barbara	$B = mA$ $C = \nu B$ $C = m\nu B$	VII. Lilii	$nB = mA$ $\mu C = B$ $n\mu C = mA$	
II. Canerent	$B = A$ $\dfrac{C}{\pi} = \dfrac{B}{\rho}$ $\dfrac{C}{\pi} = \dfrac{A}{\rho}$	VIII. Magogos	$B = A$ $\mu C = nB$ $\mu C = nA$	
III. Decane sive Celarent	$\dfrac{B}{q} = \dfrac{A}{p}$ $C = \nu B$ $\dfrac{C}{q} = \dfrac{\nu A}{p}$	IX. Negligo sive Ferio	$\dfrac{B}{q} = \dfrac{A}{p}$ $C = \nu B$ $\dfrac{\mu C}{q} = \dfrac{\nu A}{p}$	

$$nB = A$$

IV. Fideleo	$\dfrac{C}{\pi} = \dfrac{B}{\rho}$ $\dfrac{nC}{\pi} = \dfrac{A}{\rho}$	X. Pilosos	$nB = A$ $\mu C = B$ $n\mu C = A$
V. Gabini sive Darii	$B = mA$ $\mu C = \nu B$ $\mu C = m\nu A$	XI. Romano	$nB = mA$ $C = B$ $nC = mA$
VI. Hilario	$nB = mA$ $C = B$ $nC = mA$	XII. Somnio	$nB = mA$ $\mu C = B$ $n\mu C = mA$

The difficulty about "division" does not particularly affect this scheme, since it is only required that if one of the premises involve "fractions", the conclusion must also. It will be noted that the mood *Hilario* is identical in form with *Romano*, and *Lilii* with *Somnio*. The reason for this lies in the fact that $nB = mA$ has two partial meanings, one affirmative and one negative (see above). *Hilario* and *Lilii* take the affirmative interpretation, as their names indicate; *Romano* and *Somnio*, the negative.

Into the discussion of the other three figures, the reader will probably not care to go, since the manner of treatment is substantially the same as in the above.

There are various other attempts to devise a convenient symbolism and method for formal logic;[48] but these are of the same general type, and they meet with about the same degree and kind of success.

Two brief passages in which there is an anticipation of the logic of relatives possess some interest.[49] Relations, Lambert says, are "external attributes", by which he means that they do not belong to the object *an sich*. "Metaphysical" (i. e., non-logical) relations are represented by Greek letters. For example if f = fire, h = heat, and α = cause,

$$f = \alpha :: h$$

The symbol : : represents a relation which behaves like multiplication:

[48] See in *Sechs Versuche*, v and vi. Also fragments "Über die Vernunftlehre", in *Logische und Philosophische Abhandlungen*, i, xix and xx; and *Anlage zur Architektonik*, p. 190 *ff.*

[49] *Sechs Versuche*, pp. 19   *ff.*

$\alpha : : h$ is in fact what Peirce and Schröder later called a "relative produ:t".
Lambert transforms the above equation into:

$$\frac{f}{h} = \frac{\alpha}{\cdot} \qquad \text{Fire is to heat as cause to effect.}$$

$$\frac{f}{\alpha} = \frac{h}{\cdot} \qquad \text{Fire is to cause as heat to effect.}$$

$$\frac{h}{f} = \frac{\cdot}{\alpha} \qquad \text{Heat is to fire as effect to cause.}$$

The dot here represents *Wirkung* (it might be, *Wirklichkeit*, in consonance
with the metaphysical interpretation, suggestive of Aristotle, which he
gives to *Ursache*). It has the properties of 1, as is illustrated elsewhere[50]
by the fact that γ^0 may be replaced by this symbol.

Lambert also uses powers of a relation.

If $a = \varphi : : b$, and $b = \varphi : : c$,

$$a = \varphi : : \varphi : : c = \varphi^2 : : c$$

And if $a = \varphi^2 : : c$,

$$\varphi^2 = \frac{a}{c} \qquad \text{and} \qquad \varphi = \sqrt{\frac{a}{c}}$$

And more to the same effect.

No use is made of this symbolism; indeed it is difficult to see how
Lambert could have used it. Yet it is interesting that he should have felt
that the powers of a relation ought to be logically important, and that he
here hit upon exactly the concept by which the riddles of "mathematical
induction" were later to be solved.

Holland's attempt at a logical calculus is contained in a letter to Lambert.[51] He himself calls it an "unripe thought", and in a letter some three
years later[52] he expresses a doubt if logic is really a purely formal discipline
capable of mathematical treatment. But this study is of particular interest
because it treats the logical classes in extension—the only attempt at a
symbolic logic from the point of view of extension from the time of Leibniz
to the treatise of Solly in 1839.

Holland objects to Lambert's method of representing the relation of
concepts by the relation of lines, one under the other, and argues that the

[50] *Ibid.*, p. 21.
[51] *Johan. Lamberts deutscher Gelehrten Briefwechsel, Brief* III, pp. 16 *ff.*
[52] See *Ibid., Brief* XXVII, pp. 259 *ff.*

relation of "men" to "mortals" is not *sub* but *inter*.   He is apparently not aware that this means exchanging the point of view of intension for that of extension, yet all his relations are consistently represented in extension, as we shall see.

(1) If S represent the subject, P the predicate; and p, π signify undetermined variable numbers, $S/p = P/\pi$ will come to: A part of S is a part of P, or certain of the S's are certain of the P's, or (at least) an S is a P.

This expression is the general formula of all possible judgments, as is evident by the following:

(2) A member is either positive or negative, and in both cases, is either finite or infinite.   We shall see in what fashion p and π can be understood.

(3) If $p = 1$ in S/p, then is S/p as many as all S, and in this way S/p attains its logical maximum.   Since, then, p cannot become less than 1, it can still less disappear and consequently cannot become negative.

The same is true of π.

(4) Therefore p and π cannot but be positive and cannot be less than 1. If p or π becomes infinite, the concept becomes negative.

(5) If f expresses a finite number > 1, then the possible forms of judgment are as follows:

$$(1) \quad \frac{S}{1} = \frac{P}{1} \quad \text{All } S \text{ is all } P.$$

$$(2) \quad \frac{S}{1} = \frac{P}{f} \quad \text{All } S \text{ is some } P.$$

Now 0 expresses negatively what $1/\infty$ expresses positively.   To say that an infinitely small part of a curved line is straight, means exactly: No part of a curved line is straight.

$$(3) \quad \frac{S}{1} = \frac{P}{\infty} \quad \text{All } S \text{ is not } P.$$

$$(4) \quad \frac{S}{f} = \frac{P}{1} \quad \text{Some } S \text{ is all } P.$$

$$(5) \quad \frac{S}{f} = \frac{P}{f} \quad \text{Some } S \text{ is some } P.$$

$$(6) \quad \frac{S}{f} = \frac{P}{\infty} \quad \text{Some } S \text{ is not } P.$$

$$(7) \quad \frac{S}{\infty} = \frac{P}{1} \quad \text{All not-}S \text{ is all } P.$$

[53] See *Ibid., Brief* IV.

$$(8) \quad \frac{S}{\infty} = \frac{P}{f} \qquad \text{All not-}S \text{ is some } P.$$

$$(9) \quad \frac{S}{\infty} = \frac{P}{\infty} \qquad \text{All not-}S \text{ is all not-}P.$$

(1), (2), and (9) Holland says are universal affirmative propositions; (3), (7), and (8), universal negatives; (4) and (5), particular affirmatives; (6), a particular negative.

As Venn has said, this notation anticipates, in a way, the method of Boole. If instead of the fraction we take the value of the numerator indicated by it, the three values are

$$\frac{S}{1} = 1 \cdot S, \qquad \frac{S}{f} = v \cdot S,$$

where $0 < v < 1$, and $S/\infty = 0 \cdot S$. But the differences between this and Boole's procedure are greater than the resemblances. The fractional form is a little unfortunate in that it suggests that the equations may be cleared of fractions, and this would give results which are logically uninterpretable. But Holland's notation can be made the basis of a completely successful calculus. That he did not make it such, is apparently due to the fact that he did not give the matter sufficient attention to elaborate the extensional point of view.

He gives the following examples:

Example 1. All men H are mortal M
All Europeans E are men H

$$H = \frac{M}{p} \qquad E = \frac{H}{\pi}$$

Ergo, $E = \dfrac{M}{p\pi}$ [All Europeans are mortal]

Example 2. All plants are organisms $P = \dfrac{O}{p}$

All plants are no animals $P = \dfrac{A}{\infty}$

Ergo, $\dfrac{O}{p} = \dfrac{A}{\infty}$ [Some organisms are not animals]

Example 3.   All men are rational $H = \dfrac{R}{p}$

All plants are not rational $P = \dfrac{R}{\infty}$

Ergo, All plants are no men $P = \dfrac{pH}{\infty}$

In this last example, Holland has evidently transformed $H = R/p$ into $pH = R$, which is not legitimate, as we have noted. $pH = R$ would be "Some men are all the rational beings". And the conclusion $P = pHi\infty$ is also misinterpreted. It should be, "All plants are not some men". A correct reading would have revealed the invalid operation.

Lambert replied vigorously to this letter, maintaining the superiority of the intensional method, pointing out, correctly, that Holland's calculus would not distinguish the merely non-existent from the impossible or contradictory (no calculus in extension can), and objecting to the use of ∞ in this connection. It is characteristic of their correspondence that each pointed out the logical defects in the logical procedure of the other, and neither profited by the criticism.

Castillon's essay toward a calculus of logic is contained in a paper presented to the Berlin Academy in 1803.[54] The letters S, A, etc., represent concepts taken in intension, M is an indeterminate, $S + M$ represents the "synthesis" of S and M, $S - M$, the withdrawal or abstraction of M from S. $S - M$ thus represents a genus concept in which S is subsumed, M being the logical "difference" of S in $S - M$. Consonantly $S + M$, symbolizing the addition of some "further specification" to S, represents a species concept which contains (in intension) the concept S.

The predicate of a universal affirmative proposition is contained in the subject (in intension). Thus "All S is A" is represented by

$$S = A + M$$

The universal negative "No S is A" is symbolized by

$$S = - A + M = (- A) + M$$

The concept S is something, M, from which A is withdrawn—is no A.

Particular propositions are divided into two classes, "real" and "illusory". A real particular is the converse of a universal affirmative; the

[54] "Mémoire sur un nouvel algorithme logique", in *Mémoires de l'Academie des Sciences de Berlin*, 1803, *Classe de philosophie speculative*, pp. 1–14. See also his paper, "Reflexions sur la Logique", *loc. cit.*, 1802.

illusory particular, one whose converse also is particular. The real particular affirmative is

$$A = S - M$$

since this is the converse of $S = A + M$. The illusory particular affirmative is represented by

$$S = A \mp M$$

Castillon's explanation of this is that the illusory particular judgment gives us to understand that some S alone is A, or that S is got from A by abstraction ($S = A - M$), when in reality it is A which is drawn from S by abstraction ($S = M + A$). Thus this judgment puts $- M$ where it should put $+ M$; one can, then, indicate it by $S = A \mp M$.

The fact is, of course, that "Some S is A " indicates nothing about the relations of the concepts S and A except that they are not incompatible. This means, in intension, that if one *or both* be further specified in proper fashion, the results will coincide. It might well be symbolized by $S + N = A + M$. We suspect that Castillon's choice of $S = A \mp M$ is really governed by the consideration that $S = A + M$ may be supposed to give $S = A \mp M$, the universal to give its subaltern, and that $A = S - M$ will also give $S = A \mp M$, that is to say, the real particular—which is "All A is S"—will also give $S = A \mp M$. Thus "Some S is A" may be derived both from "All S is A" and from "All A is S", which is a desideratum. *

The illusory negative particular is, correspondingly,

$$S = - A \mp M$$

Immediate inference works out fairly well in this symbolism.

The universal affirmative and the real particular are converses.

$S = A + M$ gives $A = S - M$, and vice versa. The universal negative is directly convertible.

$S = - A + M$ gives $A = - S + M$, and vice versa. The illusory particular is also convertible.

$S = A \mp M$ gives $- A = - S \mp M$. Hence $A = S \mp M$, which comes back to $S = A \mp M$.

A universal gives its subaltern

$S = A + M$ gives $S = A \mp M$, and

$S = - A + M$ gives $S = - A \mp M$.

And a real particular gives also the converse illusory particular, for

$A = S - M$ gives $S = A + M$,

which gives its subaltern, $S = A \mp M$,

which gives $A = S \mp M$.

All the traditional moods and figures of the syllogism may be symbolized in this calculus, those which involve particular propositions being valid both for the real particular and for the illusory particular. For example:

$$
\begin{array}{ll}
\text{All } M \text{ is } A & M = A + N \\
\text{All } S \text{ is } M & S = M + P \\
\therefore \quad \text{All } S \text{ is } A & \therefore \quad S = A + (N + P)
\end{array}
$$

$$
\begin{array}{ll}
\text{No } M \text{ is } A & M = -A + N \\
\text{All } S \text{ is } M & S = M + P \\
\therefore \quad \text{No } S \text{ is } A & \therefore \quad S = -A + (N + P)
\end{array}
$$

$$
\begin{array}{ll}
\text{All } M \text{ is } A & M = A + N \\
\text{Some } S \text{ is } M & S = M \mp P \quad \text{or} \quad S = M - P \\
\therefore \quad \text{Some } S \text{ is } A & \therefore \quad S = (A + N) \mp P \quad \text{or} \quad S = (A + N) - P
\end{array}
$$

This is the most successful attempt at a calculus of logic in intension.

The difficulty about "subtraction" in the XIX Fragment of Leibniz, and in Lambert's calculus, arises because $M - P$ does not mean "M but not P" or "M which is not P". If it mean this, then [+] and [−] are not true inverses. If, on the other hand, $M - P$ indicates the abstraction from the concept M of all that is involved in the concept P, then $M - P$ is difficult or impossible to interpret, and, in addition, the idea of negation cannot be represented by [−]. How does it happen, then, that Castillon's notation works out so well when he uses [−] *both* for abstraction and as the sign of negation? It would seem that his calculus ought to involve him in both kinds of difficulties.

The answer is that Castillon has, apparently by good luck, hit upon a method in which nothing is ever added to or subtracted from a determined concept, S or A, except an indeterminate, M or N or P, and this indeterminate, just because it is *indeterminate*, conceals the fact that [+] and [−] are not true inverses. And when the sign [−] appears before a determinate, A, it may serve as the sign of negation, because no difficulty arises from supposing the *whole* of what is negated to be absent, or abstracted.

Castillon's calculus is theoretically as unsound as Lambert's, or more so if unsoundness admits of degree. It is quite possible that it was worked out empirically and procedures which give invalid results avoided.

Whoever studies Leibniz, Lambert and Castillon cannot fail to be convinced that a consistent calculus of concepts in intension is either immensely difficult or, as Couturat has said, impossible. Its main difficulty is not the one which troubled Leibniz and which constitutes the main defect in Lambert's system—the failure of [+] and [−] to behave like true inverses. This can be avoided by treating negative propositions as affirmatives with negative predicates, as Leibniz did. The more serious difficulty is that a calculus of "concepts" is *not* a calculus of things *in actu* but only *in possibile*, and in a rather loose sense of the latter at that. Holland pointed this out admirably in a letter to Lambert.[55] He gives the example according to Lambert's method.

$$\text{All triangles are figures.} \qquad T = tF$$
$$\text{All quadrangles are figures.} \qquad Q = qF$$

Whence, $\qquad F = \dfrac{T}{t} = \dfrac{Q}{q}, \qquad$ or $\qquad qT = tQ$

and he then proceeds:[56]

"In general, if from $A = mC$ and $B = nC$ the conclusion $nA = mB$ be drawn, the calculus cannot determine whether the ideas nA and mB consist of contradictory partial-ideas, as in the foregoing example, or not. The thing must be judged according to the matter."

This example also calls attention to the fact that Lambert's calculus, by operations which he continually uses, leads to the fallacy of the undistributed middle term. If "some A" is simply some further specification of the concept A, then this mode is *not fallacious*. And this observation brings down the whole treatment of logic as a calculus of concepts in intension like a house of cards. The relations of existent things cannot be determined from the relations of concepts alone.

The calculus of Leibniz is more successful than any invented by his continental successors—unless Ploucquet's is an exception. That the long period between him and De Morgan and Boole did not produce a successful system of symbolic logic is probably due to the predilection for this intensional point of view. It is no accident that the English were so quickly successful after the initial interest was aroused; they habitually think of logical relations in extension, and when they speak of "intension" it is usually clear that they do not mean those relations of concepts which the "intension" of traditional logic signifies.

---

[55] *Deutscher Gelehrter Briefwechsel*, i, *Brief* xxvii.
[56] *Ibid.*, pp. 262–63.

The beginning of thought upon this subject in England is marked by the publication of numerous treatises, all proposing some modification of the traditional logic by quantifying the predicate. As Sir William Hamilton notes,[57] the period from Locke to 1833 is singularly barren of any real contributions to logic. About that time, Hamilton himself proposed the quantification of the predicate. As we now know, this idea was as old at least as Leibniz. Ploucquet, Lambert, Holland, and Castillon also had quantified the predicate. Both Hamilton and his student Thomson mention Ploucquet; but this new burst of logical study in England impresses one as greatly concerned about its own innovations and sublimely indifferent to its predecessors. Hamilton quarrelled at length with De Morgan to establish his priority in the matter.[58] This is the more surprising, since George Bentham, in his *Outline of a New System of Logic*, published in 1827, had quantified the predicate and given the following table of propositions:

1. X in toto $= Y$ ex parte;
2. X in toto $||$ Y ex parte;
3. X in toto $= Y$ in toto;
4. X in toto $||$ Y in toto;
5. X ex parte $= Y$ ex parte;
6. X ex parte $||$ Y ex parte;
7. X ex parte $= Y$ in toto;
8. X ex parte $||$ Y in toto.

($||$ is here the sign of "diversity").

But Hamilton was certainly the center and inspirer of a new movement in logic, the tendency of which was toward more precise analysis of logical significances. Bayne's *Essay on the New Analytic* and Thomson's *Laws of Thought* are the most considerable permanent record of the results, but there was a continual fervid discussion of logical topics in various periodicals; logistic was in the air.

This movement produced nothing directly which belongs to the history of symbolic logic. Hamilton's rather cumbersome notation is not made the basis of operations, but is essentially only an abbreviation of language. Solly's scheme of representing syllogisms was superior as a calculus. But

---

[57] See *Discussions on Philosophy*, pp. 119 *ff*.

[58] This controversy, begun in 1846, was continued for many years (see various articles in the *London Athenæum*, from 1860 to 1867). It was concluded in the pages of the *Contemporary Review*, 1873.

this movement accomplished two things for symbolic logic: it emphasized in fact—though not always in name—the point of view of extension, and it aroused interest in the problem of a newer and more precise logic. These may seem small, but whoever studies the history of logic in this period will easily convince himself that without these things, symbolic logic might never have been revived. Without Hamilton, we might not have had Boole. The record of symbolic logic on the continent is a record of failure, in England, a record of success. The continental students habitually emphasized intension; the English, extension.

IV. DE MORGAN

De Morgan[59] is known to most students of symbolic logic only through the theorem which bears his name. But he made other contributions of permanent value—the idea of the "universe of discourse",[60] the discovery of certain new types of propositions, and a beginning of the logic of relations. Also, his originality in the invention of new logical forms, his ready wit, his pat illustrations, and the clarity and liveliness of his writing did yeoman service in breaking down the prejudice against the introduction of "mathematical" methods in logic. His important writings on logic are comprised in the *Formal Logic*, the *Syllabus of a Proposed System of Logic*, and a series of articles in the *Transactions of the Cambridge Philosophical Society*.[61]

[59] Augustus De Morgan (1806–78), A.B. (Cambridge, 1827), Professor of Mathematics in the University of London 1828–31, reappointed 1835; writer of numerous mathematical treatises which are characterized by exceptional accuracy, originality and clearness. Perhaps the most valuable of these is "Foundations of Algebra" (*Camb. Phil. Trans.*, VII, VIII); the best known, the *Budget of Paradoxes*. For a list of his papers, see the *Royal Society Catalogue*. For many years an active member of the Cambridge Philosophical Society and the Royal Astronomical Society. Father of William F. De Morgan, the novelist and poet. For a brief biography, see *Monthly Notices of the Royal Astronomical Society*, XII, 112.

[60] The idea is introduced with these words: "Let us take a pair of contrary names, as man and not-man. It is plain that between them they represent everything, imaginable or real, in the universe. But the contraries of common language embrace, not the whole universe, but some one general idea. Thus, of men, Briton and alien are contraries: every man must be one of the two, no man can be both. . . . The same may be said of integer and fraction among numbers, peer and commoner among subjects of a realm, male and female among animals, and so on. In order to express this, let us say that the whole idea under consideration is *the universe* (meaning merely the whole of which we are considering parts) and let names which have nothing in common, but which between them contain the whole of the idea under consideration, be called contraries *in, or with respect to, that universe.*" (*Formal Logic*, p. 37; see also *Camb. Phil. Trans.*, VIII, 380.)

[61] *Formal Logic: or, The Calculus of Inference, Necessary and Probable*, 1847. Hereafter to be cited as *F. L.*

Although the work of De Morgan is strictly contemporary with that of Boole, his methods and symbolism ally him rather more with his predecessors than with Boole and those who follow. Like Hamilton, he is bent upon improving the traditional Aristotelian logic. His first step in this direction is to enlarge the number of typical propositions by considering all the combinations and distributions of two terms, X and Y, *and their negatives*. It is a feature of De Morgan's notation that the distribution of each term,[62] and the quality—affirmative or negative—of the proposition are indicated, these being sufficient to determine completely the type of the proposition.

That a term X is distributed is indicated by writing half a parenthesis before or after it, with the horns turned *toward* the letter, thus: $X)$, or $(X$. An undistributed term is marked by turning the half-parenthesis the other way, thus: $X($, or $)X$. $X))Y$, for example, indicates the proposition in which the subject, X, is distributed and the predicate, Y, is undistributed, that is, "All X is Y". $X()Y$ indicates a proposition with both terms undistributed, that is, "Some X is Y".[63] The negative of a term, X, is indicated by x; of Y by y, etc. A negative proposition is indicated by a dot placed between the parenthetical curves; thus "Some X is not Y" will be $X(\cdot(Y$.[64] Two dots, or none, indicates an affirmative proposition.

All the different forms of proposition which De Morgan uses can be generated from two types, the universal, "All . . . is . . .," and the particular, "Some . . . is . . .," by using the four terms, X and its negative, x, Y and y. For the universals we have:

Syllabus of a Proposed System of Logic, 1860. Hereafter to be cited as *Syll.*

Five papers (the first not numbered; various titles) in *Camb. Phil. Trans.*, VIII, IX, X.

The articles contain the most valuable material, but they are ill-arranged and interspersed with inapposite discussion. Accordingly, the best way to study De Morgan is to get these articles and the *Formal Logic*, note in a general way the contents of each, and then use the *Syllabus* as a point of departure for each item in which one is interested.

[62] He does not speak of "distribution" but of terms which are "universally spoken of" or "particularly spoken of", or of the "quantity" of a term.

[63] This is the notation of *Syll.* and of the articles, after the first, in *Camb. Phil. Trans.* For a table comparing the different symbolisms which he used, see *Camb. Phil. Trans.*, IX, 91.

[64] It is sometimes hard to determine by the conventional criteria whether De Morgan's propositions should be classed as affirmative or negative. He gives the following ingenious rule for distinguishing them (*Syll.*, p. 13): "Let a proposition be *affirmative* which is true of X and X, false of X and not-X or x; *negative*, which is true of X and x, false of X and X. Thus 'Every X is Y' is affirmative: 'Every X is X' is true; 'Every X is x' is false. But 'Some things are neither X's nor Y's' is also *affirmative*, though in the form of a *denial*: 'Some things are neither X's nor X's' is true, though superfluous in expression; 'Some things are neither X's nor x's' is false."

(1) $X))Y$ All X is Y.

(2) $x))y$ All not-X is not-Y.

(3) $X))y$ All X is not-Y.

(4) $x))Y$ All not-X is Y.

and for particulars we have:

(5) $X()Y$ Some X is Y.

(6) $x()y$ Some not-X is not-Y.

(7) $X()y$ Some X is not-Y.

(8) $x()Y$ Some not-X is Y.

The rule for transforming a proposition into other equivalent forms may be stated as follows: Change the distribution of either term—that is, turn its parenthetic curve the other way,—change that term into its negative, and change the quality of the proposition. That this rule is valid will appear if we remember that "two negatives make an affirmative", and note that we introduce one negative by changing the term, another by changing the quality of the proposition. That the distribution of the altered term should be changed follows from the fact that whatever proposition distributes a term leaves the negative of that term undistributed, and whatever proposition leaves a term undistributed distributes the negative of that term. Using this rule of transformation, we get the following table of equivalents for our eight propositions:

	(a)	(b)	(c)	(d)
(1)	$X))Y$	$= X)\cdot(y$	$= x((y$	$= x(\cdot)Y$
(2)	$x))y$	$= x)\cdot(Y$	$= X((Y$	$= X(\cdot)y$
(3)	$X))y$	$= X)\cdot(Y$	$= x((Y$	$= x(\cdot)y$
(4)	$x))Y$	$= x)\cdot(y$	$= X((y$	$= X(\cdot)Y$
(5)	$X()Y$	$= X(\cdot(y$	$= x)(y$	$= x)\cdot)Y$
(6)	$x()y$	$= x(\cdot(Y$	$= X)(Y$	$= X)\cdot)y$
(7)	$X()y$	$= X(\cdot(Y$	$= x)(Y$	$= x)\cdot)y$
(8)	$x()Y$	$= x(\cdot(y$	$= X)(y$	$= X)\cdot)Y$

It will be observed that in each line there is one proposition with both terms positive, X and Y. Selecting these, we have the eight different types of propositions:

(1*a*) X))Y All X is Y.

(2*c*) X((Y Some X is all Y; or, All Y is X.

(3*b*) X)·(Y No X is Y.

(4*d*) X(·)Y Everything is either X or Y. (See below.)

(5*a*) X()Y Some X is Y.

(6*c*) X)(Y Some things are neither X nor Y.   (See below.)

(7*b*) X(·(Y Some X is not Y.

(8*d*) X)·)Y All X is not some Y; or, Some Y is not X.

Since the quantity of each term is indicated, any one of these propositions may be read or written backwards—that is, with Y subject and X predicate —provided the distribution of terms is preserved.   (4*d*) and (6*c*) are difficult to understand.   We might attempt to read X(·)Y "Some X is not some Y", but we hardly get from that the difference between X(·)Y and X(·(Y, "Some X is not (any) Y".   Also, X(·)Y is equivalent to universals, and the reading, "Some X is not some Y", would make it particular. X(·)Y is equivalent to x))Y, "All not-X is Y", and to x)·(y, "No not-X is not-Y".   The only equivalent of these with the terms X and Y is, "Everything (in the universe of discourse) is either X or Y (or both)".   (6*c*), X)(Y, we should be likely to read "All X is all Y", or "X and Y are equivalent"; but this would be an error,[65] since its equivalents are particular propositions.   (6*a*), x()y, is "Some not-X is not-Y". The equivalent of this in terms of X and Y is plainly, "Some things are neither X nor Y".

Contradictories[66] of propositions in line (1) will be found in line (7); of those in line (2), in line (8); of line (3), in line (5); of line (4), in line (6). We give those with both terms positive:

(1*a*) X))Y	contradicts	(7*b*) X(·(Y
(2*c*) X((Y	"	(8*d*) X)·)Y
(3*b*) X)·(Y	"	(5*a*) X()Y
(4*d*) X(·)Y	"	(6*c*) X)(Y

[65] An error into which it might seem that De Morgan himself has fallen. See e. g., *Syll.*, p. 25, and *Camb. Phil. Trans.*, IX, 98, where he translates X)(Y by "All X is all Y", or "Any one X is any one Y".   But this belongs to another interpretation, the "cumular", which requires X and Y to be singular, and not-X and not-Y will then have common members.   However, as we shall note later, there is a real difficulty.

[66] De Morgan calls *contradictory* propositions "contraries" (See *F. L.*, p. 60; *Syll.*, p. 11), just as he calls terms which are negatives of one another "contraries".

Thus the rule is that two propositions having the same terms contradict one another when one is affirmative, the other negative, and the distribution of terms is exactly opposite in the two cases.

The rule for transforming propositions which has been stated and exemplified, together with the observation that any symbolized proposition may be read or written backwards, provided the distribution of the terms be preserved, gives us the principles for the immediate inference of universals from universals, particulars from particulars. For the rest, we have the rule, "Each universal affirms the particulars of the same quality".[67]

For syllogistic reasoning, the test of validity and rule of inference are as follows:[68]

"There is inference: 1. When both the premises are universal; 2. When, one premise only being particular, the middle term has different quantities in the two premises.

"The conclusion is found by erasing the middle term and its quantities [parenthetic curves]." This rule of inference is stated for the special arrangement of the syllogism in which the minor premise is put first, and the minor term first in the premise, the major term being the last in the second premise. Since any proposition may be written backward, this arrangement can always be made. According to the rule, $X))Y$, "All X is Y", and $Y)\cdot(Z$, "No Y is Z", give $X)\cdot(Z$, "No X is Z". $X)\cdot(Y$, "No X is Y", and $Y(\cdot(Z$, "Some Y is not Z", give $X)\cdot\cdot(Z$, or $X)(Z$, which is "Some things are neither X nor Z." The reader may, by inventing other examples, satisfy himself that the rule given is sufficient for all syllogistic reasoning, with any of De Morgan's eight forms of propositions.

De Morgan also invents certain compound propositions which give compound syllogisms in a fashion somewhat analogous to the preceding:[69]

"1. $X)\bigcirc)Y$ or both $X))Y$ and $X)\cdot)Y$ — All X's and some things besides are Y's.

2. $X||Y$ or both $X))Y$ and $X((Y$ — All X's are Y's, and all Y's are X's.

3. $X(\bigcirc(Y$ or both $X((Y$ and $X(\cdot(Y$ — Among X's are all the Y's and some things besides.

4. $X)\bigcirc(Y$ or both $X)\cdot(Y$ and $X)(Y$ — Nothing both X and Y and some things neither.

[67] *Syll.*, p. 16.
[68] *Syll.*, p. 19.
[69] *Syll.*, p. 22.

5. $X|\cdot|Y$ or both $X)\cdot(Y$ and $X(\cdot)Y$ Nothing both X and Y and everything one or the other.

6. $X(\bigcirc)Y$ or both $X(\cdot)Y$ and $X()Y$ Everything either X or Y and some things both."

Each of these propositions may, with due regard for the meaning of the sign $\bigcirc$, be read or written backward, just as the simple propositions. The rule of transformation into other equivalent forms is slightly different: Change the quantity, or distribution, of any term and replace that term by its negative. We are not required, as with the simple propositions, to change at the same time the quality of the proposition. This difference is due to the manner in which the propositions are compounded.

The rules for mediate, or "syllogistic", inference for these compound propositions are as follows: [70]

"If any two be joined, each of which is [of the form of] 1, 3, 4, or 6, with the middle term of different quantities, these premises yield a conclusion of the same kind, obtained by erasing the symbols of the middle term and one of the symbols $[\bigcirc]$. Thus $X)\bigcirc(Y(\bigcirc)Z$ gives $X)\bigcirc)Z$: or if nothing be both X and Y and some things neither, and if everything be either Y or Z and some things both, it follows that all X and *two lots* of other things are Z's.

"In any one of these syllogisms, it follows that $||$ may be written for $)\bigcirc)$ or $)\bigcirc($ in one place, without any alteration of the conclusion, except reducing the *two lots* to one. But if this be done in both places, the conclusion is reduced to $||$ or $|\cdot|$, and *both lots* disappear. Let the reader examine for himself the cases in which one of the premises is cut down to a simple universal.

"The following exercises will exemplify what precedes. Letters written under one another are names of the same object. Here is a universe of 12 instances of which 3 are X's and the remainder P's; 5 are Y's and the remainder Q's; 7 are Z's and the remainder R's.

$$X\ X\ X \quad P\ P \quad P\ P \quad P\ P\ P\ P\ P$$
$$Y\ Y\ Y \quad Y\ Y \quad Q\ Q \quad Q\ Q\ Q\ Q\ Q$$
$$Z\ Z\ Z \quad Z\ Z \quad Z\ Z \quad R\ R\ R\ R\ R$$

We can thus verify the eight complex syllogisms

$X)\bigcirc)Y)\bigcirc)Z$	$P(\bigcirc)Y)\bigcirc)Z$	$P(\bigcirc(Q(\bigcirc)Z$	$P(\bigcirc(Q(\bigcirc(R$
$P(\bigcirc)Y)\bigcirc(R$	$X)\bigcirc)Y)\bigcirc(R$	$X)\bigcirc(Q(\bigcirc(R$	$X)\bigcirc(Q(\bigcirc)Z$

[70] *Syll.*, p. 23.

In every case it will be seen that the two lots in the middle form the quantity of the particular proposition of the conclusion."

In so much of his work as we have thus far reviewed, De Morgan is still too much tied to his starting point in Aristotelian logic. He somewhat simplifies traditional methods and makes new generalizations which include old rules, but it is still distinctly the old logic. He does not question the inference from universals to particulars nor observe the problems there involved.[71] He does not seek a method by which any number of terms may be dealt with but accepts the limitation to the traditional two. And his symbolism has several defects. The dot introduced between the parenthetic curves is not the sign of negation, so as to make it possible to read $(\cdot)$ as, "It is false that ()". The negative of () is $) \cdot ($, so that this simplest of all relations of propositions is represented by a complex transformation applicable only when no more than two terms are involved in the propositional relation. Also, there are two distinct senses in which a term in a proposition may be distributed or "mentioned universally", and De Morgan, following the scholastic tradition, fails to distinguish them and symbolizes both the same way. This is the secret of the difficulty in reading $X)(Y$, which looks like "All X is all Y", and really is "Some things are neither X nor Y".[72] Mathematical symbols are introduced but without any corresponding mathematical operations. The sign of equality is used both for the symmetrical relation of equivalent propositions and for the unsymmetrical relation of premises to their conclusion.[73]

His investigation of the logic of relations, however, is more successful, and he laid the foundation for later researches in that field. This topic is suggested to him by consideration of the formal and material elements in logic. He says:[74]

[71] But he does make the assumption upon which all inference (in extension) of a particular from a universal is necessarily based: the assumption that a class denoted by a simple term has members. He says (*F. L.*, pp. 110), "Existence as objects, or existence as ideas, is tacitly claimed for the terms of every syllogism".

[72] A universal affirmative distributes its subject in the sense that it indicates the class to which every member of the subject belongs, i. e., the class denoted by the predicate. Similarly, the universal negative, No X is Y, indicates that every X is not-Y, every Y is not-X. No particular proposition distributes a term in that sense. The particular negative tells us only that the predicate is excluded from *some unspecified portion* of the class denoted by the subject. $X)(Y$ distributes X and Y in this sense only. Comparison with its equivalents shows us that it can tell us, of X, only that it is excluded from some unspecified portion of not-Y; and of Y, only that it is excluded from some unspecified portion of not-X. We cannot infer that X is wholly included in Y, or Y in X, or get any other relation of inclusion out of it.

[73] In one passage (*Camb. Phil. Trans.*, x, 183) he suggests that the relation of two premises to their conclusion should be symbolized by $A\ B < C$.

[74] *Camb. Phil. Trans.*, x, 177, footnote.

"Is there any *consequence* without *form*? Is not *consequence* an action of the machinery? Is not logic the science of the action of the machinery? Consequence is always an *act* of the mind: on every consequence logic ought to ask, What kind of act? What is the *act*, as distinguished from the *acted on*, and from any inessential concomitants of the action? For these are of the form, as distinguished from the matter.

". . . The copula performs certain functions; it is competent to those functions . . . because it has certain properties, which are sufficient to validate its use. . . . The word 'is,' which identifies, does not do its work because it identifies, except insofar as identification is a *transitive* and *convertible* motion: '*A* is *that which is B*' means '*A* is *B*'; and '*A* is *B*' means '*B* is *A*'. Hence every transitive and convertible relation is as fit to validate the syllogism as the copula '*is*', and by the same proof in each case. Some forms are valid when the relation is only transitive and not convertible; as in 'give'. Thus if *X—Y* represent *X* and *Y* connected by a transitive copula, *Camestres* in the second figure is valid, as in

$$\text{Every } Z—Y, \quad \text{No } X—Y, \quad \text{therefore} \quad \text{No } X—Z.$$

. . . In the following chain of propositions, there is exclusion of matter, form being preserved at every step:

		Hypothesis
(Positively true)	Every man is animal	
"	Every man is Y	Y has existence.
"	Every X is Y	X has existence.
"	Every $X—Y$	— is a transitive relation.
"	α of $X—Y$	α is a fraction $<$ or $= 1$.
(Probability β)	α of $X—Y$	β is a fraction $<$ or $= 1$.

The last is *nearly* the purely formal judgment, with not a single material point about it, except the transitiveness of the copula.[75]

". . . I hold the supreme *form* of the syllogism of one middle term to be as follows: There is the probability α that X is in the relation L to Y; there is the probability β that Y is in the relation M to Z; whence there is the probability $\alpha\beta$ that X is in the relation L of M to Z.[76]

". . . The copula of cause and effect, of motive and action, of all which *post hoc* is of the form and *propter hoc* (perhaps) of the matter, will one day be carefully considered in a more complete system of logic."[77]

[75] *Ibid.*, pp. 177–78.
[76] *Ibid.*, p. 339.
[77] *Ibid.*, pp. 179–80.

De Morgan is thus led to a study of the categories of exact thinking in general, and to consideration of the types and properties of relations. His division of categories into logico-mathematical, logico-physical, logico-metaphysical, and logico-contraphysical,[78] is inauspicious, and nothing much comes of it. But in connection with this, and an attempt to rebuild logic in the light of it, he propounds the well-known theorem: "The contrary [negative] of an aggregate [logical sum] is the compound [logical product] of the contraries of the aggregants: the contrary of a compound is the aggregate of the contraries of the components." [79]

For the logic of relations, X, Y, and Z will represent the class names; L, M, N, relations. $X . . LY$ will signify that X is some one of the objects of thought which stand to Y in the relation L, or is one of the L's of Y.[80] $X . LY$ will signify that X is not any one of the L's of Y. $X . . (LM)Y$ or $X . . LM\ Y$ will express the fact that X is one of the L's of one of the M's of Y, or that X has the relation L to some Z which has the relation M to Y. $X . LM\ Y$ will mean that X is not an L of any M of Y.

It should be noted that the union of the two relations L and M is what we should call today their "relative product"; that is, $X . . LY$ and $Y . . MZ$ together give $X . . LM\ Z$, but $X . . LY$ and $X . . MY$ do *not* give $X . . LM\ Y$. If L is the relation "brother of" and M is the relation "aunt of", $X . . LM\ Y$ will mean "X is a brother of an aunt of Y". (Do not say hastily, "X is uncle of Y". "Brother of an aunt" is not equivalent to "uncle" since some uncles have no sisters.) L, or M, written by itself, will represent *that which has* the relation L, or M, that is, a brother, or an aunt, and LY stands for any X which has the relation L to Y, that is, a brother of Y.[81]

In order to reduce ordinary syllogisms to the form in which the copula has that abstractness which he seeks, that is, to the form in which the copula may be *any* relation, or any relation of a certain type, it is necessary to introduce symbols of quantity. Accordingly LM^* is to signify an L of *every* M, that is, something which has the relation L to every member of the class M (say, a lover of every man). $L*M$ is to indicate an L of *none but* M's (a lover of none but men). The mark of quantity, * or *, always

---

[78] See *ibid.*, p. 190.

[79] *Ibid.*, p. 208. See also *Syll.*, p. 41. Pp. 39–60 of *Syll.* present in summary the ideas of the paper, "On the Syllogism, No. 3, and on Logic in General."

[80] *Camb. Phil. Trans.*, x, 341. We follow the order of the paper from this point on.

[81] I tried at first to make De Morgan's symbolism more readily intelligible by introducing the current equivalents of his characters. But his systematic ambiguities, such as the use of the same letter for the relation and for that which has the relation, made this impossible. For typographical reasons, I use the asterisk where he has a small accent.

goes with the letter which precedes it, but L_*M is read *as if* [*] modified the letter which follows. To obviate this difficulty, De Morgan suggests that L_*M be read, "An every- L of M; an L of M in every way in which it is an L," but we shall stick to the simpler reading, "An L of none but M's".

LM^*X means an L of every M of X: L_*MX, an L of none but M's of X: L_*M^*, an L of every M and of none but M's: LMX^*, an L of an M of every X, and so on.

Two more symbols are needed. The converse of L is symbolized by L^{-1}. If L is "lover of", L^{-1} is "beloved of"; if L is "aunt", L^{-1} is "niece or nephew". The contrary (or as we should say, the negative) of L is symbolized by l; the contrary of M by m.

In terms of these relations, the following theorems can be stated:

(1) Contraries of converses are themselves contraries.

(2) Converses of contraries are contraries.

(3) The contrary of the converse is the converse of the contrary.

(4) If the relation L be contained in, or imply, the relation M, then (a) the converse of L, L^{-1}, is contained in the converse of M, M^{-1}; and (b) the contrary of M, m, is contained in the contrary of L, l.

For example, if "parent of" is contained in "ancestor of", (a) "child of" is contained in "descendent of", and (b) "not ancestor of" is contained in "not parent of".

(5) The conversion of a compound relation is accomplished by converting both components and inverting their order; thus, $(LM)^{-1} = M^{-1}L^{-1}$.

If X be teacher of the child of Y, Y is parent of the pupil of X.

When a sign of quantity is involved in the conversion of a compound relation, the sign of quantity changes its place on the letter; thus, $(LM^*)^{-1} = M_*^{-1}L^{-1}$.

If X be teacher of *every* child of Y, Y is parent of *none but* pupils of X.

(6) When, in a compound relation, there is a sign of quantity, if each component be changed into its contrary, and the sign of quantity be shifted from one component to the other and its position on the letter changed, the resulting relation is equivalent to the original; thus $LM^* = l_*m$ and $L_*M = lm^*$.

A lover of every man is a non-lover of none but non-men; and a lover of none but men is a non-lover of every non-man.

(7) When a compound relation involves no sign of quantity, its contrary is found by taking the contrary of either component and giving quantity to the other. The contrary of LM is lM^* or L_*m.

"*Not* (lover of a man)" is "non-lover of every man" or "lover of none but non-men"; and there are two equivalents, by (6).

But if there be a sign of quantity in one component, the contrary is taken by dropping that sign and taking the contrary of the other component. The contrary of LM^* is lM; of L_*M is Lm.

"*Not* (lover of every man)" is "non-lover of a man"; and "*not* (lover of none but men)" is "lover of a non-man".

So far as they do not involve quantifications, these theorems are familiar to us today, though it seems not generally known that they are due to De Morgan. The following table contains all of them:

Combination	Converse	Contrary	Converse of Contrary Contrary of Converse
LM	$M^{-1}L^{-1}$	lM^* or L_*M	$M_*{}^{-1}l^{-1}$ or $m^{-1}L^{-1}*$
LM^* or l_*m	$M_*{}^{-1}L^{-1}$ or $m^{-1}l^{-1}*$	lM	$M^{-1}l^{-1}$
L_*M or lm^*	$M^{-1}L^{-1}*$ or $m_*{}^{-1}l^{-1}$	Lm	$m^{-1}L^{-1}$

The sense in which one relation is said to be "contained in" or to "imply" another should be noted: L is contained in M in case every X which has the relation L to any Y has also the relation M to that Y. This must not be confused with the relation of *class* inclusion between two relative terms. Every grandfather is also a father, the *class* of grandfathers is contained in the *class* of fathers, but "grandfather of" is not contained in "father of", because the grandfather of Y is not also the father of Y. The relation "grandfather of" *is* contained in "ancestor of", since the grandfather of Y is also the ancestor of Y. But De Morgan appropriately uses the same *symbol* for the relation "L contained in M" that he uses for "All L is M", where L and M are class terms, that is, $L))M$.

In terms of this relation of relations, the following theorems can be stated:

(8) If $L))M$, then the contrary of M is contained in the contrary of L,— that is, $L))M$ gives $m))l$.

Applying this theorem to compound relations, we have:

(8') $LM))N$ gives $n))lM^*$ and $n))L_*m$.

(8'') If $LM))N$, then $L^{-1}n))m$ and $nM^{-1}))l$.

Proof: If $LM))N$, then $n))lM^*$. Whence $nM^{-1}))lM^*M^{-1}$. But an l of every M of an M^{-1} of Z must be an l of Z. Hence $nM^{-1}))l$. Again; if $LM))N$, then $n))L*m$. Whence $L^{-1}n))L^{-1}L*m$. But whatever has the relation converse-of-L to an L of none but m's must be itself an m. Hence $L^{-1}n))m$.

De Morgan calls this "theorem K" from its use in *Baroko* and *Bokardo*.

(9) If $LM = N$, then $L))NM^{-1}$ and $M))L^{-1}N$.

Proof: If $LM = N$, then $LMM^{-1} = NM^{-1}$ and $L^{-1}LM = L^{-1}N$. Now for any X, $MM^{-1}X$ and $L^{-1}LX$ are classes which contain X; hence the theorem.

We do not have $L = NM^{-1}$ and $M = L^{-1}N$, because it is not generally true that $MM^{-1}X = X$ and $L^{-1}LX = X$. For example, the child of the parent of X may not be X but X's brother: but the class "children of the parent of X" will *contain* X. The relation MM^{-1} or $M^{-1}M$ will not always cancel out. MM^{-1} and $M^{-1}M$ are always *symmetrical* relations; if $XMM^{-1}Y$ then $YMM^{-1}X$. If X is child of a parent of Y, then Y is child of a parent of X. But MM^{-1} and $M^{-1}M$ are *not exclusively* reflexive. $XMM^{-1}X$ does not always hold. If we know that a child of the parent of X is a celebrated linguist we may not hastily assume that X is the linguist in question.

With reference to transitive relations, we may quote: [82]

"A relation is transitive when a relative of a relative is a relative of the same kind; as symbolized in $LL))L$, whence $LLL))LL))L$; and so on.

"A transitive relation has a transitive *converse*, but not necessarily a transitive contrary: for $L^{-1}L^{-1}$ is the converse of LL, so that $LL))L$ gives $L^{-1}L^{-1}))L^{-1}$. From these, by contraposition, and also by theorem K and its contrapositions, we obtain the following results:

$$L \text{ is contained in } LL^{-1}*, \; l*l^{-1}, \; l^{-1}l*, \; L*^{-1}L$$
$$L^{-1} \ldots \ldots \ldots L*L^{-1}, \; ll^{-1}*, \; l*^{-1}l, \; L^{-1}L*$$
$$l \ldots \ldots \ldots \ldots lL*, \; L*l$$
$$l^{-1} \ldots \ldots \ldots L*^{-1}l^{-1}, \; l^{-1}L^{-1}*$$
$$LL \ldots \ldots \ldots \ldots L$$
$$L^{-1}L^{-1} \ldots \ldots \ldots L^{-1}$$
$$L^{-1}l, \; lL^{-1} \ldots \ldots l$$
$$Ll^{-1}, \; l^{-1}L \ldots \ldots \ldots l^{-1}$$

"I omit demonstration, but to prevent any doubt about correctness of printing, I subjoin instances in words: L signifies *ancestor* and L^{-1} *descendent*.

[82] *Camb. Phil. Trans.*, x, 346. For this discussion of transitive relations, De Morgan treats all reciprocal relations, such as $XLL^{-1}Y$, as also reflexive, though not necessarily exclusively reflexive.

"An ancestor is always an ancestor of all descendents, a non-ancestor of none but non-descendents, a non-descendent of all non-ancestors, and a descendent of none but ancestors. A descendent is always an ancestor of none but descendents, a non-ancestor of all non-descendents, a non-descendent of none but non-ancestors, and a descendent of all ancestors. A non-ancestor is always a non-ancestor of all ancestors, and an ancestor of none but non-ancestors. A non-descendent is a descendent of none but non-descendents, and a non-descendent of all descendents. Among non-ancestors are contained all descendents of non-ancestors, and all non-ancestors of descendents. Among non-descendents are contained all ancestors of non-descendents, and all non-descendents of ancestors."

In terms of the general relation, L, or M, representing *any* relation, the syllogisms of traditional logic may be tabulated as follows: [83]

"

	1	2	3	4
	$X .. LY$	$X . LY$	$X .. LY$	$X . LY$
I	$Y .. LZ$	$Y .. MZ$	$Y . MZ$	$Y . MZ$
	$X .. LMZ$	$X .. lMZ$	$X .. LmZ$	$X .. lmZ$
	$X . LY$	$X .. LY$	$X .. LY$	$X . LY$
II	$Z .. MY$	$Z .. MY$	$Z . MY$	$Z . MY$
	$X .. lM^{-1}Z$	$X .. LM^{-1}Z$	$X .. Lm^{-1}Z$	$X .. lm^{-1}Z$
	$Y .. LX$	$Y . LX$	$Y .. LX$	$Y . LX$
III	$Y . MZ$	$Y .. MZ$	$Y .. MZ$	$Y . MZ$
	$X .. L^{-1}mZ$	$X .. l^{-1}MZ$	$X .. L^{-1}MZ$	$X .. l^{-1}mZ$
	$Y . LX$	$Y .. LX$	$Y . LX$	$Y .. LX$
IV	$Z . MY$	$Z . MY$	$Z .. MY$	$Z .. MY$
	$X .. l^{-1}m^{-1}Z$	$X .. L^{-1}m^{-1}Z$	$X .. l^{-1}M^{-1}Z$	$X .. L^{-1}M^{-1}Z$"

The Roman numerals here indicate the traditional figures. All the conclusions are given in the affirmative form; but for each affirmative conclusion, there are two negative conclusions, got by negating the relation and replacing it by one or the other of its contraries. Thus $X .. LMZ$ gives $X . lM*Z$ and $X . L*mZ$; $X .. lM^{-1}Z$ gives $X . LM^{-1}*Z$ and $X . l*m^{-1}Z$, and so on for each of the others.

[83] *Ibid.*, p. 350.

When the copula of all three propositions is limited to the *same transitive* relation, *L*, or its converse, the table of syllogisms will be: [84]

"	$X \mathbin{..} LY$	$X . LY$	$X \mathbin{..} LY$	
I	$Y \mathbin{..} LZ$	$Y \mathbin{..} L^{-1}Z$	$Y . L^{-1}Z$	———
	$X \mathbin{..} LZ$	$X . LZ$	$X . L^{-1}Z$	
	$X . LY$	$X \mathbin{..} LY$	$X \mathbin{..} LY$	
II	$Z \mathbin{..} LY$	$Z \mathbin{..} L^{-1}Y$	$Z . LY$	———
	$X . LZ$	$X \mathbin{..} LZ$	$X . L^{-1}Z$	
	$Y \mathbin{..} LX$	$Y . LX$	$Y \mathbin{..} LX$	
III	$Y . LZ$	$Y \mathbin{..} LZ$	$Y \mathbin{..} L^{-1}Z$	———
	$X . LZ$	$X . L^{-1}Z$	$X \mathbin{..} L^{-1}Z$	
		$Y \mathbin{..} LX$	$Y . LX$	$Y \mathbin{..} LX$
IV	———	$Z . L^{-1}Y$	$Z \mathbin{..} L^{-1}Y$	$Z \mathbin{..} LY$
		$X . LZ$	$X . L^{-1}Z$	$X \mathbin{..} L^{-1}Z$ "

Here, again, in the logic of relations, De Morgan would very likely have done better if he had left the traditional syllogism to shift for itself. The introduction of quantifications and the systematic ambiguity of *L, M*, etc., which are used to indicate both the relation and that which has the relation, hurry him into complications before the simple analysis of relations, and types of relations, is ready for them. This logic of relations was destined to find its importance in the logistic of mathematics, not in any applications to, or modifications of, Aristotelian logic. And these complications of De Morgan's, due largely to his following the clues of formal logic, had to be discarded later, after Peirce discovered the connection between Boole's algebra and relation theory. The logic of relative terms has been reintroduced by the work of Frege and Peano, and more especially of Whitehead and Russell, in the logistic development of mathematics. But it is there separated—and has to be separated—from the simpler analysis of the relations themselves. Nevertheless, it should always be remembered that it was De Morgan who laid the foundation; and if some part of his work had to be discarded, still his contribution was indispensable and of permanent value. In concluding his paper on relations, he justly remarks: [85]

[84] *Ibid.*, p. 354.
[85] *Ibid.*, p. 358.

"And here the general idea of relation emerges, and for the first time in the history of knowledge, the notions of relation and *relation* of *relation* are symbolized. And here again is seen the scale of graduation of forms, the manner in which what is difference of form at one step of the ascent is difference of *matter* at the next. But the relation of algebra to the higher developments of logic is a subject of far too great extent to be treated here. It will hereafter be acknowledged that, though the geometer did not think it necessary to throw his ever-recurring *principium et exemplum* into imitation of *Omnis homo est animal, Sortes est homo*, etc., yet the algebraist was living in the higher atmosphere of syllogism, the unceasing composition of relation, before it was admitted that such an atmosphere existed." [86]

V. Boole

The beginning from which symbolic logic has had a continuous development is that made by George Boole.[87] His significant and vital contribution was the introduction, in a fashion more general and systematic than before, of mathematical operations. Indeed Boole allows operations which have no direct logical interpretation, and is obviously more at home in mathematics than in logic. It is probably the great advantage of Boole's work that he either neglected or was ignorant of those refinements of logical theory which hampered his predecessors. The precise mathematical development of logic needed to make its own conventions and interpretations; and this could not be done without sweeping aside the accumulated traditions of the non-symbolic Aristotelian logic. As we shall see, all the nice problems of intension and extension, of the existential import of universals and particulars, of empty classes, and so on, return later and demand consideration. It is well that, with Boole, they are given a vacation long enough to get the subject started in terms of a simple and general procedure.

Boole's first book, *The Mathematical Analysis of Logic, being an Essay toward a Calculus of Deductive Reasoning*, was published in 1847, on the

[86] I omit, with some misgivings, any account of De Morgan's contributions to probability theory as applied to questions of authority and judgment. (See *Syll.*, pp. 67–72; *F. L.*, Chap. ix, x; and *Camb. Phil. Trans.*, viii, 384–87, and 393–405.) His work on this topic is less closely connected with symbolic logic than was Boole's. The allied subject of the "numerically definite syllogism" (see *Syll.*, pp. 27–30; *F. L.*, Chap. viii; and *Camb. Phil. Trans.*, x, *355–*358) is also omitted.

[87] George Boole (1815–1864) appointed Professor of Mathematics in Queen's College, Cork, 1849; LL.D. (Dublin, 1852), F.R.S. (1857), D.C.L. (Oxford, 1859). For a biographical sketch, by Harley, see *Brit. Quart. Rev.*, xliv (1866), 141–81. See also *Proc. Roy. Soc.*, xv (1867), vi–xi.

same day as De Morgan's *Formal Logic*.[88] The next year, his article, "The Calculus of Logic," appeared in the *Cambridge Mathematical Journal*. This article summarizes very briefly and clearly the important innovations proposed by Boole. But the authoritative statement of his system is found in *An Investigation of the Laws of Thought, on which are founded the Mathematical Theories of Logic and Probability*, published in 1854.[89]

Boole's algebra, unlike the systems of his predecessors, is based squarely upon the relations of extension. The three fundamental ideas upon which his method depends are: (1) the conception of "elective symbols"; (2) the laws of thought expressed as rules for operations upon these symbols; (3) the observation that these rules of operation are the same which would hold for an algebra of the numbers 0 and 1.[90]

For reasons which will appear shortly, the "universe of conceivable objects" is represented by 1. All other classes or aggregates are supposed to be formed from this by selection or limitation. This operation of *electing*, in 1, all the X's, is represented by $1 \cdot x$ or x; the operation of electing all the Y's is similarly represented by $1 \cdot y$ or y, and so on. Since Boole does not distinguish between this operation of election represented by x, and the result of performing that operation—an ambiguity common in mathematics—x becomes, in practice, the symbol for the class of all the X's. Thus x, y, z, etc., representing ambiguously operations of election or classes, are the variables of the algebra. Boole speaks of them as "elective symbols" to distinguish them from coefficients.

This operation of election suggests arithmetical multiplication: the suggestion becomes stronger when we note that it is not confined to 1. $1 \cdot x \cdot y$ or xy will represent the operation of electing, first, all the X's in the "universe", and from this class by a second operation, all the Y's. The result of these two operations will be the class whose members are both X's and Y's. Thus xy is the class of the common members of x and y; xyz, the class of those things which belong at once to x, to y, and to z, and so on. And for any x, $1 \cdot x = x$.

The operation of "aggregating parts into a whole" is represented by $+$. $x + y$ symbolizes the class formed by combining the two distinct classes, x and y. It is a distinctive feature of Boole's algebra that x and y in $x + y$ must have no common members. The relation may be read, "that which

---

[88] See De Morgan's note to the article "On Propositions Numerically Definite", *Camb. Phil. Trans.*, xi (1871), 396.

[89] London, Walton and Maberly.

[90] This principle appears for the first time in the *Laws of Thought*. See pp. 37–38. Work hereafter cited as *L. of T.*

is either x or y *but not both*". Although Boole does not remark it, $x + y$ cannot be as completely analogous to the corresponding operation of ordinary algebra as xy is to the ordinary algebraic product. In numerical algebras a number may be added to itself: but since Boole conceives the terms of any logical sum to be "quite distinct",[91] mutually exclusive classes, $x + x$ cannot have a meaning in his system. As we shall see, this is very awkward, because such expressions still occur in his algebra and have to be dealt with by troublesome devices.

But making the relation $x + y$ completely disjunctive has one advantage —it makes possible the inverse relation of "subtraction". The "separation of a part, x, from a whole, y", is represented by $y - x$. If $x + z = y$, then since x and z have nothing in common, $y - x = z$ and $y - z = x$. Hence $[+]$ and $[-]$ are strict inverses.

$x + y$, then, symbolizes the class of those things which are *either* members of x *or* members of y, but not of both. $x \cdot y$ or xy symbolizes the class of those things which are *both* members of x *and* members of y. $x - y$ represents the class of the members of x which are not members of y—the x's except the y's. $[=]$ represents the relation of two classes which have the same members, i. e., have the same extension. These are the fundamental relations of the algebra.

The entity $(1 - x)$ is of especial importance. This represents the universe except the x's, or all things which are not x's. It is, then, the supplement or negative of x.

With the use of this symbolism for the negative of a class, the sum of two classes, x and y, which have members in common, can be represented by

$$xy + x(1 - y) + (1 - x)y.$$

The first term of this sum is the class which are both x's and y's; the second, those which are x's but not y's; the third, those which are y's but not x's. Thus the three terms represent classes which are all mutually exclusive, and the sum satisfies the meaning of $+$. In a similar fashion, $x + y$ may be expanded to

$$x(1 - y) + (1 - x)y.$$

Consideration of the laws of thought and of the meaning of these symbols will show us that the following principles hold:

(1) $xy = yx$ What is both x and y is both y and x.

(2) $x + y = y + x$ What is either x or y is either y or x.

[91] See *L. of T.*, pp. 32–33.

(3) $z(x + y) = zx + zy$ That which is both z and (either x or y) is either both z and x or both z and y.

(4) $z(x - y) = zx - zy$ That which is both z and (x but not y) is both z and x but not both z and y.

(5) If $x = y$, then $zx = zy$
$$z + x = z + y$$
$$x - z = y - z$$

(6) $x - y = - y + x$

This last is an arbitrary convention: the first half of the expression gives the *meaning* of the last half.

It is a peculiarity of "logical symbols" that if the operation x, upon 1, be repeated, the result is not altered by the repetition:

$1 \cdot x = 1 \cdot x \cdot x = 1 \cdot x \cdot x \cdot x \ldots$ Hence we have:

(7) $x^2 = x$

Boole calls this the "index law".[92]

All these laws, except (7), hold for numerical algebra. It may be noted that, in logic, "If $x = y$, then $zx = zy$" is not reversible. At first glance, this may seem to be another difference between numerical algebra and the system in question. But "If $zx = zy$, then $x = y$" does not hold in numerical algebra when $z = 0$. Law (7) is, then, the distinguishing principle of this algebra. The only finite numbers for which it holds are 0 and 1. *All the above laws hold for an algebra of the numbers 0 and 1.* With this observation, Boole adopts the entire procedure of ordinary algebra, modified by the law $x^2 = x$, introduces numerical *coefficients* other than 0 and 1, and makes use, on occasion, of the operation of division, of the properties of functions, and of any algebraic transformations which happen to serve his purpose.[93]

This borrowing of algebraic operations which often have no logical interpretation is at first confusing to the student of logic; and commentators have seemed to smile indulgently upon it. An example will help: the derivation of the "law of contradiction" or, as Boole calls it, the "law of duality", from the "index law".[94]

---

[92] In *Mathematical Analysis of Logic* he gives it also in the form $x^n = x$, but in *L. of T.* he avoids this, probably because the factors of $x^n - x$ (e. g., $x^3 - x$) are not always logically interpretable.

[93] This procedure characterizes *L. of T.* Only 0 and 1, and the fractions which can be formed from them appear in *Math. An. of Logic*, and the use of division and of fractional coefficients is not successfully explained in that book.

[94] *L. of T.*, p. 49.

Since $x^2 = x$, $\quad x - x^2 = 0$.

Hence, factoring, $x(1 - x) = 0$.

This transformation hardly represents any process of logical deduction. Whoever says "What is both x and x, x^2, is equivalent to x; *therefore* what is both x and not-x is nothing" may well be asked for the steps of his reasoning. Nor should we be satisfied if he reply by interpreting in logical terms the intermediate expression, $x - x^2 = 0$.

Nevertheless, this apparently arbitrary way of using uninterpretable algebraic processes is thoroughly sound. Boole's algebra may be viewed as an abstract mathematical system, generated by the laws we have noted, which has two interpretations. On the one hand, the "logical" or "elective" symbols may be interpreted as variables whose value is either numerical 0 or numerical 1, although numerical *coefficients* other than 0 and 1 are admissible, provided it be remembered that such coefficients do not obey the "index law" which holds for "elective" symbols. All the usual algebraic transformations will have an interpretation in these terms. On the other hand, the "logical" or "elective" symbols may be interpreted as logical classes. For this interpretation, *some* of the algebraical processes of the system and *some* resultant expressions will not be expressible in terms of logic. But whenever they are interpretable, they will be valid consequences of the premises, and even when they are not interpretable, any further results, derived from them, which *are* interpretable, will *also* be valid consequences of the premises.

It must be admitted that Boole himself does not observe the proprieties of his procedure. His consistent course would have been to develop this algebra without reference to logical meanings, and then to discuss in a thorough fashion the interpretation, and the limits of that interpretation, for logical classes. By such a method, he would have avoided, for example, the difficulty about $x + x$. We should have $x + x = 2x$, the interpretation of which for the numbers 0 and 1 is obvious, and its interpretation for logical classes would depend upon certain conventions which Boole made and which will be explained shortly. The point is that the two interpretations should be kept separate, although the processes of the system need not be limited by the narrower interpretation—that for logical classes. Instead of making this separation of the abstract algebra and its two interpretations, Boole takes himself to be developing a calculus of logic; he observes that its "axioms" are identical with those of an algebra of the numbers 0 and 1; [95]

[95] *L. of T.*, pp. 37–38.

hence he applies the whole machinery of that algebra, yet arbitrarily rejects from it any expressions which are not finally interpretable in terms of logical relations. The retaining of non-interpretable expressions which can be transformed into interpretable expressions he compares to "the employment of the uninterpretable symbol $\sqrt{-1}$ in the intermediate processes of trigonometry."[96] It would be a pretty piece of research to take Boole's algebra, find independent postulates for it (his laws are entirely insufficient as a basis for the operations he uses), complete it, and systematically investigate its interpretations.

But neglecting these problems of method, the expression of the simple logical relations in Boole's symbolism will now be entirely clear. Classes will be represented by x, y, z, etc.; their negatives, by $(1 - x)$, $(1 - y)$, etc. That which is both x and y will be xy; that which is x but not y will be $x(1 - y)$, etc. That which is x or y but not both, will be $x + y$, or $x(1 - y) + (1 - x)y$. That which is x or y or both will be $x + (1 - x)y$—i. e., that which is x or not x but y—or

$$xy + x(1 - y) + (1 - x)y$$

—that which is both x and y or x but not y or y but not x. 1 represents the "universe" or "everything". The logical significance of 0 is determined by the fact that, for any y, $0y = 0$: the only class which remains unaltered by any operation of electing from it whatever is the class "nothing".

Since Boole's algebra is the basis of the classic algebra of logic—which is the topic of the next chapter—it will be unnecessary to comment upon those parts of Boole's procedure which were taken over into the classic algebra. These will be clear to any who understand the algebra of logic in its current form or who acquaint themselves with the content of Chapter II. We shall, then, turn our attention chiefly to those parts of his method which are peculiar to him.

Boole does not symbolize the relation "x is included in y". Consequently the only copula by which the relation of terms in a proposition can be represented is the relation $=$. And since all relations are taken in extension, $x = y$ symbolizes the fact that x and y are classes with identical membership. Propositions must be represented by equations in which something is put $= 0$ or $= 1$, or else the predicate must be quantified. Boole uses both methods, but mainly relies upon quantification of the predicate. This involves an awkward procedure, though one which still survives—the introduction of a symbol v or w, to represent an indefinite class and symbolize "Some". Thus "All x is (some) y" is represented by $x = vy$: "Some x is (some) y", by $wx = vy$. If v, or w, were here "the indefinite class" or "any class", this method would be less objectionable. But in such cases v, or w, must be very definitely specified: it must be a class "indefinite in all respects but this, that it contains some members of the class to whose expression it is prefixed".[97] The universal affirmative can also be expressed, without this symbol for the indeterminate, as $x(1 - y) = 0$; "All x is y" means "That which is x but not y is nothing". Negative propositions are treated as affirmative propositions with a negative predicate. So the four typical propositions of traditional logic are expressed as follows: [98]

All x is y:	$x = vy,$	or,	$x(1 - y) = 0.$
No x is y:	$x = v(1 - y),$	or	$xy = 0.$
Some x is y:	$vx = w(1 - y),$	or,	$v = xy.$
Some x is not y:	$vx = w(1 - y),$	or,	$v = x(1 - y).$

Each of these has various other equivalents which may be readily determined by the laws of the algebra.

To *reason* by the aid of this symbolism, one has only to express his premises explicitly in the proper manner and then operate upon the resultant equation according to the laws of the algebra. Or, as Boole more explicitly puts it, valid reasoning requires: [99]

"1st, That a fixed interpretation be assigned to the symbols employed in the expression of the data; and that the laws of the combination of these symbols be correctly determined from that interpretation.

"2nd, That the formal processes of solution or demonstration be conducted throughout in obedience to all the laws determined as above, without regard to the question of the interpretation of the particular results obtained.

"3rd, That the final result be interpretable in form, and that it be actually interpreted in accordance with that system of interpretation which has been employed in the expression of the data."

As we shall see, Boole's methods of solution sometimes involve an uninterpretable stage, sometimes not, but there is provided a machinery by

[97] *L. of T.*, p. 63. This translation of the arbitrary v by "Some" is unwarranted, and the above statement is inconsistent with Boole's later treatment of the arbitrary coefficient. There is no reason why such an arbitrary coefficient may not be null.

[98] See *Math. An. of Logic*, pp. 21–22; *L. of T.*, Chap. IV.

[99] *L. of T.*, p. 68.

which any equation may be reduced to a form which is interpretable.   To comprehend this we must first understand the process known as the development of a function.   With regard to this, we can be brief, because Boole's method of development belongs also to the classic algebra and is essentially the process explained in the next chapter.[100]

Any expression in the algebra which involves x or $(1 - x)$ may be called a function of x.   A function of x is said to be developed when it has the form $Ax + B(1 - x)$.   It is here required that x be a "logical symbol", susceptible only of the values 0 and 1.   But the coefficients, A and B, are not so limited: A, or B, *may be* such a "logical symbol" which obeys the "law of duality", or it may be some number other than 0 or 1, or involve such a number.   If the function, as given, does not have the form $Ax + B(1 - x)$, it may be put into that form by observing certain interesting laws which govern coefficients.

Let	$f(x) = Ax + B(1 - x)$
Then	$f(1) = A \cdot 1 + B(1 - 1) = A$
And	$f(0) = A \cdot 0 + B(1 - 0) = B$
Hence	$f(x) = f(1) \cdot x + f(0) \cdot (1 - x)$
Thus if	$f(x) = \dfrac{1 + x}{2 - x},$
	$f(1) = \dfrac{1 + 1}{2 - 1} = 2; \qquad f(0) = \dfrac{1 + 0}{2 - 0} = \dfrac{1}{2}$
Hence	$f(x) = 2x + \dfrac{1}{2}(1 - x)$

A developed function of two variables, x and y, will have the form:

$$Axy + Bx(1 - y) + C(1 - x)y + D(1 - x)(1 - y)$$

And for any function, $f(x, y)$, the coefficients are determined by the law:

$$f(x, y) = f(1, 1) \cdot xy + f(1, 0) \cdot x(1 - y) + f(0, 1) \cdot (1 - x)y$$
$$+ f(0, 0) \cdot (1 - x)(1 - y)$$

[100] See *Math. An. of Logic*, pp. 60–69; *L. of T.*, pp. 71–79; "The Calculus of Logic," *Cambridge and Dublin Math. Jour.*, III, 188–89.   That this same method of development should belong both to Boole's algebra and to the remodeled algebra of logic, in which $+$ is not completely disjunctive, is at first surprising.   But a completely developed function, in either algebra, is always a sum of terms any two of which have nothing in common. This accounts for the identity of form where there is a real and important difference in the meaning of the symbols.

Thus if
$$f(x, y) = ax + 2by,$$
$$f(1, 1) = a \cdot 1 + 2b \cdot 1 = a + 2b$$
$$f(1, 0) = a \cdot 1 + 2b \cdot 0 = a$$
$$f(0, 1) = a \cdot 0 + 2b \cdot 1 = 2b$$
$$f(0, 0) = a \cdot 0 + 2b \cdot 0 = 0$$

Hence
$$f(x, y) = (a + 2b)xy + ax(1 - y) + 2b(1 - x)y$$

An exactly similar law governs the expansion and the determination of coefficients, for functions of any number of variables. In the words of Boole: [101]

"The general rule of development will . . . consist of two parts, the first of which will relate to the formation of the *constituents* of the expansion, the second to the determination of their respective coefficients. It is as follows:

"1st. *To expand any function of the symbols x, y, z*—Form a series of constituents in the following manner: Let the first constituent be the product of the symbols: change in this product any symbol z into $1 - z$, for the second constituent. Then in both these change any other symbol y into $1 - y$, for two more constituents. Then in the four constituents thus obtained change any other symbol x into $1 - x$, for four new constituents, and so on until the number of possible changes has been exhausted.

"2ndly. *To find the coefficient of any constituent*—If that constituent involves x as a factor, change in the original function x into 1; but if it involves $1 - x$ as a factor, change in the original function x into 0. Apply the same rule with reference to the symbols y, z, etc.: the final calculated value of the function thus transformed will be the coefficient sought."

Two further properties of developed functions, which are useful in solutions and interpretations, are: (1) The product of any two constituents is 0. If one constituent be, for example, xyz, any other constituent will have as a factor one or more of the negatives, $1 - x$, $1 - y$, $1 - z$. Thus the product of the two will have a factor of the form $x(1 - x)$. And where x is a "logical symbol", susceptible only of the values 0 and 1, $x(1 - x)$ is always 0. And (2) if each constituent of any expansion have the coefficient 1, the sum of all the constituents is 1.

All information which it may be desired to obtain from a given set of premises, represented by equations, will be got either (1) by a solution, to determine the equivalent, in other terms, of some "logical symbol" x, or

[101] *L. of T.*, pp. 75–76.

(2) by an elimination, to discover what statements (equations), which are *independent* of some term x, are warranted by given equations which involve x, or (3) by a combination of these two, to determine the equivalent of x in terms of t, u, v, from equations which involve x, t, u, v, and some other "logical" symbol or symbols which must be eliminated in the desired result. "Formal" reasoning is accomplished by the elimination of "middle" terms.

The student of symbolic logic in its current form knows that any set of equations may be combined into a single equation, that any equation involving a term x may be given the form $Ax + B(1 - x) = 0$, and that the result of eliminating x from such an equation is $AB = 0$. Also, the solution of any such equation, provided the condition $AB = 0$ be satisfied, will be $x = B + v(1 - A)$, where v is undetermined. Boole's methods achieve these same results, but the presence of numerical coefficients other than 0 and 1, as well as the inverse operations of subtraction and division, necessarily complicates his procedure. And he does not present the matter of solutions in the form in which we should expect to find it but in a more complicated fashion which nevertheless gives equivalent results. We have now to trace the procedures of interpretation, reduction, etc. by which Boole obviates the difficulties of his algebra which have been mentioned.

The simplest form of equation is that in which a developed function, of any number of variables, is equated to 0, as:

$$Ax + B(1 - x) = 0, \qquad \text{or,}$$
$$Axy + Bx(1 - y) + C(1 - x)y + D(1 - x)(1 - y) = 0, \qquad \text{etc.}$$

It is an important property of such equations that, since the product of any two constituents in a developed function is 0, any such equation gives any one of its constituents, whose coefficient does not vanish in the development, $= 0$. For example, if we multiply the second of the equations given by xy, all constituents after the first will vanish, giving $Axy = 0$. Whence we shall have $xy = 0$.

Any equation in which a developed function is equated to 1 may be reduced to the form in which one member is 0 by the law; If $V = 1$, $1 - V = 0$.

The more general form of equation is that in which some "logical symbol", w, is equated to some function of such symbols. For example, suppose $x = yz$, and it be desired to interpret z as a function of x and y. $x = yz$ gives $z = x/y$; but this form is not interpretable. We shall, then, develop x/y by the law

$$f(x, y) = f(1, 1) \cdot xy + f(1, 0) \cdot x(1 - y) + f(0, 1) \cdot (1 - x)y$$
$$+ f(0, 0) \cdot (1 - x)(1 - y)$$

By this law:

If $z = \dfrac{x}{y}$, then

$$z = xy + \frac{1}{0}x(1 - y) + 0(1 - x)y + \frac{0}{0}(1 - x)(1 - y)$$

These fractional coefficients represent the sole necessary difference of Boole's methods from those at present familiar—a difference due to the presence of division in his system. Because any function can always be developed, and the difference between any two developed functions, of the same variables, is always *confined to the coefficients*. If, then, we can interpret and successfully deal with such fractional coefficients, one of the difficulties of Boole's system is removed.

The fraction $0/0$ is indeterminate, and this suggests that a proper interpretation of the coefficient $0/0$ would be to regard it as indicating an undetermined portion of the class whose coefficient it is. This interpretation may be corroborated by considering the symbolic interpretation of "All x is y", which is $x(1 - y) = 0$.

If $x(1 - y) = 0$, then $x - xy = 0$ and $x = xy$.
Whence $y = x/x$.

Developing x/x, we have $y = x + \dfrac{0}{0}(1 - x)$.

If "All x is y", the class y is made up of the class x plus an undetermined portion of the class not-x. Whence $0/0$ is equivalent to an arbitrary parameter v, which should be interpreted as "an undetermined portion of" or as "All, some, or none of".

The coefficient $1/0$ belongs to the general class of symbols which do not obey the "index law", $x^2 = x$, or its equivalent, the "law of duality", $x(1 - x) = 0$. At least Boole says it belongs to this class, though the numerical properties of $1/0$ would, in fact, depend upon laws which do not belong to Boole's system. But in any case, $1/0$ belongs with the class of such coefficients so far as its logical interpretation goes. *Any constituent of a developed function which does not satisfy the index law must be separately equated to* 0. Suppose that in any equation

$$w = At + P$$

w be a "logical symbol", and t be a constituent of a developed function whose coefficient A does not satisfy the index law, $A^2 = A$. And let P be the sum of the remaining constituents whose coefficients do satisfy this law. Then

$$w^2 = w, \qquad t^2 = t, \qquad \text{and} \qquad P^2 = P$$

Since the product of any two constituents of a development is 0,

$$w^2 = (At + P)^2 = A^2t^2 + P^2$$

Hence

$$w = A^2t + P$$

Subtracting this from the original equation,

$$(A - A^2)t = 0 = A(1 - A)t$$

Hence since

$$A(1 - A) \neq 0, \qquad t = 0$$

Hence any equation of the form

$$w = P + 0Q + \frac{0}{0}R + \frac{1}{0}S$$

is equivalent to the two equations

$$w = P + vR^{\cdot} \qquad \text{and} \qquad S = 0$$

which together represent its complete solution.

It will be noted that a fraction, in Boole's algebra, is always an ambiguous function. Hence the division operation *must never be performed:* the value of a fraction is to be determined by the law of development only, except for the numerical coefficients, which are elsewhere discussed. We have already remarked that $ax = bx$ does not give $a = b$, because x may have the value 0. But we may transform $ax = bx$ into $a = bx/x$ and determine this fraction by the law

$$f(b, x) = f(1, 1) \cdot bx + f(1, 0) \cdot b(1 - x) + f(0, 1) \cdot (1 - b)x$$
$$+ f(0, 0) \cdot (1 - b)(1 - x)$$

We shall then have

$$a = \frac{bx}{x} = bx + \frac{0}{0}b(1 - x) + \frac{0}{0}(1 - b)(1 - x)$$

and this is not, in general, equivalent to b. Replacing $0/0$ by indeterminate coefficients, v and w, this gives us,

If $ax = bx$, then

$$a = bx + v \cdot b(1 - x) + w \cdot (1 - b)(1 - x)$$

And this result is always valid. Suppose, for example, the logical equation

$$\text{rational men} = \text{married men}$$

and suppose we wish to discover who are the rational beings. Our equation will not give us

$$\text{rational} = \text{married}$$

but instead

$$\text{rational} = \text{married men} + v \cdot \text{married non-men} + w \cdot \text{non-married non-men}$$

That is, our hypothesis is satisfied if the class "rational beings" consist of the married men together with any portion (which may be null) of the class "married women" and a similarly undetermined portion of the class "unmarried women".

If we consider Boole's system as an algebra of 0 and 1, and the fact that for any fraction, x/y,

$$\frac{x}{y} = xy + \frac{1}{0}x(1 - y) + \frac{0}{0}(1 - x)(1 - y)$$

we shall find, by investigating the cases

(1) $x = 1$ and $y = 1$;   (2) $x = 1, y = 0$;   (3) $x = 0, y = 1$;

and   (4) $x = 0, y = 0$,

that it requires these three possible cases:

$$(1)\ \frac{0}{0} = 1$$

$$(2)\ \frac{0}{0} = 0$$

$$(3)\ \frac{0}{0} = \frac{1}{0} \cdot 0$$

Or, to speak more accurately, it requires that 0/0 be an ambiguous function susceptible of the values 0 and 1.

Since there are, in general, only four possible coefficients, 1, 0, 0/0, and such as do not obey the index law, of which 1/0 is a special case, this means that any equation can be interpreted, and the difficulty due to the presence of an uninterpretable division operation in the system has disappeared. And any equation can be solved for any "logical symbol" x, by transferring all other terms to the opposite side of the equation, by subtraction or division or both, and developing that side of the equation.

Any equation may be put in the form in which one member is 0 by bringing all the terms to one side. When this is done, and the equation fully expanded, all the coefficients which do not vanish may be changed to unity, except such as already have that value. Boole calls this a "rule of interpretation".[102] Its validity follows from two considerations: (1) Any constituent of an equation with one member 0, whose coefficient does not vanish in development, may be separately equated to 0; (2) the sum of the constituents thus separately equated to 0 will be an equation with one member 0 in which each coefficient will be unity.

Negative coefficients may be eliminated by squaring both sides of any equation in which they appear. The "logical symbols" in any function are not altered by squaring, and any expression of the form $(1 - x)$, where x is a "logical symbol", is not altered, since it can have only the values 0 and 1. Hence no constituent is altered, except that its coefficient may be altered. And any negative coefficient will be made positive. No new terms will be introduced by squaring, since the product of any two terms of a developed function is always null. Hence the only change effected by squaring any developed function is the alteration of any negative coefficients into positive. Their actual numerical value is of no consequence, because coefficients other than 1 can be dealt with by the method described above.

For reducing any two or more equations to a single equation, Boole first proposed the "method of indeterminate multipliers",[103] by which each equation, after the first, is multiplied by an arbitrary constant and the equations then added. But these indeterminate multipliers complicate the process of elimination, and the method is, as he afterward recognized, an inferior one. More simply, such equations may be reduced, by the methods just described, to the form in which one member is 0, and each coefficient is 1. They may then be simply added; the resulting equation will combine the logical significance of the equations added.

Any "logical symbol" which is not wanted in an equation may be eliminated by the method which is familiar to all students of symbolic logic. To eliminate x, the equation is reduced to the form

$$Ax + B(1 - x) = 0$$

The result of elimination will be[104]

$$AB = 0$$

---

[102] *L. of T.*, p. 90.

[103] See *Math. An. of Logic*, pp. 78–81; *L. of T.*, pp. 115–120.

[104] See *L. of T.*, p. 101. We do not pause upon this or other matters which will be entirely clear to those who understand current theory.

By these methods, the difference between Boole's algebra and the classic algebra of logic which grew out of it is reduced to a minimum. Any logical results obtainable by the use of the classic algebra may also be got by Boole's procedures. The difference is solely one of ease and mathematical neatness in the method. Two important laws of the classic algebra which do not appear among Boole's principles are:

$$(1) \ x + x = x, \qquad \text{and} \qquad (2) \ x = x + xy$$

These seem to be inconsistent with the Boolean meaning of $+$; the first of them does not hold for $x = 1$; the second does not hold for $x = 1$, $y = 1$. But although they do not belong to Boole's system as an abstract algebra, the methods of reduction which have been discussed will always give x in place of $x + x$ or of $x + xy$, in any equation in which these appear. The expansion of $x + x$ gives $2x$; the expansion of $x + xy$ gives $2xy + x(1 - y)$. By the method for dealing with coefficients other than unity, $2x$ may be replaced in the equation by x, and $2xy + x(1 - y)$ by $xy + x(1 - y)$, which is equal to x.

The methods of applying the algebra to the relations of logical classes should now be sufficiently clear. The application to *propositions* is made by the familiar device of correlating the "logical symbol", x, with the *times* when some proposition, X. is true. xy will represent the times when X and Y are both true; $x(1 - y)$, the times when X is true and Y is false, and so on. Congruent with the meaning of $+$, $x + y$ will represent the times when either X or Y (but not both) is true. In order to symbolize the times when X or Y or both are true, we must write $x + (1 - x)y$, or $xy + x(1 - y) + (1 - x)y$. 1, the "universe", will represent "all times" or "always"; and 0 will be "no time" or "never". $x = 1$ will represent "X is always true"; $x = 0$ or $(1 - x) = 1$, "X is never true; is always false".

Just as there is, with Boole, no symbol for the inclusion relation of classes, so there is no symbol for the implication relation of propositions. For classes, "All X is Y" or "X is contained in Y" becomes $x = vy$. Correspondingly, "All times when X is true are times when Y is true" or "If X then Y" or "X implies Y" is $x = vy$. $x = y$ will mean, "The times when X is true and the times when Y is true are the same" or "X implies Y and Y implies X".

The entire procedure for "secondary propositions" is summarized as follows: [105]

[105] *L. of T.*, p. 178.

"Rule.—Express symbolically the given propositions. . . .

"Eliminate separately from each equation in which it is found the indefinite symbol v.

"Eliminate the remaining symbols which it is desired to banish from the final solution: always before elimination, reducing to a single equation those equations in which the symbol or symbols to be eliminated are found. Collect the resulting equations into a single equation [one member of which is 0], $V = 0$.

"Then proceed according to the particular form in which it is desired to express the final relation, as

1st. If in the form of a denial, or system of denials, develop the function V, and equate to 0 all those constituents whose coefficients do not vanish.

2ndly. If in the form of a disjunctive proposition, equate to 1 the sum of those constituents whose coefficients vanish.

3rdly. If in the form of a conditional proposition having a simple element, as x or $1 - x$, for its antecedent, determine the algebraic expression of that element, and develop that expression.

4thly. If in the form of a conditional proposition having a compound expression, as xy, $xy + (1 - x)(1 - y)$, etc., for its antecedent, equate that expression to a new symbol t, and determine t as a developed function of the symbols which are to appear in the consequent. . . .

5thly. . . . If it only be desired to ascertain whether a particular elementary proposition x is true or false, we must eliminate all the symbols but x; then the equation $x = 1$ will indicate that the proposition is true, $x = 0$ that it is false, $0 = 0$ that the premises are insufficient to determine whether it is true or false."

It is a curious fact that the one obvious law of an algebra of 0 and 1 which Boole does *not* assume is exactly the law which would have *limited* the logical interpretation of his algebra to propositions. The law

$$\text{If } x \neq 1, \ x = 0 \text{ and if } x \neq 0, \ x = 1$$

is exactly the principle which his successors added to his system when it is to be considered as a calculus of propositions. This principle would have made his system completely inapplicable to logical classes.

For propositions, this principle means, "If x is not true, then x is false, and if x is not false, it is true". But careful attention to Boole's interpretation for "propositions" shows that in his system $x = 0$ should be interpreted "x is false *at all times* (or in all cases)", and $x = 1$ should be interpreted "x is true at all times". This reveals that fact that what Boole calls "propositions" are what we should now call "propositional functions", that is, *statements* which may be true under some circumstances and false under others. The limitation put upon what we *now* call "propositions"—namely that they must be absolutely determinate, and hence simply true or false—does not belong to Boole's system. And his treatment of "propositional symbols" in the application of the algebra to probability theory gives them the character of "propositional functions" rather than of our absolutely determinate propositions.

The last one hundred and seventy-five pages of the *Laws of Thought* are devoted to an application of the algebra to the solution of problems in probabilities.[106] This application amounts to the invention of a new method—a method whereby any logical analysis involved in the problem is performed as automatically as the purely mathematical operations. We can make this provisionally clear by a single illustration:

All the objects belonging to a certain collection are classified in three ways—as A's or not, as B's or not, and as C's or not. It is then found that (1) a fraction m/n of the A's are also B's and (2) the C's consist of the A's which are not B's together with the B's which are not A's.

Required: the probability that if one of the A's be taken at random, it will also be a C.

By premise (2)

$$C = A(1 - B) + (1 - A)B$$

Since A, B, and C are "logical symbols", $A^2 = A$ and $A(1 - A) = 0$. Hence, $AC = A^2(1 - B) + A(1 - A)B = A(1 - B)$.

The A's which are also C's are identical with the A's which are not B's. Thus the probability that a given A is also a C is exactly the probability that it is not a B; or by premise (1), $1 - m/n$, which is the required solution.

In any problem concerning probabilities, there are usually two sorts of difficulties, the purely mathematical ones, and those involved in the logical analysis of the situation upon which the probability in question depends. The methods of Boole's algebra provide a means for expressing the relations of classes, or events, given in the data, and then transforming these logical

---

[106] Chap. 16 *ff.* See also the Keith Prize essay "On the Application of the Theory of Probabilities to the Question of the Combination of Testimonies or Judgments", *Trans. Roy. Soc. Edinburgh*, xxi, 597 *ff.* Also a series of articles in *Phil. Mag.*, 1851–54 (see *Bibl*). An article on the related topic "Of Propositions Numerically Definite" appeared posthumously; *Camb. Phil. Trans.*, xi, 396–411.

equations so as to express the class which the *quaesitum* concerns as a function of the other classes involved. It thus affords a method for untangling the problem—often the most difficult part of the solution.

The parallelism between the logical relations of classes as expressed in Boole's algebra and the corresponding probabilities, numerically expressed, is striking. Suppose x represent the class of cases (in a given total) in which the event X occurs—or those which "are favorable to" the occurrence of X.[107] And let p be the probability, numerically expressed, of the event X. The total class of cases will constitute the logical "universe", or 1; the null class will be 0. Thus, if $x = 1$—if all the cases are favorable to X—then $p = 1$—the probability of X is "certainty". If $x = 0$, then $p = 0$. Further, the class of cases in which X does not occur, will be expressed by $1 - x$; the probability that X will not occur is the numerical $1 - p$. Also, $x + (1 - x) = 1$ and $p + (1 - p) = 1$.

This parallelism extends likewise to the combinations of two or more events. If x represent the class of cases in which X occurs, and y the class of cases in which Y occurs, then xy will be the class of cases in which X and Y both occur; $x(1 - y)$, the cases in which X occurs without Y; $(1 - x)y$, the cases in which Y occurs without X; $(1 - x)(1 - y)$, the cases in which neither occurs; $x(1 - y) + y(1 - x)$, the cases in which X or Y occurs but not both, and so on. Suppose that X and Y are "simple" and "independent" events, and let p be the probability of X, q the probability of Y. Then we have:

Combination of events expressed in Boole's algebra	Corresponding probabilities numerically expressed
xy	pq
$x(1 - y)$	$p(1 - q)$
$(1 - x)y$	$(1 - q)p$
$(1 - x)(1 - y)$	$(1 - p)(1 - q)$
$x(1 - y) + (1 - x)y$	$p(1 - q) + (1 - p)q$
Etc. etc.	

In fact, this parallelism is complete, and the following rule can be formulated: [108]

---

[107] Boole prefers to consider x as representing the times when a certain proposition, asserting an occurrence, will be true. But this interpretation comes to exactly the same thing.

[108] *L. of T.*, p. 258.

"If $p, q, r, \ldots$ are the respective probabilities of unconditioned simple events, $x, y, z, \ldots$, the probability of any compound event V will be $[V]$, this function $[V]$ being formed by changing, in the function V, the symbols $x, y, z, \ldots$ into $p, q, r, \ldots$.

"According to the well-known law of Pascal, the probability that if the event V occur, the event V' will occur with it, is expressed by a fraction whose numerator is the probability of the joint occurrence of V and V', and whose denominator is the probability of the occurrence of V. We can then extend the rule just given to such cases:

"The probability that if the event V occur, any other event V' will also occur, will be $\dfrac{[V\,V']}{[V]}$, where $[V\,V']$ denotes the result obtained by multiplying together the logical functions V and V', and changing in the result $x, y, z, \ldots$ into $p, q, r, \ldots$."

The inverse problem of finding the absolute probability of an event when its probability upon a given condition is known can also be solved.

Given: The probabilities of simple events $x, y, z, \ldots$ are respectively $p, q, r, \ldots$ when a certain condition V is satisfied.

To determine: the absolute probabilities $l, m, n, \ldots$ of $x, y, z, \ldots$.

By the rule just given,

$$\frac{[xV]}{[V]} = p, \qquad \frac{[yV]}{[V]} = q, \qquad \frac{[zV]}{[V]} = r, \qquad \text{etc.}$$

And the number of such equations will be equal to the number of unknowns, $l, m, n, \ldots$ to be determined.[109] The determination of any logical expression of the form xV is peculiarly simple since the product of x into any developed function V is the sum of those constituents of V which contain x as a factor. For example:

$$\text{if } V = xyz + x(1 - y)z + (1 - x)y(1 - z) + (1 - x)(1 - y)z,$$
$$xV = xyz + x(1 - y)z$$
$$yV = xyz + (1 - x)y(1 - z)$$
$$zV = xyz + x(1 - y)z + (1 - x)(1 - y)z$$

Thus any equation of the form

$$\frac{[xV]}{[V]} = p$$

[109] On certain difficulties in this connection, and their solution, see Cayley, "On a Question in the Theory of Probability" (with discussion by Boole), *Phil. Mag.*, Ser. IV, XXIII (1862), 352–65, and Boole, "On a General Method in the Theory of Probabilities", *ibid.*, XXV (1863), 313–17.

is readily determined as a numerical equation. Boole gives the following example in illustration: [110]

"Suppose that in the drawings of balls from an urn, attention had only been paid to those cases in which the balls drawn were either of a particular color, 'white,' or of a particular composition, 'marble,' or were marked by both of these characters, no record having been kept of those cases in which a ball which was neither white nor of marble had been drawn. Let it then have been found, that whenever the supposed condition was satisfied, there was a probability p that a white ball would be drawn, and a probability q that a marble ball would be drawn: and from these data alone let it be required to find the probability m that in the next drawing, without reference at all to the condition above mentioned, a white ball will be drawn; also a probability n that a marble ball will be drawn.

"Here if x represent the drawing of a white ball, y that of a marble ball, the condition V will be represented by the logical function

$$xy + x(1 - y) + (1 - x)y$$

Hence we have

$$xV = xy + x(1 - y) = x$$
$$yV = xy + (1 - x)y = y$$

Whence

$$[xV] = m, \qquad [yV] = n$$

and the final equations of the problem are

$$\frac{m}{mn + m(1 - n) + (1 - m)n} = p$$

$$\frac{n}{mn + m(1 - n) + (1 - m)n} = q$$

from which we find

$$m = \frac{p + q - 1}{q}, \qquad n = \frac{p + q - 1}{p}$$

. . . To meet a possible objection, I here remark that the above reasoning does not require that the drawings of a white and a marble ball should be independent, in virtue of the physical constitution of the balls.

"In general, the probabilities of any system of independent events being given, the probability of any event X may be determined by finding a logical equation of the form

$$x = A + 0B + \frac{0}{0}C + \frac{1}{0}D$$

[110] *L. of T.*, p. 262. I have slightly altered the illustration by a change of letters.

where A, B, C, and D are functions of the symbols of the other events. As has already been shown, this is the general type of the logical equation, and its interpretation is given by

$$x = A + vC, \qquad \text{where } v \text{ is arbitrary and}$$
$$D = 0$$

By the properties of constituents, we have also the equation,

$$A + B + C + D = 1$$

and, since $D = 0$,

$$A + B + C = 1$$

$A + B + C$ thus gives the 'universe' of the events in question, and the probabilities given in the data are to be interpreted as conditioned by $A + B + C = 1$, since $D = 0$ is the condition of the solution $x = A + vC$. If the given probability of some event S is p, of T is q, etc., then the supposed 'absolute' probabilities of S, T, etc., may be determined by the method which has been described. Let $V = A + B + C$, then

$$\frac{[sV]}{[V]} = p, \qquad \frac{[tV]}{[V]} = q, \qquad \text{etc.}$$

where $[sV]$, $[tV]$, *etc.* are the "absolute probabilities" sought. These, being determined, may be substituted in the equation

$$\text{Prob. } w = \frac{[A + vC]}{[V]}$$

which will furnish the required solution.

"The term vC will appear only in cases where the data are insufficient to determine the probability sought. Where it does appear, the limits of this probability may be determined by giving v the limiting values, 0 and 1. Thus

$$\text{Lower limit of Prob. } w = \frac{[A]}{[V]}$$

$$\text{Upper limit} \qquad = \frac{[A + C]}{[V]}"$$

With the detail of this method, and with the theoretical difficulties of its application and interpretation, we need not here concern ourselves. Suffice it to say that, with certain modifications, it is an entirely workable method and seems to possess certain marked advantages over those more generally in use. It is a matter of surprise that this immediately useful application of symbolic logic has been so generally overlooked.

VI. Jevons

It has been shown that Boole's "calculus of logic" is not so much a system of logic as an algebra of the numbers 0 and 1, some of whose expressions are capable of simple interpretation as relations of logical classes, or propositions, and some of whose transformations represent processes of reasoning. If the entire algebra can, with sufficient ingenuity, be interpreted as a system of logic, still Boole himself failed to recognize this fact, and this indicates the difficulty and unnaturalness of some parts of this interpretation.

Jevons[111] pointed a way to the simplification of Boole's algebra, discarding those expressions which have no obvious interpretation in logic, and laying down a procedure which is just as general and is, in important respects, superior. In his first book on this subject, Jevons says:[112]

"So long as Professor Boole's system of mathematical logic was capable of giving results beyond the power of any other system, it had in this fact an impregnable stronghold. Those who were not prepared to draw the same inferences in some other manner could not quarrel with the manner of Professor Boole. But if it be true that the system of the foregoing chapters is of equal power with Professor Boole's system, the case is altered. There are now two systems of notation, giving the same formal results, one of which gives them with self-evident force and meaning, the other by dark and symbolic processes. The burden of proof is shifted, and it must be for the author or supporters of the dark system to show that it is in some way superior to the evident system."

He sums up the advantages of his system, compared with Boole's, as follows:[113]

"1. Every process is of self-evident nature and force, and governed by laws as simple and primary as those of Euclid's axioms.

"2. The process is infallible, and gives us no uninterpretable or anomalous results.

"3. The inferences may be drawn with far less labor than in Professor Boole's system, which generally requires a separate computation and development for each inference."

---

[111] William Stanley Jevons (1835–1882), B.A., M.A. (London), logician and economist; professor of logic and mental and moral philosophy and Cobden professor of political economy in Owens College, Manchester, 1866–76; professor of political economy, University College, London, 1876–80.

[112] *Pure Logic, or the Logic of Quality apart from Quantity*, p. 75.

[113] *Ibid.*, p. 74.

The third of these observations is not entirely warranted. Jevons unduly restricts the operations and methods of Boole in such wise that his own procedure is often cumbersome and tedious where Boole's would be expeditious. Yet the honor of first pointing out the simplifications which have since been generally adopted in the algebra of logic belongs to Jevons.

He discards Boole's inverse operations, $a - b$ and a/b, and he interprets the sum of a and b as "either a or b, where a and b are not necessarily exclusive classes". (We shall symbolize this relation by $a + b$: Jevons has $A + B$ or $A \cdot | \cdot B$.)[114] Thus, for Jevons, $a + a = a$, whereas for Boole $a + a$ is not interpretable as any relation of logical classes, and if it be taken as an expression in the algebra of 0 and 1, it obeys the usual arithmetical laws, so that $a + a = 2a$. As has been indicated, this is a source of much awkward procedure in Boole's system. The law $a + a = a$ eliminates numerical coefficients, other than 0 and 1, and this is a most important simplification.

Jevons supposes that the fundamental difference between himself and Boole is that Boole's system, being mathematical, is a calculus of things taken in their logical extension, while his own system, being "pure logic", is a calculus of terms in intension. It is true that mathematics requires that classes be taken in extension, but it is not true that the calculus of logic either requires or derives important advantage from the point of view of intension. Since Jevons's system can be interpreted in extension without the slightest difficulty, we shall ignore this supposed difference.

The fundamental ideas of the system are as follows:

(1) $a\,b$ denotes that which is both a and b, or (in intension) the sum of the meanings of the two terms combined.

(2) $a + b$ denotes that which is either a or b or both, or (in intension) a term with one of two meanings.[115]

(3) $a = b$ a is identical with b, or (in intension) a means the same as b.

(4) $-b$ Not-b, the negative of b, symbolized in Boole's system by $1 - b$.[116]

(5) 0   According to Jevons, 0 indicates that which is contradictory or "excluded from thought". He prefers it to appear as a factor rather than

---

[114] $A + B$ in *Pure Logic;* $A \cdot | \cdot B$ in the other papers. (See *Bibl.*)

[115] Jevons would add "but it is not known which". (See *Pure Logic*, p. 25.) But this is hardly correct; it makes no difference if it *is* known which, since the meaning of $a + b$ does not depend on the state of our knowledge. Perhaps a better qualification would be "but it is not specified which".

[116] Jevons uses capital roman letters for positive terms and the corresponding small italics for their negatives. Following De Morgan, he calls A and a "contrary" terms.

by itself.[117] The meaning given is a proper interpretation of the symbol in intension. Its meaning in extension is the null-class or "nothing", as with Boole.

Jevons does not use any symbol for the "universe", but writes out the "logical alphabet". This "logical alphabet", for any number n of elements, a, b, c, . . . , consists of the 2^n terms which, in Boole's system, form the constituents of the expansion of 1. Thus, for two elements, a and b, the "logical alphabet" consists of $a\,b$, $a\,-b$, $-a\,b$, and $-a\,-b$. For three terms, x, y, z, it consists of $x\,y\,z$, $x\,y\,-z$, $x\,-y\,z$, $x\,-y\,-z$, $x\,y\,-z$, $-x\,-y\,z$, and $-x\,-y\,-z$. Jevons usually writes these in a column instead of adding them and putting the sum $= 1$. Thus the absence of 1 from his system is simply a whim and represents no real difference from Boole's procedure.

The fundamental laws of the system of Jevons are as follows:

(1) If $a = b$ and $b = c$, then $a = c$.

(2) $a\,b = b\,a$.

(3) $a\,a = a$.

(4) $a\,-a = 0$.

(5) $a + b = b + a$.

(6) $a + a = a$.

(7) $a + 0 = a$. This law is made use of but is not stated.

(8) $a(b + c) = a\,b + a\,c$ and $(a + b)(c + d) = a\,c + a\,d + b\,c + b\,d$.

(9) $a + a\,b = a$. This law, since called the "law of absorption", allows a direct simplification which is not possible in Boole. Its analogue for multiplication

$$a(a + b) = a$$

follows from (8), (3), and (9). The law of absorption extends to any number of terms, so that we have also

$$a + a\,b + a\,c + a\,b\,d + \ldots = a$$

(10) $a = a(b + -b)(c + -c) \ldots.$ This is the rule for the expansion of any term, a, with reference to any other terms, b, c, etc. For three terms it gives us

$$a = a(b + -b)(c + -c) = a\,b\,c + a\,b\,-c + a\,-b\,c + a\,-b\,-c$$

This expansion is identical with that which appears in Boole's system, except for the different meaning of $+$. But the product of any two terms of such an expansion will always have a factor of the form $a\,-a$, and hence, by (4), will be null. Thus the terms of any expansion will always represent classes

[117] See *Pure Logic*, pp. 31–33.

which are mutually exclusive. This accounts for the fact that, in spite of the different meaning of $+$, developed functions in Boole's system and in Jevons's always have the same form.

(11) The "logical alphabet" is made up of any term plus its negative, $a + -a$. It follows immediately from this and law (10) that the logical alphabet for any number of terms, $a, b, c, \ldots$, will be

$$(a + -a)(b + -b)(c + -c)\ldots$$

and will have the character which we have described. It corresponds to the expansion of 1 in Boole's system because it is a developed function and its terms are mutually exclusive.

A procedure by which Jevons sets great store is the "substitution of similars", of a for b or b for a when $a = b$. Not only is this procedure valid when the expressions in which a and b occur belong to the system, but it holds good whatever the rational complex in which a and b stand. He considers this the first principle of reasoning, more fundamental than Aristotle's *dictum de omni et nullo*.[118] In this he is undoubtedly correct, and yet there is another principle, which underlies Aristotle's dictum, which is equally fundamental—the substitution for variables of values of these variables. And this procedure is not reducible to any substitution of equivalents.

The only copulative relation in the system is $[=]$; hence the expression of simple logical propositions is substantially the same as with Boole:

All a is b: $\quad a = a\,b$
No a is b: $\quad a = a\,-b$
Some a is b: $\quad c\,a = c\,a\,b \quad$ or $\quad U\,a = V\,a\,b$

"U" is used to suggest "Unknown".

The methods of working with this calculus are in some respects simpler than Boole's, in some respects more cumbersome. But, as Jevons claims, they are obvious while Boole's are not. Eliminations are of two sorts, "intrinsic" and "extrinsic". Intrinsic eliminations may be performed by substituting for any part of one member of an equation the whole of the other. Thus from $a = b\,c\,d$, we get

$$a = a\,c\,d = a\,b\,d = a\,c = a\,d$$

This rule follows from the principles $a\,a = a$, $a\,b = b\,a$, and if $a = b$, $a\,c = b\,c$. For example

If $\quad a = b\,c\,d$
$\quad a \cdot a = b\,c\,d \cdot b\,c\,d = b\,b \cdot c\,c \cdot d\,d = b\,c\,d \cdot d = a\,d.$

[118] See *Substitution of Similars*, passim.

Also, in cases where a factor or a term of the form $a(b + -b)$, or of the form $a -a$, is involved, eliminations may be performed by the rules $a(b + -b) = a$ and $a -a = 0$.

Extrinsic elimination is that simplification or "solution" of equations which may occur when two or more are united. Jevons does not add or multiply such equations but uses them as a basis for striking out terms in the same "logical alphabet".

This method is equivalent, in terms of current procedures, to first forming the expansion of 1 (which contains the terms of the logical alphabet) and then putting any equations given in the form in which one member is 0 and "subtracting" them from the expansion of 1. But Jevons did not hit upon the current procedures. His own is described thus: [119]

"1. Any premises being given, form a combination containing every term involved therein. Change successively each simple term of this into its contrary [negative], so as to form all the possible combinations of the simple terms and their contraries. [E. g., if a, b, and c are involved, form the "logical alphabet" of all the terms in the expansion of

$$(a + -a)(b + -b)(c + -c).]$$

"2. Combine successively each such combination [or term, as $a\,b\,c$,] with both members of a premise. When the combination forms a contradiction [an expression having a factor of the form $(a -a)$] with neither side of a premise, call it an *included subject* of the premise; when it forms a contradiction with both sides, call it an *excluded* subject of the premise; when it forms a contradiction with one side only, call it a *contradictory combination* or *subject*, and strike it out.

"We may call an included or excluded subject a *possible subject* as distinguished from a contradictory combination or *impossible subject*.

"3. Perform the same process with each premise. Then a combination is an included subject of a series of premises, when it is an included subject of any one; it is a contradictory subject when it is a contradictory subject of any one; it is an excluded subject when it is an excluded subject of *every* premise.

"4. The expression of any term [as a or b] involved in the premises consists of all the included and excluded subjects containing the term, treated as alternatives [in the relation +].

"5. Such expressions may be simplified by reducing all dual terms [of

[119] *Pure Logic*, pp. 44–46.

the form $a(b + -b)$], and by intrinsic elimination of all terms not required in the expression.

"6. When it is observed that the expression of a term contains a combination which would not occur in the expression of any contrary of that term, we may eliminate the part of the combination common to the term and its expression. . . .

"7. Unless each term of the premises and the contrary of each appear in one or other of the possible subjects, the premises must be deemed inconsistent or contradictory. Hence there must always remain at least two possible subjects.

"Required by the above process the inferences of the premise $a = b c$.

"The possible combinations of the terms a, b, c, and their contraries are as given [in the column at the left, which is, for this case, the 'logical alphabet']. Each of these being combined with both sides of the premise, we have the following results:

$a\,b\,c$	$a\,b\,c$	$= a\,b\,c$		$a\,b\,c$	included subject
$a\,b\,-c$	$a\,b\,-c$	$= a\,b\,c\,-c$	$= 0$	$a\,b\,-c$	contradiction
$a\,-b\,c$	$a\,-b\,c$	$= a\,b\,-b\,c$	$= 0$	$a\,-b\,c$	contradiction
$a\,-b\,-c$	$a\,-b\,-c$	$= a\,b\,-b\,c\,-c$	$= 0$	$a\,-b\,-c$	.contradiction
$-a\,b\,c$	$0 = a\,-a\,b\,c$	$= -a\,b\,c$		$-a\,b\,c$	contradiction
$-a\,b\,-c$	$0 = a\,-a\,b\,-c$	$= -a\,b\,c\,-c$	$= 0$	$-a\,b\,-c$	excluded subject
$-a\,-b\,c$	$0 = a\,-a\,-b\,c$	$= -a\,b\,-b\,c$	$= 0$	$-a\,-b\,c$	excluded subject
$-a\,-b\,-c$	$0 = a\,-a\,-b\,-c$	$= -a\,b\,-b\,c\,-c$	$= 0$	$-a\,-b\,-c$	excluded subject

"It appears, then, that the four combinations $a\,b\,-c$ to $-a\,b\,c$ are to be struck out, and only the rest retained as possible subjects. Suppose we now require an expression for the term $-b$ as inferred from the premise $a = b c$. Select from the included and excluded subjects such as contain $-b$, namely $-a\,-b\,c$ and $-a\,-b\,-c$.

"Then $-b = -a\,-b\,c + -a\,-b\,-c$, but as $-a\,c$ occurs only with $-b$, and not with b, its contrary, we may, by Rule 6, eliminate $-b$ from $-a\,-b\,c$; hence $-b = -a\,c + -a\,-b\,-c$."

This method resembles nothing so much as solution by means of the Venn diagrams (to be explained in Chapter III). The "logical alphabet" is a list of the different compartments in such a diagram; those marked "contradiction" are the ones which would be struck out in the diagram by transforming the equations given into the form in which one member is 0.

The advantage which Jevons claims for his method, apart from its obviousness,—namely, that the solutions for different terms do not require to be separately performed,—is also an advantage of the diagram, which exhibits all the possibilities at once.

If any problem be worked out by this method of Jevons and also that of Boole, it will be found that the comparison is as follows: The "logical alphabet" consists of the terms which when added give 1, or the universe. Any term marked "contradiction" will, by Boole's method, have the coefficient 0 or 1/0; any term marked "included subject" will have the coefficient 1; any marked "excluded subject" will have the coefficient 0/0, or v where v is arbitrary. If, then, we remember that, according to Boole, terms with the coefficient 1/0 are equated to 0 and thus eliminated, we see that the two methods give substantially the same results. The single important difference is in Boole's favor: the method of Jevons does not distinguish decisively between the coefficients 1 and v. If, for example, the procedure of Jevons gives $x = x - y z$, Boole's will give either $x = -y z$ or $x = v - y z$.

One further, rather obvious, principle may be mentioned: [120]

Any subject of a proposition remains an included, excluded, or contradictory subject, after combination with any unrelated terms. This means simply that, in any problem, the value of a term remains its value as a factor when the term is multiplied by any new terms which may be introduced into the problem. In a problem involving a, b, and c, let $a - b c$ be a "contradictory" term. Then if x be introduced, $a - b c x$ and $a - b c - x$ will be "contradictory".

On the whole Jevons's methods are likely to be tedious and have little of mathematical nicety about them. Suppose, for example, we have three equations involving altogether six terms. The "logical alphabet" will consist of sixty-four members, each of which will have to be investigated separately for each equation, making one hundred and ninety-two separate operations. Jevons has emphasized his difference from Boole to the extent of rejecting much that would better have been retained. It remained for others, notably Mrs. Ladd-Franklin and Schröder, to accept Jevons's amended meaning of addition and its attendant advantages, yet retain Boole's methods of development and similar methods of elimination and solution. But Jevons should have credit for first noting the main clue to this simplification—the laws $a + a = a$ and $a + a b = a$.

[120] *Pure Logic*, p. 48.

VII. Peirce

The contributions of C. S. Peirce[121] to symbolic logic are more numerous and varied than those of any other writer—at least in the nineteenth century. He understood how to profit by the work of his predecessors, Boole and De Morgan, and built upon their foundations, and he anticipated the most important procedures of his successors even when he did not work them out himself. Again and again, one finds the clue to the most recent developments in the writings of Peirce. These contributions may be summed up under three heads: (1) He improved the algebra of Boole by distinguishing the relations which are more characteristic of logical classes (such as multiplication in Boole's algebra) from the relations which are more closely related to arithmetical operations (such as subtraction and division in Boole). The resulting algebra has certain advantages over the system of Jevons because it retains the mathematical methods of development, transformation, elimination, and solution, and certain advantages over the algebra of Boole because it distinguishes those operations and relations which are always interpretable for logical classes. Also Peirce introduced the "illative" relation, "is contained in", or "implies", into symbolic logic. (2) Following the researches of De Morgan, he made marked advance in the treatment of relations and relative terms. The method of dealing with these is made more precise and "mathematical", and the laws which govern them are related to those of Boole's algebra of classes. Also the method of treating "some" and "all" propositions as sums (Σ) and products (Π) respectively of "propositions" containing variables was here first introduced. This is the historic origin of "formal implication" and all that has been built upon it in the more recent development of the logic of mathematics. (3) Like Leibniz, he conceived symbolic logic to be the science of mathematical form in general, and did much to revive the sense of logistic proper, as we have used that term. He worked out in detail the derivation of various multiple algebras from the calculus of relatives, and he improved Boole's method of applying symbolic logic to problems in probability.

[121] Charles Saunders Peirce (1839–1914), son of Benjamin Peirce, the celebrated mathematician, A.B. (Harvard, 1859), B.S. (Harvard, 1863), lecturer in logic at Johns Hopkins, 1890– ?. For a number of years, Peirce was engaged in statistical researches for the U. S. Coast Survey, and was at one time head of the Department of Weights and Measures. His writings cover a wide variety of topics in the history of science, metaphysics, mathematics, astronomy, and chemistry. According to William James, his articles on "Some Illustrations of the Science of Logic", *Pop. Sci. Mo.*, 1877–78, are the source of pragmatism.

We shall take up these contributions in the order named.

The improvement of the Boolian algebra is set forth mainly in the brief article, "On an Improvement in Boole's Calculus of Logic",[122] and in two papers, "On the Algebra of Logic".[123]

It will be remembered that Boole's calculus has four operations, or relations: $a + b$ indicates the class made up of the two *mutually exclusive* classes, a and b; $[-]$ is the strict inverse of $[+]$, so that if $x + b = a$, then $x = a - b$; $a \times b$ or $a\,b$ denotes the class of those things which are common to a and b; and division is the strict inverse of multiplication, so that if $x\,b = a$, then $x = a/b$. These relations are not homogeneous in type. Boole's $[+]$ and $[-]$ have properties which approximate closely those of arithmetical addition and subtraction. If $[n]x$ indicate the number of members of the class x,

$$[n]a + [n]b = [n](a + b)$$

because a and b are mutually exclusive classes, and every member of a is a member of $(a + b)$ and every member of b is a member of $(a + b)$. This relation, then, differs from arithmetical addition only by the fact that a and b are not necessarily to be regarded as numbers or quantities. Similarly,

$$[n]a - [n]b = [n](a - b)$$

But in contrast to this, for Boole's $a \times b$ or $a\,b$,

$$[n]a \times [n]b = [n](a\,b)$$

will not hold except for 0 and 1: this relation is not of the type of its arithmetical counterpart. And the same is true of its inverse, a/b. Thus, in Boole's calculus, addition and subtraction are relations of the same type as arithmetical addition and subtraction; but multiplication and division are different in type from arithmetical multiplication and division.

Peirce rounds out the calculus of Boole by completing both sets of these relations, adding multiplication and division of the arithmetical type, and addition and subtraction of the non-arithmetical type.[124] The general character of these relations is as follows:

---

[122] *Proc. Amer. Acad.*, VII, 250–61. This paper will be referred to hereafter as "Boole's Calculus"

[123] *Amer. Jour. Math.*, III (1880), 15–57, and VII (1885), 180–202. These two papers will be referred to hereafter as *Alg. Log.* 1880, and *Alg. Log.* 1885, respectively.

[124] "Boole's Calculus," pp. 250–54.

A. *The "Non-Arithmetical" or Logical Relations*

(1) $a + b$ denotes the class of those things which are either a's or b's *or both*.[125]

(2) The inverse of the above, $a \vdash b$, is such that if $x + b = a$, then $x = a \vdash b$.

Since x and b, in $x + b$, need not be mutually exclusive classes, $a \vdash b$ is an ambiguous function. Suppose $x + b = a$ and all b is x. Then

$$a \vdash b = x, \quad \text{and} \quad a \vdash b = a$$

Thus $a \vdash b$ has an upper limit, a. But suppose that $x + b = a$ and no b is x. Then $a \vdash b$ coincides with $a - b$ (a which is not b)—i. e.,

$$a \vdash b = x, \quad \text{and} \quad a \vdash b = a - b$$

Thus $a \vdash b$ has a lower limit, $a - b$, or (as we elsewhere symbolize it) $a - b$. And in any case, $a \vdash b$ is not interpretable unless all b is a, the class b contained in the class a. We may summarize all these facts by

$$a \vdash b = a - b + v \, a \, b + [0] - a \, b$$

where v is undetermined, and [0] indicates that the term to which it is prefixed must be null.

(3) $a \, b$ denotes the class of those things which are both a's and b's. This is Boole's $a \, b$.

(4) The inverse of the preceding, a/b such that if $b \, x = a$, then $x = a/b$. This is Boole's a/b.

a/b is an ambiguous function. Its upper limit is $a + -b$; its lower limit, a.[126] It is uninterpretable unless a is contained in b—i.e.,

$$a/b = a \, b + v - a - b + [0] \, a - b$$

B. *The "Arithmetical" Relations*

(5) $a + b$ denotes the class of those things which are either a's or b's, where a and b are mutually exclusive classes. This is Boole's $a + b$.

$$a + b = a - b + -a \, b + [0] \, a \, b$$

(6) The inverse of the preceding. $a - b$ signifies the class "a which is not b". As has been mentioned, it coincides with the lower limit of $a \vdash b$.

(7) $a \times b$ and $a \div b$ are strictly analogous to the corresponding relations

---

[125] Peirce indicates the logical relations by putting a comma underneath the sign of the relation: that which is both a and b is a, b.

[126] Peirce indicates the upper limit by $a : b$, the lower limit by $a \div b$. These occur only in the paper "Boole's Calculus".

of arithmetic. They have no such connection with the corresponding "logical" relations as do $a + b$ and $a - b$. Peirce does not use them except in applying this system to probability theory.

For the "logical" relations, the following familiar laws are stated: [127]

$$a + a = a \qquad\qquad a\,a = a$$
$$a + b = b + a \qquad\qquad a\,b = b\,a$$
$$(a + b) + c = a + (b + c) \qquad (a\,b)c = a(b\,c)$$
$$(a + b)c = a\,c + b\,c \qquad a\,b + c = (a + c)(b + c)$$

The last two are derived from those which precede.

Peirce's discussion of transformations and solutions in this system is inadequate. Any sufficient account would carry us quite beyond what he has given or suggested, and require our report to be longer than the original paper. We shall be content to suggest ways in which the methods of Boole's calculus can be extended to functions involving those relations which do not appear in Boole. As has been pointed out, if any function be developed by Boole's laws,

$$f(x) = f(1) \cdot x + f(0) \cdot -x,$$
$$\varphi(x, y) = \varphi(1, 1) \cdot x\,y + \varphi(1, 0) \cdot x\,-y + \varphi(0, 1) \cdot -x\,y + \varphi(0, 0) \cdot -x\,-y,$$

Etc., etc.,

the terms on the right-hand side of these equations will always represent mutually exclusive classes. That is to say, the difference between the "logical" relation, $+$, and the "arithmetical" relation, $+$, here vanishes. Thus any relation in this system of Peirce's can be interpreted by developing it according to the above laws, provided that we can interpret these relations when they appear in the *coefficients*. And the correct interpretation of these coefficients can always be discovered.

Developing the "logical" sum, $x + y$, we have,

$$x + y = (1 + 1) \cdot x\,y + (1 + 0) \cdot x\,-y + (0 + 1) \cdot -x\,y + (0 + 0) \cdot -x\,-y$$

Comparing this with the meaning of $x + y$ given above, we find that $(1 + 1) = 1$, $(1 + 0) = 1$, $(0 + 1) = 1$, and $(0 + 0) = 0$.

Developing the "logical" difference, $a \vdash b$, we have

$$x \vdash y = (1 \vdash 1) \cdot x\,y + (1 \vdash 0) \cdot x\,-y + (0 \vdash 1) \cdot -x\,y + (0 \vdash 0) \cdot -x\,-y$$

Comparing this with the discussion of $x \vdash y$ above, we see that $(1 \vdash 1)$ is equivalent to the undetermined coefficient v; that $(1 \vdash 0) = 1$; that

[127] "Boole's Calculus," pp. 250–53.

(0 ⊢1) is equivalent to [0], which indicates that the term to which it is prefixed must be null, and that (0 ⊢0) = 0.

The interpretation of the "arithmetical" relations, × and ÷, in coefficients of class-symbols is not to be attempted. These are of service only in probability theory, where the related symbols are numerical in their significance.

The reader does not require to be told that this system is too complicated to be entirely satisfactory. In the "Description of a Notation for the Logic of Relatives", all these relations except ÷ are retained, but in later papers we find only the "logical" relations, $a + b$ and $a\,b$.

The relation of "inclusion in" or "being as small as" (which we shall symbolize by ⊂)[128] appears for the first time in the "Description of a Notation for the Logic of Relatives".[129] Aside from its treatment of relative terms and the use of the "arithmetical" relations, this monograph gives the laws of the logic of classes almost identically as they stand in the algebra of logic today. The following principles are stated.[130]

(1) If $x \subset y$ and $y \subset z$, then $x \subset z$.

(2) If $a \subset b$, then there is such a term x that $a + x = b$.

(3) If $a \subset b$, then there is such a term y that $b\,y = a$.

(4) If $b\,x = a$, then $a \subset b$.

(5) If $a \subset b$, $(c + a) \subset (c + b)$.

(6) If $a \subset b$, $c\,a \subset c\,b$.

(7) If $a \subset b$, $a\,c \subset b\,c$.

(8) $a\,b \subset a$.

(9) $x \subset (x + y)$.

(10) $x + y = y + x$.

(11) $(x + y) + z = x + (y + z)$.

(12) $x(y + z) = x\,y + x\,z$.

(13) $x\,y = y\,x$.

(14) $(x\,y)z = x(y\,z)$.

(15) $x\,x = x$.

(16) $x - x = 0$.[131]

(17) $x + -x = 1$.

---

[128] Peirce's symbol is $-\!\!<$ which he explains as meaning the same as $\leq$ but being simpler to write.

[129] *Memoirs of the Amer. Acad.*, n. s., IX (1867), 317–78.

[130] "Description of a Notation for the Logic of Relatives," *loc. cit.*, pp. 334–35, 338–39, 342.

[131] In this paper, not-x is symbolized by $\mathfrak{n}^x$, "different from every x," or by σ^{-x}.

(18) $x + 0 = x$.

(19) $x + 1 = 1$.

(20) $\varphi(x) = \varphi(1) \cdot x + \varphi(0) \cdot -x$.

(21) $\varphi(x) = [\varphi(1) + x][\varphi(0) + -x]$.

(22) If $\varphi(x) = 0$, $\varphi(1) \cdot \varphi(0) = 0$.

(23) If $\varphi(x) = 1$, $\varphi(1) + \varphi(0) = 1$.

The last of these gives the equation of condition and the elimination resultant for equations with one member 1. Boole had stated (22), which is the corresponding law for equations with one member 0, but not (23). Most of the above laws, beyond (9), had been stated either by Boole or by Jevons. (1) to (9) are, of course, novel, since the relation $\subset$ appears here for the same time since Lambert.

Later papers state further properties of the relation $\subset$, notably,—

If $x \subset y$, then $-y \subset -x$.

And the methods of elimination and solution are given in terms of this relation.[132] Also, these papers extend the relation to propositions. In this interpretation, Peirce reads $x \subset y$, "If x is true, y is true," but he is well aware of the difference between the meaning of $x \subset y$ and usual significance of "x implies y". He says: [133]

"It is stated above that this means 'if x is true, y is true'. But this meaning is greatly modified by the circumstance that only the actual state of things is referred to. . . . Now the peculiarity of the hypothetical proposition [ordinarily expressed by 'if x is true, y is true'] is that it goes out beyond the actual state of things and declares what *would* happen were things other than they are or may be. The utility of this is that it puts us in possession of a rule, say that 'if A is true, B is true', such that should we afterward learn something of which we are now ignorant, namely that A is true, then, by virtue of this rule, we shall find that we know something else, namely, that B is true. [In contrast to this] . . . the proposition, $a \subset b$, is true if a is false or if b is true, but is false if a is true while b is false. . . . For example, we shall see that from $-(x \subset y)$ [the negation of $x \subset y$] we can infer $z \subset x$. This does not mean that because in the actual state of things x is true and y false, therefore in every state of things either z is false or x true; but it does mean that in whatever state of things we find x true and y false, in that state of things either z is false or x is true [since, *ex hypothesi*, x is true anyway]."

[132] *Alg. Log.* 1880, see esp. § 2.

[133] *Alg. Log.* 1885, pp. 186–87.

We now call this relation, $x \subset y$, "material implication," and the peculiar theorems which are true of it are pretty well known. Peirce gives a number of them. They will be intelligible if the reader remember that $x \subset y$ means, "The actual state of things is not one in which x is true and y false".

(1) $x \subset (y \subset x)$. This is the familiar theorem: "A true proposition is implied by any proposition".

(2) $[(x \subset y) \subset x] \subset x$. If "$x$ implies y" implies that x is true, then x is true.

(3) $[(x \subset y) \subset \alpha] \subset x$, where α is used in such a sense that $(x \subset y) \subset \alpha$ means that from $x \subset y$ every proposition follows.

The difference between "material implication" and the more usual meaning of "implies" is a difficult topic into which we need not go at this time.[134] But it is interesting to note that Peirce, who introduced the relation, understood its limitations as some of his successors have not.

Other theorems in terms of this relation are:

(4) $x \subset x$.

(5) $[x \subset (y \subset z)] \subset [y \subset (x \subset z)]$.

(6) $x \subset [(x \subset y) \subset y]$.

(7) $(x \subset y) \subset [(y \subset z) \subset (x \subset z)]$. This is a fundamental law, since called the "Principle of the Syllogism".

Peirce worked most extensively with the logic of relatives. His interest here reflects a sense of the importance of relative terms in the analyses of mathematics, and he anticipates to some extent the methods of such later researches as those of Peano and of *Principia Mathematica*. To follow his successive papers on this topic would probably result in complete confusion for the reader. Instead, we shall make three divisions of this entire subject as treated by Peirce: (1) the modification and extension of De Morgan's calculus of relatives by the introduction of a more "mathematical" symbolism—for the most part contained in the early paper, "Description of a Notation for the Logic of Relatives"; (2) the calculus of relations, expressed without the use of exponents and in a form which makes it an extension of the Boolean algebra—a later development which may be seen at its best in "The Logic of Relatives", Note B in the *Studies in Logic by members of Johns Hopkins University;* and (3) the systematic consideration of the *theory* of relatives, which is scattered throughout the papers, but has almost complete continuity.

[134] But see below, Chap. IV, Sect. I.

The terms of the algebra of relatives may usually be regarded as simple relative terms, such as "ancestor", "lover," etc. Since they are also class names, they will obey all the laws of the logic of classes, which may be taken for granted without further discussion. But relative terms have additional properties which do not belong to non-relatives; and it is to these that our attention must be given. If w signifies "woman" and s, "servant," logic is concerned not only with such relations as $s\,w$, the "logical product" "servant woman", $s+w$, the "logical sum" "either servant or woman (or both)", and $s \subset w$, "the class 'servants' is contained in the class 'women',—relations which belong to class-terms in general— but also with the relations first symbolized by De Morgan, "servant *of a* woman," "servant of every woman," and "servant of none but women".

We may represent "servant of a woman" by $s\,|\,w$.[135] This is a kind of "multiplication" relation. It is associative,

$$s\,|\,(l\,|\,w) = (s\,|\,l)\,|\,w$$

"Servant of a lover-of-a-woman" is "servant-of-a-lover of a woman". Also, it is distributive with respect to the non-relative "addition" symbolized by $+$,

$$s\,|\,(m+w) = s\,|\,m + s\,|\,w$$

"Servant of either a man or a woman" is "servant of a man or servant of a woman". But it is not commutative: $s\,|\,l$ is not $l\,|\,s$, "servant of a lover" is not equivalent to "lover of a servant". To distinguish $s\,|\,w$ from $s\,w$, or $s \times w$—the class of those who are both servants and women—we shall call $s\,|\,w$ the *relative product* of s and w.

For "servant of every woman" Peirce proposed s^w, and for "servant of none but women" ^sw. As we shall see, this notation is suggested by certain mathematical analogies. We may represent individual members of the class w as W_1, W_2, W_3, etc., and the *class* of all the W's as $W_1 + W_2 + W_3 + \ldots$. Remembering the interpretation of $+$, we may write

$$w = W_1 + W_2 + W_3 + \ldots$$

and this means, "The class-term, w, denotes W_1 or W_2 or W_3 or $\ldots$," that is, w denotes an unspecified member of the class of W's. The servant of a (some, any) woman is, then, $s\,|\,w$.

$$s\,|\,w = s\,|\,(W_1 + W_2 + W_3 + \ldots) = s\,|\,W_1 + s\,|\,W_2 + s\,|\,W_3 + \ldots$$

"A woman" is *either* W_1 *or* W_2 *or* W_3, etc.; "servant of a woman" is either

---

[135] Peirce's notation for this is $s\,w$; he uses s,w for the simple logical product.

servant of W_1 or servant of W_2 or servant of W_3, etc. Similarly, "servant of every woman" is servant of W_1 *and* servant of W_2 *and* servant of W_3, etc.; or remembering the interpretation of ✕,

$$s^w = s^{(W_1+W_2+W_3+\cdots)} = (s\,|\,W_1) \times (s\,|\,W_2) \times (s\,|\,W_3) \times \ldots$$

where, of course, $s\,|\,W_n$ represents the relative product, "s of W_n," and ✕ represents the non-relative logical product translated by "and". The above can be more briefly symbolized, following the obvious mathematical analogies,

$$w = \Sigma\,W$$
$$s\,|\,w = \Sigma_w(s\,|\,W)$$
$$s^w = \Pi_w(s\,|\,W)$$

Unless w represent a null class, we shall have

$$\Pi_w(s\,|\,W) \subset \Sigma_w(s\,|\,W), \qquad \text{or} \qquad s^w \subset s\,|\,w$$

The class "servants of *every* woman" is contained in the class "servants of *a* woman". This law has numerous consequences, some of which are:

$$(l\,|\,s)^w \subset (l\,|\,s\,|\,w)$$

A lover of a servant of all women is a lover of a servant of a woman.

$$l^{s^w} \subset (l\,|\,s)^w$$

A lover of every servant-of-all-women stands to every woman in the relation of lover-of-a-servant of hers (unless the class s^w be null).

$$l^{s\,|\,w} \subset l^s\,|\,w$$

A lover of every servant-of-a-woman stands to a (some) woman in the relation of lover-of-a-servant of hers.

From the general principle,[136]

$$m\,|\,[\Pi_x\,f(x)] \subset \Pi_x[m\,|\,f(x)]$$

[136] The proof of this theorem is as follows:

$$a = a\,b\,c\ldots + a\,b\,-c\ldots + a\,-b\,c\ldots + \ldots,$$

or $a = a\,b\,c\ldots + P$, where P is the sum of the remaining terms.

Whence, if $\bigcirc$ represent any relation distributive with respect to $+$,

$$m \bigcirc a = m \bigcirc a\,b\,c\ldots + m \bigcirc P$$

Similarly, $\qquad m \bigcirc b = m \bigcirc a\,b\,c\ldots + m \bigcirc Q$

$$m \bigcirc c = m \bigcirc a\,b\,c\ldots + m \bigcirc R$$

Etc., etc.

Now let a, b, c, etc., be respectively $f(x_1)$, $f(x_2)$, $f(x_3)$, etc., and multiply together all the above equations. On the left side, we have

$$[m \bigcirc f(x_1)][m \bigcirc f(x_2)][m \bigcirc f(x_3)]\ldots$$

we have also,

$$l \,|\, [\Pi_w(s \,|\, w)] \subset \Pi_w[(l \,|\, s) \,|\, w], \qquad \text{or} \qquad l \,|\, s^w \subset (l \,|\, s)^w$$

A lover of a (some) servant-of-every-woman stands to every woman in the relation of lover-of-a-servant of hers.

We have also the general formulae of inclusion,

$$\text{If } \ l \subset s, \text{ then } l^w \subset s^w$$

and, $\qquad$ If $\ s \subset w$, then $l^w \subset l^s$

The first of these means: If all lovers are servants, then a lover of every woman is also a servant of every woman. The second means: If all servants are women, then a lover of every woman is also a lover of every servant. These laws are, of course, general. We have also: [137]

$$(l \,|\, s) \,|\, w = l \,|\, (s \,|\, w)$$
$$(l^s)^w = l^{(s \,|\, w)}$$
$$l^{s+w} = l^s \times l^w$$

The last of these is read: A lover of every person who is either a servant or a woman is a lover of every servant and a lover of every woman. An interesting law which reminds us of Lambert's "Newtonian formula" is,

$$(l + s)^w = l^w + \Sigma_q(l^{w-q} \times s^q) + s^w$$

One who is either-lover-or-servant of every woman, is either lover of every woman or, for some portion q of the class *women*, is lover of every woman except members of q and servant of every member of q, or, finally, is servant of every woman. Peirce also gives this law in a form which approximates even more closely the binomial theorem. The corresponding law for the product is simpler,

$$(l \times s)^w = l^w \times s^w$$

which is

$$\Pi_x[m \bigcirc f(x)]$$

On the right side, we have

$$(m \bigcirc a \, b \, c \, \dots) + (m \bigcirc P) + (m \bigcirc Q) + (m \bigcirc R) + \dots, \qquad \text{or} \qquad (m \bigcirc a \, b \, c \dots) + K$$

where K is a sum of other terms.

But $(m \bigcirc a \, b \, c \, \dots)$ is $m \bigcirc [f(x_1) \times f(x_2) \times f(x_3) \dots]$, which is

$$m \bigcirc \Pi_x f(x)$$

Hence $[m \bigcirc \Pi f(x)] + K = \Pi_x[m \bigcirc f(x)]$.

Hence $m \bigcirc \Pi f(x) \subset \Pi_x[m \bigcirc f(x)]$.

Peirce does not prove this theorem, but illustrates it briefly for logical multiplication (see "Description of a Notation", p. 346).

[137] "Description of a Notation, p. 334.

One who is both-lover-and-servant of every woman, is both a lover of every woman and a servant of every woman.

Peirce introduces a fourth term, and summarizes in a diagram the inclusion relations obtained by extending the formulae already given.[138]   The number of such inclusions, for four relatives, is somewhat more than one hundred eighty.   He challenges the reader to accomplish the precise formulation of these by means of ordinary language and formal logic.

An s of none but members of w, Peirce symbolizes by ^sw.   He calls this operation "backward involution", and relatives of the type ^sw he refers to as "infinitesimal relatives", on account of an extended and difficult mathematical analogy which he presents.[139]   The laws of this relation are analogous to those of s^w.

$$\text{If } s \subset w, \text{ then } {}^ls \subset {}^lw$$

If all servants are women, then a lover of none but servants is lover of none but women.

$$\text{If } l \subset s, \text{ then } {}^sw \subset {}^lw$$

If all lovers are servants, then a servant of none but women is a lover of none but women.

$$l({}^sw) = {}^{(l \mid s)}w$$

The lovers of none but servants-of-none-but-women are the lovers-of-servants of none but women.

$$^{l+s}w = {}^lw \times {}^sw$$

Those who are either-lovers-or-servants of none but women are those who are lovers of none but women and servants of none but women.

$$^s(w \times v) = {}^sw \times {}^sv$$

The servants of none but those who are both women and violinists are those who are servants of none but women and servants of none but violinists.

$$^{(l \mid s)}w \subset {}^{(l^s)}w$$

Whoever is lover-of-a-servant of none but women is a lover-of-every-servant of none but women.

$$l \mid {}^sw \subset {}^{(l_s)}w$$

A lover of one who is servant to none but women is a lover-of-none-but-servants to none but women.

$$^ls\,w \subset {}^l(s \mid w)$$

[138] *Ibid.*, p. 347.
[139] *Ibid.*, pp. 348 *ff.*

Whoever stands to a woman in the relation of lover-of-nothing-but-servants of hers is a lover of nothing but servants of women.

The two kinds of involution are connected by the laws:

$$l(s^w) = (^ls)^w$$

A lover of none but those who are servants of every woman is the same as one who stands to every woman in the relation of a lover of none but servants of hers.

$$^ls = -l^{-s}\ [140]$$

Lover of none but servants is non-lover of every non-servant. It appears from this last that x^y and ^xy are connected through negation:

$-(l^s) = -l|s$, Not a lover of every servant is non-lover of a servant.

$-(^ls) = l|-s$, Not a lover of none but servants is lover of a non-servant.

$^l-s = -(l|s) = -l^s$, A lover of none but non-servants is one who is not lover-of-a-servant, a non-lover of every servant.

$^{-l}s = -(-l|-s) = l^{-s}$, A non-lover of none but servants is one who is not a non-lover-of-a-non-servant, a lover of every non-servant.

We have the further laws governing negatives: [141]

$$-[(l \times s)^w] = -(l^w) \,\textbf{+}\, -(s^w)$$
$$-[^l(s \times w)] = -(^ls) \,\textbf{+}\, -(^lw)$$
$$-(^{l+s}w) = -(^lw) \,\textbf{+}\, -(^sw)$$
$$-(l^{s+w}) = -(l^s) \,\textbf{+}\, -(l^w)$$

In the early paper, "On the Description of a Notation for the Logic of Relatives", negatives are treated in a curious fashion. A symbol is used for "different from" and the negative of s is represented by $\mathfrak{n}^s$, "different from every s". Converses are barely mentioned in this study. In the paper of 1880, converses and negatives appear in their usual notation, "relative addition" is brought in to balance "relative multiplication", and the two kinds of involution are retained. But in "The Logic of Relatives" in the Johns Hopkins *Studies in Logic*, published in 1882, involution has disappeared, converses and negatives and "relative addition" are retained. This last represents the final form of Peirce's calculus of relatives. We have here,

(1) Relative terms, $a, b, \ldots x, y, z$.

(2) The negative of x, $-x$.

[140] See *ibid.*, p. 353. Not-x is here symbolized by $(1 - x)$.
[141] *Alg. Log.* 1880, p. 55.

(3) The converse of x, $\smile x$. If x is "lover", $\smile x$ is "beloved"; if $\smile x$ is "lover", x is "beloved".

(4) Non-relative addition, $a + b$, "either a or b".

(5) Non-relative multiplication, $a \times b$, or $a\,b$, "both a and b".

(6) Relative multiplication, $a|b$, "a of a b".

(7) Relative addition, $a \dagger b$, "a of everything but b's, a of every non-b".

(8) The relations $=$ and $\subset$, as before.

(9) The universal relation, 1, "consistent with," which pairs every term with itself and with every other.

(10) The null-relation, 0, the negative of 1.

(11) The relation "identical with", I, which pairs every term with itself.

(12) The relation "different from", N, which pairs any term with every other term which is distinct.[142]

In terms of these, the fundamental laws of the calculus, in addition to those which hold for class-terms in general, are as follows:

(1) $\smile(\smile a) = a$

(2) $-(\smile a) = \smile(-a)$

(3) $(a \subset b) = (\smile b \subset \smile a)$

(4) If $a \subset b$, then $(a|x) \subset (b|x)$ and $(x|a) \subset (x|b)$.

(5) If $a \subset b$, then $(a \dagger x) \subset (b \dagger x)$ and $(x \dagger a) \subset (x \dagger b)$.

(6) $x|(a|b) = (x|a)|b$

(7) $x \dagger (a \dagger b) = (x \dagger a) \dagger b$

(8) $x|(a \dagger b) \subset (x|a) \dagger b$

(9) $(a \dagger b)\,x \subset a \dagger (b\,x)$

(10) $(a|x) + (b|x) \subset (a + b)|x$

(11) $x|(a \dagger b) \subset (x \dagger a)(x \dagger b)$

(12) $(a + b)\,x \subset (a|x) + (b|x)$

(13) $(a \dagger x)(b \dagger x) \subset (a|b) \dagger x$

(14) $-(a \dagger b) = -a|-b$

(15) $-(a|b) = -a \dagger -b$

(16) $\smile(a + b) = \smile a + \smile b$

(17) $\smile(a\,b) = \smile a \smile b$

(18) $\smile(a \dagger b) = \smile a \dagger \smile b$

(19) $\smile(a|b) = \smile a|\smile b$

For the relations 1, 0, I, and N, the following additional formulae are given:

---

[142] I have altered Peirce's notation, as the reader may see by comparison.

(20) $0 \subset x$ (21) $x \subset 1$

(22) $x + 0 = x$ (23) $x \cdot 1 = x$

(24) $x + 1 = 1$ (25) $x \cdot 0 = 0$

(26) $x \dagger 1 = 1$ (27) $x \,|\, 0 = 0$

(28) $1 \dagger x = 1$ (29) $0 \,|\, x = 0$

(30) $x \dagger N = x$ (31) $x \,|\, I = x$

(32) $N \dagger x = x$ (33) $I \,|\, x = x$

(34) $x + -x = 1$ (35) $x -x = 0$

(36) $I \subset [x \dagger \smile(-x)]$ (37) $[x \,|\, \smile(-x)] \subset N$

This calculus is, as Peirce says, highly multiform, and no general principles of solution and elimination can be laid down.[143] Not only the variety of relations, but the lack of symmetry between relative multiplication and relative addition, e. g., in (10)–(13) above, contributes to this multiformity. But, as we now know, the chief value of any calculus of relatives is not in any elimination or solution of the algebraic type, but in deductions to be made directly from its formulae. Peirce's devices for solution are, therefore, of much less importance than is the theoretic foundation upon which his calculus of relatives is built. It is this which has proved useful in later research and has been made the basis of valuable additions to logistic development.

This theory is practically unmodified throughout the papers dealing with relatives, as a comparison of "Description of a Notation for the Logic of Relatives" with "The Logic of Relatives" in the Johns Hopkins studies and with the paper of 1884 will indicate.

"Individual" or "elementary" relatives are the pairs (or triads, etc.) of individual things.   If the objects in the universe of discourse be A, B, C: etc., then the individual relatives will constitute the two-dimensional array,

$$A : A, \ A : B, \ A : C, \ A : D, \ \ldots$$
$$B : A, \ B : B, \ B : C, \ B : D, \ \ldots$$
$$C : A, \ C : B, \ C : C, \ C : D, \ \ldots$$
$$\ldots \text{ Etc., etc.}$$

It will be noted that any individual thing coupled with itself is an individual relative but that in general $A : B$ differs from $B : A$—individual relatives are *ordered* couples.

A *general* relative is conceived as an aggregate or logical sum of such

[143] "Logic of Relatives" in *Studies in Logic by members of Johns Hopkins University*, p. 193.

individual relatives. If b represent "benefactor", then

$$b = \Sigma_i \Sigma_j (b)_{ij} (I : J),$$

where $(b)_{ij}$ is a numerical coefficient whose value is 1 in case I is a bene-factor of J, and otherwise 0, and where the sums are to be taken for all the individuals in the universe. That is to say, b is the logical sum of all the benefactor-benefitted pairs in the universe. This is the first formulation of "definition in extension", now widely used in logistic, though seldom in exactly this form. By this definition, b is the aggregate of all the individual relatives in our two-dimensional array which do not drop out through having the coefficient 0. It is some expression of the form,

$$b = (X : Y)_1 + (X : Y)_2 + (X : Y)_3 + \ldots$$

If, now, we consider the logical meaning of $+$, we see that this may be read, "b is either $(X : Y)_1$ or $(X : Y)_2$ or $(X : Y)_3$ or ...". To say that b represents the *class* of benefactor-benefitted couples is, then, inexact: b represents an unspecified individual relative, *any one* of this class. (That it should represent "some" in a sense which denotes more than one at once—which the meaning of $+$ in the general case admits—is precluded by the fact that any two distinct individual relatives are *ipso facto* mutually exclusive.) A general relative, so defined, is what Mr. Russell calls a "real variable". Peirce discusses the idea of such a variable in a most illuminating fashion.[144]

"Demonstration of the sort called mathematical is founded on suppo-sition of particular cases. The geometrician draws a figure; the algebraist assumes a letter to signify a certain quantity fulfilling the required condi-tions. But while the mathematician supposes a particular case, his hypoth-esis is yet perfectly general, because he considers no characters of the individual case but those which must belong to every such case. The ad-vantage of his procedure lies in the fact that the logical laws of individual terms are simpler than those which relate to general terms, because indi-viduals are either identical or mutually exclusive, and cannot intersect or be subordinated to one another as classes can. . . .

"The old logics distinguish between *individuum signatum* and *indi-viduum vagum*. 'Julius Caesar' is an example of the former; 'a certain man', of the latter. The *individuum vagum*, in the days when such con-ceptions were exactly investigated, occasioned great difficulty from its having a certain generality, being capable, apparently, of logical division.

[144] "Description of a Notation, pp. 342–44.

If we include under *individuum vagum* such a term as 'any individual man', these difficulties appear in a strong light, for what is true of any individual man is true of all men. Such a term is in one sense not an individual term; for it represents every man. But it represents each man as capable of being denoted by a term which is individual; and so, though it is not itself an individual term, it stands for any one of a class of such terms. . . . The letters which the mathematician uses (whether in algebra or in geometry) are such individuals by second intention. . . . All the formal logical laws relating to individuals will hold good of such individuals by second intention, and at the same time a universal proposition may be substituted for a proposition about such an individual, for nothing can be predicated of such an individual which cannot be predicated of the whole class."

The relative b, denoting ambiguously any one of the benefactor-benefitted pairs in the universe, is such an individual by second intention. It is defined by means of the "propositional function", "I benefits J", as the logical sum of the $(I : J)$ couples for which "I benefits J" is true. The compound relations of the calculus can be similarly defined.

$$\text{If } a = \Sigma_i \Sigma_j (a)_{ij} (I : J), \text{ and } b = \Sigma_i \Sigma_j (b)_{ij} (I : J),$$
$$\text{then } a + b = \Sigma_i \Sigma_j [(a)_{ij} + (b)_{ij}] (I : J)$$

That is, if "agent" is the logical sum of all the $(I : J)$ couples for which "I is agent of J" is true, and "benefactor" is the sum of all the $(I : J)$ couples for which "I benefits J" is true, then "either agent or benefactor" is the logical sum of all the $(I : J)$ couples for which "Either I is agent of J or I benefits J" is true. We might indicate the same facts more simply by defining only the "propositional function", $(a + b)_{ij}$.[145]

$$(a + b)_{ij} = (a)_{ij} + (b)_{ij}$$

The definition of $a + b$ given above, follows immediately from this simpler equation. The definitions of the other compound relations are similar:

$$(a \times b)_{ij} = (a)_{ij} \times (b)_{ij}$$
$$\text{or} \quad a \times b = \Sigma_i \Sigma_j [(a)_{ij} \times (b)_{ij}] (I : J)$$

"Both agent and benefactor" is the logical sum of the $(I : J)$ couples for which "I is agent of J and I is benefactor of J" is true.

$$(a | b)_{ij} = \Sigma_h \{ (a)_{ih} \times (b)_{hj} \}$$
$$\text{or} \quad a | b = \Sigma_i \Sigma_j [\Sigma_h \{ (a)_{ih} \times (b)_{hj} \}] (I : J)$$

---

[145] See "Logic of Relatives", *loc. cit.*, p. 188.

"Agent of a benefactor" is the logical sum of all the $(I : J)$ couples such that, for some H, "I is agent of H and H is benefactor of J" is true.

There are two difficulties in the comprehension of this last. The first concerns the meaning of "agent of a benefactor". Peirce, like De Morgan, treats his relatives as denoting ambiguously either the relation itself or the things which have the relation—either relations or relative terms. a is either the relation "agent of" or the class name "agent". Now note that the class name denotes the *first* term in the *pairs* which have the relation. With this in mind, the compound relation, $a|b$, will become clear. "Agent of a benefactor" names the I's in the $I : J$ pairs which make up the field of the relation, "agent of a benefactor of". Any reference to the J's at the other end of the relation is gone, just as "agent" omits any reference to the J's in the field of the relation "agent of". The second difficulty concerns the operator, Σ_h, which we have read, "For some H". Consider any statement involving a "propositional function", φz, where z is the variable representing the individual of which φ is asserted.

$$\Sigma_z \varphi z = \varphi Z_1 + \varphi Z_2 + \varphi Z_3 + \ldots$$

That is, $\Sigma_z \varphi z$ symbolizes "Either φ is true of Z_1 or φ is true of Z_2 or φ is true of Z_3 or ... ", and this is most simply expressed by "For *some* z (some z or other), φz". In the particular case in hand, φz is $(a)_{ih} \times (b)_{hj}$, "I is agent of H and H is benefactor of J". The terms, I and J, which stand in the relation "I is agent of a benefactor of J", are those for which *there is some H or other* such that I is agent of H and H is benefactor of J.

Suppose we consider any "propositional function", φz with the operator Π.

$$\Pi_z \varphi z = \varphi Z_1 \times \varphi Z_2 \times \varphi Z_3 \times \ldots$$

That is, $\Pi_z \varphi z$ symbolizes "φ is true of Z_1 and φ is true of Z_2 and φ is true of Z_3 and ... ", or "φ is true for *every* z". This operator is needed in the definition of $a \dagger b$.

$$(a \dagger b)_{ij} = \Pi_h \{(a)_{ih} + (b)_{hj}\}$$

"I is agent of everyone but benefactors of J" is equivalent to "For every H, either I is agent of H or H is benefactor of J".

$$a \dagger b = \Sigma_i \Sigma_j [\Pi_h \{(a)_{ih} + (b)_{hj}\}](I : J)$$

"Agent of all non-benefactors" is the logical sum of all the $(I : J)$ couples such that, for every H, either I is agent of H or H is benefactor of J. The same considerations about the ambiguity of relatives—denoting either the relation itself or those things which are *first terms* of the relation—applies in this case also. We need not, for the relations still to be discussed, consider the step from the definition of the compound "propositional functions", $(a \dagger b)_{ij}$ in the above, to the definition of the corresponding relation, $a \dagger b$. This step is always taken in exactly the same way.

The converse, converse of the negative, and negative of the converse, are very simply defined.

$$(\smile b)_{ij} = (b)_{ji}$$
$$[\smile(-b)]_{ij} = (-b)_{ji}$$
$$[-(\smile b)]_{ij} = -(b)_{ji}$$

That the negative of the converse is the converse of the negative follows from the obvious fact that $-(b)_{ij} = (-b)_{ji}$.

All the formulae of the calculus of relatives, beyond those which belong also to the calculus of non-relative terms,[146] may be proved from such definitions. For example:

To prove, $\smile(a + b) = \smile a + \smile b$

$\smile(a + b)_{ij} = (a + b)_{ji} = (a)_{ji} + (b)_{ji}$

But $(a)_{ji} = (\smile a)_{ij}$, and $(b)_{ji} = (\smile b)_{ij}$

Hence $\smile(a + b)_{ij} = (\smile a)_{ij} + (\smile b)_{ij}$

Hence $\Sigma_i \Sigma_j \{\smile(a + b)_{ij}\}(I : J) = \Sigma_i \Sigma_j \{(\smile a)_{ij} + (\smile b)_{ij}\}(I : J)$ Q E.D.

For the complete development of this theory, there must be a discussion of the laws which govern such expressions as $(a)_{ij}$, or in general, expressions of the form φx, where φx is a statement which involves a variable, x, and φx is either true or false whenever any individual value of the variable is specified. Such expressions are now called "propositional functions".[147] $(a)_i$, or in the more convenient notation, φx, is a propositional function of one variable; $(a)_{ij}$, or $\varphi(x, y)$, may be regarded as a propositional function of two variables, or as a function of the single variable, the individual relative $(I : J)$, or $(X : Y)$.

This theory of propositional functions is stated in the paper of 1885, 'On the Algebra of Logic". It is assumed, as also in earlier papers, that the laws of the algebra of classes hold for propositions as well.[148] The *additional* law which propositions obey is stated here for the first time.

---

[146] The formulae of the calculus of classes can also be derived from these, considered as themselves laws of the calculus of propositions.

[147] Peirce has no name for such expressions, though he discusses their properties acutely (see *Alg. Log.* 1880, § 2).

[148] This assumption first appears in *Alg. Log.* 1880.

The current form of this law is "If $x \neq 0$, then $x = 1$",—which gives immediately "If $x \neq 1$, then $x = 0$"—"If x is not false, then x is true, and if x is not true, then x is false". Peirce uses v and f for "true" and "false", instead of 1 and 0, and the law is stated in the form

$$(x - f)(v - x) = 0$$

But the calculus of propositional functions, though derived from the algebra for propositions, is not identical with it. "x is a man" is neither true nor false. A propositional function may be true in some cases, false in some cases. "If x is a man, then x is a mortal" is true in all cases, or true of *any* x; "x is a man" is true in *some* cases, or true for some values of x. For reasons already suggested,

$$\Sigma_x \varphi x = \varphi x_1 + \varphi x_2 + \varphi x_3 + \ldots$$

$\Sigma_x \varphi x$ represents "φx is true for some value of the variable, x—that is, either φx_1 is true or φx_2 is true or φx_3 is true or . . ." Similarly,

$$\Pi_x \varphi x = \varphi x_1 \times \varphi x_2 \times \varphi x_3 \times \ldots$$

$\Pi_x \varphi x$ represents "φx is true for all values of the variable, x—that is, φx_1 is true and φx_2 is true and φx_3 is true and . . ."

If $(a)_{xy}$, or more conveniently, $\varphi(x, y)$, represent "x is agent of y", and $(b)_{xy}$, or more conveniently, $\psi(x, y)$, mean "x is benefactor of y", then

$$\Pi_x \Sigma_y [\varphi(x, y) \times \psi(x, y)]$$

will mean that for all values of x and some values of y, "x is agent of y and x is benefactor of y" is true—that is, it represents the proposition "Everyone is both agent and benefactor of someone". This will appear if we expand $\Pi_x \Sigma_y [\varphi(x, y) \times \psi(x, y)]$:

$$\Pi_x \Sigma_y [\varphi(x, y) \times \psi(x, y)]$$
$$= \{ [\varphi(x_1, y_1) \times \psi(x_1, y_1)] + [\varphi(x_1, y_2) \times \psi(x_1, y_2)] + \ldots \}$$
$$\times \{ [\varphi(x_2, y_1) \times \psi(x_2, y_1)] + [\varphi(x_2, y_2) \times \psi(x_2, y_2)] + \ldots \}$$
$$\times \{ [\varphi(x_3, y_1) \times \psi(x_3, y_1)] + [\varphi(x_3, y_2) \times \psi(x_3, y_2)] + \ldots \}$$
$$\times \ldots \text{ Etc., etc.}$$

This expression reads directly "{*Either* [x_1 is agent of y_1 and x_1 is benefactor of y_1] *or* [x_1 is agent of y_2 and x_1 is benefactor of y_2] *or* . . .} *and* {*either* [x_2 is agent of y_1 and x_2 is benefactor of y_1] *or* [x_2 is agent of y_2 and x_2 is benefactor of y_2] *or* . . .} *and* {*either* [x_3 is agent of y_1 and x_3 is benefactor of y_1] *or* [x_3 is agent of y_2 and x_3 is benefactor of y_2] *or* . . .} *and* . . . Etc., etc".

The operator Σ, which is nearer the argument, or "Boolian" as Peirce calls it, indicates the operation, $+$, within the lines. The outside operator, Π, indicates the operation, $\times$, between the lines—i. e., in the columns; and the subscript of the operator nearer the Boolian indicates the letter which varies within the lines, the subscript of the outside operator, the letter which varies from line to line. Three operators would give a three-dimensional array. With a little patience, the reader may learn to interpret any such expression directly from the meaning of simple logical sums and logical products. For example, with the same meanings of $\varphi(x, y)$ and $\psi(x, y)$,

$$\Pi_x \Sigma_y [\varphi(x, y) \times \psi(y, x)]$$

will mean "Everyone (x) is agent of some (y) benefactor of himself". (Note the order of the variables in the Boolian.)   And

$$\Sigma_x \Sigma_y \Pi_z [\varphi(x, z) + \psi(z, y)]$$

will symbolize "There is some x and some y such that, for every z, either x is agent of z or z is benefactor of y"; or, more simply, "There is some pair, x and y, such that x is agent of all non-benefactors of y".

The laws for the manipulation of such Boolians with Π and Σ operators are given as follows: [149]

"1st. The different premises having been written with distinct indices (the same index not being used in two propositions) are written together, and all the Π's and Σ's are to be brought to the left. This can evidently be done, for

$$\Pi_i x_i . \Pi_j x_j = \Pi_i \Pi_j x_i x_j$$
$$\Sigma_i x_i . \Pi_j x_j = \Sigma_i \Pi_j x_i x_j$$
$$\Sigma_i x_i . \Sigma_j x_j = \Sigma_i \Sigma_j x_i x_j$$

[Or in the more convenient, and probably more familiar, notation,

$$\Pi_x \varphi x \times \Pi_y \varphi y = \Pi_x \Pi_y (\varphi x \times \varphi y)$$
$$\Sigma_x \varphi x \times \Pi_y \varphi y = \Sigma_x \Pi_y (\varphi x \times \varphi y)$$
$$\Sigma_x \varphi x \times \Sigma_y \varphi y = \Sigma_x \Sigma_y (\varphi x \times \varphi y)]$$

"2d. Without deranging the order of the indices of any one premise, the Π's and Σ's belonging to different premises may be moved relatively to one another, and as far as possible the Σ's should be carried to the left

[149] *Alg. Log.* 1885, pp. 196–98.

of the Π's.   We have

$$\Pi_i\Pi_j x_{ij} = \Pi_j\Pi_i x_{ij} \qquad [\text{Or,} \quad \Pi_x\Pi_y\varphi(x,\,y) = \Pi_y\Pi_x\varphi(x,\,y)]$$

$$\Sigma_i\Sigma_j x_{ij} = \Sigma_j\Sigma_i x_{ij} \qquad [\text{Or,} \quad \Sigma_x\Sigma_y\varphi(x,\,y) = \Sigma_y\Sigma_x\varphi(x,\,y)]$$

and also $\Sigma_i\Pi_j x_i y_j = \Pi_j\Sigma_i x_i y_j \qquad [\text{Or,} \ \Sigma_x\Pi_y(\varphi x \times \psi y) = \Pi_y\Sigma_x(\varphi x \times \psi y)]$

But this formula does not hold when i and j are not separated.   We do have, however,

$$\Sigma_i\Pi_j x_{ij} \ -< \ \Pi_j\Sigma_i x_{ij} \qquad [\text{Or,} \ \Sigma_x\Pi_y\varphi(x,\,y) \subset \Pi_y\Sigma_x\varphi(x,\,y)]$$

It will, therefore, be well to begin by putting the Σ's to the left as far as possible, because at a later stage of the work they can be carried to the right but not [always] to the left.   For example, if the operators of two premises are $\Pi_i\Sigma_j\Pi_k$ and $\Sigma_x\Pi_y\Sigma_z$, we can unite them in either of the two orders

$$\Sigma_x\Pi_y\Sigma_z\Pi_i\Sigma_j\Pi_k$$

$$\Sigma_x\Pi_i\Sigma_j\Pi_y\Sigma_z\Pi_k$$

and shall usually obtain different conclusions accordingly.   There will often be room for skill in choosing the most suitable arrangement.

. . . "5th.   The next step consists in multiplying the whole Boolian part, by the modification of itself produced by substituting for the index of any Π any other index standing to the left of it in the Quantifier.   Thus, for

$$\Sigma_i\Pi_j l_{ij} \qquad\qquad [\text{Or, for } \Sigma_x\Pi_y\varphi(x,\,y),$$

we can write $\Sigma_i\Pi_j l_{ij} l_{ii} \qquad\qquad\qquad \Sigma_x\Pi_y\{ \varphi(x,\,y) \times \varphi(x,\,x)\}]$

"6th.   The next step consists in the re-manipulation of the Boolian part, consisting, 1st, in adding to any part any term we like; 2d, in dropping from any part any factor we like, and 3d, in observing that

$$x\bar{x} = f, \qquad x + \bar{x} = v,$$

so that $x\bar{x}y + z = z \qquad (x + \bar{x} + y)z = z$

"7th. Π's and Σ's in the Quantifier whose indices no longer appear in the Boolian are dropped.

"The fifth step will, in practice, be combined with part of the sixth and seventh.   Thus, from $\Sigma_i\Pi_j l_{ij}$ we shall at once proceed to $\Sigma_i l_{ii}$ if we like."

We may say, in general, that the procedures which are valid in this calculus are those which can be performed by treating $\Sigma_x\varphi x$ as a sum, $\varphi x_1 + \varphi x_2 + \varphi x_3 + \ldots$, and $\Pi_x\varphi x$ as a product, $\varphi x_1 \times \varphi x_2 \times \varphi x_3 \times \ldots$; $\Sigma_x\Pi_y\psi(x,\,y)$ as a sum, for the various values of x, of products, each for the various values of y, and so on. Thus this calculus may be derived from the calculus of propositions. But Peirce does not carry out any proofs of the principles of the system, and he notes that this method of proof would be theoretically unsound.[150] "It is to be remarked that $\Sigma_i x_i$ and $\Pi_i x_i$ are only *similar* to a sum and a product; they are not strictly of that nature, because the individuals of the universe may be innumerable."

Another way of saying the same thing would be this: The laws of the calculus of propositions cannot extend to $\Sigma_i x_i$ and $\Pi_i x_i$, because the extension of these laws to aggregates in general, by the method which the mathematical analogies of sum and product suggest, would require the principle of mathematical induction, which is not sufficient for proof in case the aggregate is infinite.

The whole of the calculus of relatives may be derived from this calculus of propositional functions by the methods which have been exemplified—that is, by representing any relation, b, as $\Sigma_i \Sigma_j (b)_{ij} (I : J)$, and defining the relations, such as "converse of", "relative-product," etc., which distinguish the calculus, as Π and Σ functions of the elementary relatives. We need not enter into the detail of this matter, since Sections II and III of Chapter IV will develop the calculus of propositional functions by a modification of Peirce's method, while Section IV of that chapter will show how the calculus of classes can be derived from this calculus of propositional functions, Section V will indicate the manner in which the calculus of relations may be similarly derived, and Section VI will suggest how, by a further important modification of Peirce's method, a theoretically adequate logic of mathematics may be obtained.

It remains to consider briefly Peirce's studies toward the derivation of other mathematical relations, operations, and systems from symbolic logic. The most important paper, in this connection, is "Upon the Logic of Mathematics".[151] Certain portions of the paper, "On an Improvement in Boole's Calculus of Logic", and of the monograph, "Description of a Notation for the Logic of Relatives", are also of interest.

The first-mentioned of these is concerned to show how the relations $+$, $=$, etc., of arithmetic can be defined in terms of the corresponding logical relations, and the properties of arithmetical relations deduced from theorems concerning their logical analogues.[152]

"Imagine . . . a particular case under Boole's calculus, in which the

---

[150] *Alg. Log.* 1885, p. 195.
[151] *Proc. Amer. Acad.*, VII, 402–12.
[152] *Loc. cit.*, pp. 410–11.

letters are no longer terms of first intention, but terms of second intention, and that of a special kind. . . . Let the letters . . . relate exclusively to the extension of first intensions. Let the differences of the characters of things and events be disregarded, and let the letters signify only the differences of classes as wider or narrower. In other words, the only logical comprehension which the letters considered as terms will have is the greater or less divisibility of the class. Thus, n in another case of Boole's calculus might, for example, denote 'New England States'; but in the case now supposed, all the characters which make these states what they are, being neglected, it would signify only what essentially belongs to a class which has the same relation to higher and lower classes which the class of New England States has,—that is, a collection of *six*.

"In this case, the sign of identity will receive a special meaning. For, if m denotes what essentially belongs to a class of the rank of 'sides of a cube', then [the logical] $m = n$ will imply, not that every New England State is the side of a cube, and conversely, but that whatever essentially belongs to a class of the numerical rank of 'New England States' essentially belongs to a class of the rank of 'sides of a cube', and conversely. *Identity* of this particular sort may be termed equality. . . ."

If a, b, c, etc. represent thus the number of the classes, a, b, c, etc., then the arithmetical relations can be defined as logical relations. The logical relation $a + b$, already defined, will represent arithmetical addition: And from the fact that the logical $+$ is commutative and associative, it will follow that the arithmetical $+$ is so also. Arithmetical multiplication is more difficult to deal with but may be defined as follows: [153]

$a \times b$ represents an event when a and b are events only if these events are independent of each other, in which case $a \times b = a\,b$ [where $a\,b$ is the logical product]. By the events being independent is meant that it is possible to take two series of terms, A_1, A_2, A_3, etc., and B_1, B_2, B_3, etc., such that the following conditions are satisfied. (Here x denotes any individual or class, not nothing; A_m, A_n, B_m, B_n, any members of the two series of terms, and ΣA, ΣB, $\Sigma (A\,B)$ logical sums of some of the A_n's, the B_n's, and the $(A_n\,B_n)$'s respectively.)

> Condition 1.   No A_m is A_n
> "   2.   No B_m is B_n
> "   3. $x = \Sigma (A\,B)$
> "   4. $a = \Sigma A$

[153] *Loc. cit.*, p. 403.

Condition 5. $b = \Sigma B$

"   6.   Some A_m is B_n

This definition is somewhat involved: the crux of the matter is that $a\,b$ will, in the case described, have as many members as there are combinations of a member of a with a member of b. Where the members of a are distinct (condition 1) and the members of b are distinct (condition 2), these combinations will be of the same multitude as the arithmetical $a \times b$.

It is worthy of remark that, in respect both to addition and to multiplication, Peirce has here hit upon the same fundamental ideas by means of which arithmetical relations are defined in *Principia Mathematica*.[154] The "second intention" of a class term is, in *Principia*, Nc'α; $a + b$, in Peirce's discussion, corresponds to what is there called the "arithmetical sum" of two logical classes, and $a \times b$ to what is called the "arithmetical product". But Peirce's discussion does not meet all the difficulties—that could hardly be expected in a short paper. In particular, it does not define the arithmetical sum in case the classes summed have members in common, and it does not indicate the manner of defining the *number* of a class, though it does suggest exactly the mode of attack adopted in *Principia*, namely, that number be considered as a property of cardinally similar classes taken in extension.

The method suggested for the derivation of the laws of various numerical algebras from those of the logic of relatives is more comprehensive, though here it is only the *order* of the systems which is derived from the *order* of the logic of relatives; there is no attempt to define the number or multitude of a class in terms of logical relations.[155]

We are here to take a closed system of elementary relatives, every individual in which is either a T or a P and none is both.

$$\text{Let } c = (T : T)$$
$$s = (P : P)$$
$$p = (P : T)$$
$$t = (T : P)$$

Suppose T here represent an individual teacher, and P an individual pupil: the system will then be comparable to a school in which every person is either teacher or pupil, and none is both and every teacher teaches every pupil. The *relative* term, c, will then be defined as the relation of one

---

[154] See Vol. II, Section A.

[155] "Description of a Notation, pp. 359 *ff*.

teacher to another, that is, "colleague". Similarly, s is $(P : P)$, the relation of one pupil to another, that is, "schoolmate". The *relative* term, p,
is $(P : T)$, the relation of any pupil to any teacher, that is, "pupil". And
the *relative* term, t, is $(T : P)$, the relation of any teacher to any pupil,
that is, "teacher". Thus from the two non-relative terms, T and P, are
generated the four elementary relatives, c, s, t, and p.

The properties of this system will be clearer if we venture upon certain
explanations of the properties of elementary relatives—which Peirce does
not give and to the form of which he might object. For *any* such relative
$(I : J)$, where the I's and the J's are distinct, we shall have three laws:

(1) $(I : J) | J = I$

Whatever has the $(I : J)$ relation to a J must be an I: whoever has the
teacher-pupil relation to a pupil must be a teacher.

(2) $(I : J) | I = 0$

Whatever has the teacher-pupil relation to a teacher (where teachers and
pupils are distinct) does not exist.

(3) $(I : J) | (H : K) = [(I : J) | H] : K$

The relation of those which have the $(I : J)$ relation to those which have
the $(H : K)$ relation is the relation of those-which-have-the-$(I : J)$-relation-
to-an-H to a K.

It is this third law which is the source of the important properties of
the system. For example:

$$t | p = (T : P) | (P : T) = [(T : P) | P] : T = (T : T) = c$$

The teachers of any person's pupils are that person's colleagues. (Our
illustration, to fit the system, requires that one may be his own colleague
or his own schoolmate.)

$$c | c = (T : T) | (T : T) = [(T : T) | T] : T = (T : T) = c$$

The colleagues of one's colleagues are one's colleagues.

$$t | t = (T : P) | (T : P) = [(T : P) | T] : P = (0 : P) = 0$$

There are no teachers of teachers in the system.

$$p | s = (P : T) | (P : P) = [(P : T) | P] : P = (0 : P) = 0$$

There are no pupils of anyone's schoolmates in the system.

The results may be summarized in the following multiplication table,
in which the multipliers are in the column at the right and the multiplicands

at the top (relative multiplication not being commutative): [156]

·	c	t	p	s
c	c	t	0	0
t	0	0	c	t
p	p	s	0	0
s	0	0	p	s

The symmetry of the table should be noted. The reader may easily interpret the sixteen propositions which it gives.

To the algebra thus constituted may be added modifiers of the terms, symbolized by small roman letters. If f is "French", f will be a modifier of the system in case French teachers have only French pupils, and vice versa. Such modifiers are "scalars" of the system, and any expression of the form

$$a\,c + b\,t + c\,p + d\,s$$

where c, t, p, and s are the relatives, as above, and a, b, c, d are scalars, Peirce calls a "logical quaternion". The product of a scalar with a term is commutative,

$$b\,t = t\,b$$

since this relation is that of the non-relative logical product. Inasmuch as any (dyadic, triadic, etc.) relative is resolvable into a logical sum of (pairs, triads, etc.) elementary relatives, it is plain that any general relative whatever is resolvable into a sum of logical quaternions.

If we consider a system of relatives, each of which is of the form

$$a\,i + b\,j + c\,k + d\,l + \ldots$$

where i, j, k, l, etc. are each of the form

$$m\,u + n\,v + o\,w + \ldots$$

where m, n, o, etc. are scalars, and u, v, w, etc. are elementary relatives, we shall have a more complex algebra. By such processes of complication, multiple algebras of various types can be generated. In fact, Peirce says: [157]

"I can assert, upon reasonable inductive evidence, that all such [linear associative] algebras can be interpreted on the principles of the present notation in the same way as those given above. In other words, all such algebras are complications and modifications of the algebra of (156) [for which the multiplication table has been given]. It is very likely that this is true of all algebras whatever.   The algebra of (156), which is of such a fundamental character in reference to pure algebra and our logical notation, has been shown by Professor [Benjamin] Peirce to be the algebra of Hamilton's quaternions."

Peirce gives the form of the four fundamental factors of quaternions and of scalars, tensors, vectors, etc., with their logical interpretations as relative terms with modifiers such as were described above.

One more item of importance is Peirce's modification of Boole's calculus of probabilities.   This is set forth with extreme brevity in the paper, "On an Improvement in Boole's Calculus of Logic".[158]   For the expression of the relations involved, we shall need to distinguish the logical relation of identity of two classes in extension from the relation of numerical equality. We may, then, express the fact that the class a has the same membership as the class b, or all a's are all b's, by $a \equiv b$, and the fact that the number of members of a is the same as the number of members of b, by $a = b$. Also we must remember the distinction between the logical relations expressed by $a + b$, $a\,b$, $a \vdash b$, and the corresponding arithmetical relations expressed by $a + b$, $a \times b$, and $a - b$.   Peirce says: [159]

"Let every expression for a class have a second meaning, which is its meaning in a [numerical] equation.   Namely, let it denote the proportion of individuals of that class to be found among all the individuals examined in the long run.

"Then we have

$$\text{If } a \equiv b \qquad a = b$$
$$a + b = (a + b) + a\,b$$

"Let b_a denote the frequency of the b's among the a's.   Then considered as a class, if a and b are events b_a denotes the fact that if a happens b happens.

$$a \times b_a = a\,b$$

"It will be convenient to set down some obvious and fundamental properties of the function b_a.

$$a \times b_a = b \times a_b$$
$$\varphi(b_a, c_a) = \varphi(b, c)_a$$
$$(1 - b)_a = 1 - b_a$$
$$b_a = \frac{b}{a} + b_{1-a}\left(1 - \frac{1}{a}\right)$$

[158] *Proc. Amer. Acad.*, VII, 255 *ff.*
[159] *Ibid.*, pp. 255–56.

$$a_b = 1 - \frac{1 - a}{b} \times b_{(1-a)}$$

$$(\varphi a)_a = (\varphi(1))_a \text{ ''}$$

The chief points of difference between this modified calculus of probabilities and the original calculus of Boole are as follows:

(1) Where Boole puts p, q, etc. for the "probability of a, of b, etc.", in passing from the logical to the arithmetical interpretation of his equations, Peirce simply changes the relations involved from logical relations to the corresponding arithmetical relations, in accordance with the foregoing, and lets the terms a, b, etc. stand for the frequency of the a's, b's, etc. in the system under discussion.

(2) Boole has no symbol for the frequency of the a's amongst the b's, which Peirce represents by a_b. As a result, Boole is led to treat the probabilities of all unconditioned simple events as independent—a procedure which involved him in many difficulties and some errors.

(3) Peirce has a complete set of four logical operations, and four analogous operations of arithmetic. This greatly facilitates the passage from the purely logical expression of relations of classes or events to the arithmetical expression of their relative frequencies or probabilities.

Probably there is no one piece of work which would so immediately reward an investigator in symbolic logic as would the development of this calculus of probabilities in such shape as to make it simple and practicable. Except for a monograph by Poretsky and the studies of H. MacColl,[160] the subject has lain almost untouched since Peirce wrote the above in 1867.

Peirce's contribution to our subject is the most considerable of any up to his time, with the doubtful exception of Boole's. His papers, however, are brief to the point of obscurity: results are given summarily with little or no explanation and only infrequent demonstrations. As a consequence, the most valuable of them make tremendously tough reading, and they have never received one-tenth the attention which their importance deserves.[161] If Peirce had been given to the pleasantly discursive style of De Morgan, or the detailed and clearly accurate manner of Schröder, his work on symbolic logic would fill several volumes.

[160] Since the above was written, a paper by Couturat, posthumously published, gives an unusually clear presentation of the fundamental laws of probability in terms of symbolic logic. See *Bibl.*

[161] Any who find our report of Peirce's work unduly difficult or obscure are earnestly requested to consult the original papers.

VIII. Developments since Peirce

Contributions to symbolic logic which have been made since the time of Peirce need be mentioned only briefly. These are all accessible and in a form sufficiently close to current notation to be readily intelligible. Also, they have not been superseded, as have most of the papers so far discussed; consequently they are worth studying quite apart from any relation to later work. And finally, much of the content and method of the most important of them is substantially the same with what will be set forth in later chapters, or is such that its connection with what is there set forth will be pointed out. But for the sake of continuity and perspective, a summary account may be given of these recent developments.

We should first mention three important pieces of work contemporary with Peirce's later treatises.[162]

Robert Grassmann had included in his encyclopedic *Wissenschaftslehre* a book entitled *Die Begriffslehre oder Logik*,[163] containing (1) *Lehre von den Begriffen*, (2) *Lehre von den Urtheilen*, and (3) *Lehre von den Schlüssen*. The *Begriffslehre* is the second book of *Die Formenlehre oder Mathematik*, and as this would indicate, the development of logic is entirely mathematical. An important character of Grassmann's procedure is the derivation of the laws of classes, or *Begriffe*, as he insists upon calling them, from the laws governing individuals. For example, the laws $a + a = a$ and $a \cdot a = a$, where a is a class, are derived from the laws $e + e = e$, $e \cdot e = e$, $e_1 \cdot e_2 = 0$, where e, e_1, e_2 represent individuals. This method has much to commend it, but it has one serious defect—the supposition that a class can be treated as an aggregate of individuals and the laws of such aggregates proved generally by mathematical induction. As Peirce has observed, this method breaks down when the number of individuals may be infinite. Another difference between Grassmann and others is the use throughout of the language of intension. But the method and the laws are those of extension, and in the later treatise, there are diagrammatic illustrations in which "concepts" are represented by areas. Although somewhat incomplete, in

---

[162] Alexander MacFarlane, *Principles of the Algebra of Logic*, 1879, gives a masterly presentation of the Boolean algebra. There are some notable extensions of Boole's methods and one or two emendations, but in general it is the calculus of Boole unchanged. MacFarlane's paper "On a Calculus of Relationship" (*Proc. Roy. Soc. Edin.*, x, 224–32) resembles somewhat, in its method, Peirce's treatment of "elementary relatives". But the development of it seems never to have been continued.

[163] There are two editions, 1872 and 1890. The later is much expanded, but the plan and general character is the same.

other respects Grassmann's calculus is not notably different from others which follow the Boolean tradition.

Hugh MacColl's first two papers on "The Calculus of Equivalent Statements",[164] and his first paper "On Symbolical Reasoning",[165] printed in 1878–80, present a calculus of propositions which has essentially the properties of Peirce's, without Π and Σ operators. In others words, it is a calculus of propositions, like the Two-Valued Algebra of Logic as we know it today. And the date of these papers indicates that their content was arrived at independently of Peirce's studies which deal with this topic. In fact, MacColl writes, in 1878, that he has not seen Boole.[166]

The calculus set forth in MacColl's book, *Symbolic Logic and its Applications*,[167] is of an entirely different character. Here the fundamental symbols represent propositional functions rather than propositions; and instead of the two traditional truth values, "true" and "false", we have "true", "false", "certain", "impossible" and "variable" (not certain and not impossible). These are indicated by the exponents τ, ι, ϵ, η, θ respectively. The result is a highly complex system, the fundamental ideas and procedures of which suggest somewhat the system of Strict Implication to be set forth in Chapter V.

The calculus of Mrs. Ladd-Franklin, set forth in the paper "On the Algebra of Logic" in the Johns Hopkins studies,[168] differs from the other systems based on Boole by the use of the copula $\vee$. Where a and b are classes, $a \vee b$ represents "a is-partly b", or "Some a is b", and its negative, $a \barvee b$, represents "a is-wholly-not-b", or "No a is b". Thus $a \vee b$ is equivalent to $a b \neq 0$, and $a \barvee b$ to $a b = 0$. These two relations can, between them, express any assertable relation in the algebra. $a \subset b$ will be $a \barvee -b$, and $a = b$ is represented by the pair, $(a \barvee -b)(-a \barvee b)$. For propositions, $a \vee b$ denotes that a and b are consistent—a does not imply that b is false and b does not imply that a is false. And $a \barvee b$ symbolizes "a and b are inconsistent"—if a is true, b is false; if b is true, a is false. The use of the terms "consistent" and "inconsistent" in this connection is possibly misleading: any two true propositions or any two false propositions are con-

---

[164] (1) *Proc. London Math. Soc.*, IX, 9–20; (2) *ibid.*, IX, 177–86.

[165] *Mind*, v (1880), 45–60.

[166] *Proc. London Math. Soc.*, IX, 178.

[167] Longmans, 1906.

[168] The same volume contains an interesting and somewhat complicated system by O. H. Mitchell. Peirce acknowledged this paper as having shown us how to express universal and particular propositions as Π and Σ functions. B. I. Gilman's study of relative number, also in that volume, belongs to the number of those papers which are important in connecting symbolic logic with the theory of probabilities.

sistent in this sense, and any two propositions one of which is true and the other false are inconsistent. This is not quite the usual meaning of "consistent" and "inconsistent"—it is related to what is usually meant by these terms exactly as the "material implication $a \subset b$ is related to what is usually meant by "b can be inferred from a".

That a given class, x, is empty, or a given proposition, x, is false, $x = 0$, may be expressed by $x \bar{\vee} \infty$, where ∞ is "everything"—in most systems represented by 1. That a class, y, has members, is symbolized by $y \vee \infty$. This last is of doubtful interpretation where y is a proposition, since Mrs. Ladd-Franklin's system does not contain the assumption which is true for propositions but not for classes, usually expressed, "If $x \neq 0$, then $x = 1$, and if $x \neq 1$, then $x = 0$". $x \vee \infty$ may be abbreviated to $x \vee$, $a b \vee \infty$ to $a b \vee$, and $y \bar{\vee} \infty$ to $y \bar{\vee}$, $c d \bar{\vee} \infty$ to $c d \bar{\vee}$, etc., since it is always understood that if one term of a relation $\vee$ or $\bar{\vee}$ is missing, the missing term is ∞. This convention leads to a very pretty and convenient operation: $\vee$ or $\bar{\vee}$ may be moved past its terms in either direction. Thus,

$$(a \vee b) = (a b \vee) = (\vee a b)$$
$$\text{and} \quad (x \bar{\vee} y) = (x y \bar{\vee}) = (\bar{\vee} x y)$$

But the forms ($\vee a b$) and ($\bar{\vee} x y$) are never used, being redundant both logically and psychologically.

Mrs. Ladd-Franklin's system symbolizes the relations of the traditional logic particularly well:

All a is b.	$a \bar{\vee} -b$,	or	$a -b \bar{\vee}$
No a is b.	$a \bar{\vee} b$,	or	$a b \bar{\vee}$
Some a is b.	$a \vee b$,	or	$a b \vee$
Some a is not b.	$a \vee -b$,	or	$a -b \vee$

Thus $\bar{\vee}$ characterizes a universal, $\vee$ a particular proposition. And any pair of contradictories will differ from one another simply by the difference between $\vee$ and $\bar{\vee}$. The syllogism, "If all a is b and all b is c, then all a is c," will be represented by

$$(a \bar{\vee} -b)(b \bar{\vee} -c) \bar{\vee} (a \vee c)$$

where $\bar{\vee}$, or $\vee$, *within* the parentheses is interpreted for classes, and $\bar{\vee}$ *between* the parentheses takes the propositional interpretation. This expression may also be read, "'All a is b and all b is c' is inconsistent with the negative (contradictory) of 'Some a is not c'". It is equivalent to

$$(a \bar{\vee} -b)(b \bar{\vee} -c)(a \vee -c) \bar{\vee}$$

"The three propositions, 'All a is b', 'All b is c,' and 'Some a is not c', are inconsistent—they cannot all three be true". This expresses at once *three* syllogisms:

$$(1) \quad (a \,\bar{\vee}\, -b)(b \,\bar{\vee}\, -c) \,\bar{\vee}\, (a \,\vee\, -c)$$

"If all a is b and all b is c, then all a is c";

$$(2) \quad (a \,\bar{\vee}\, -b)(a \,\vee\, -c) \,\bar{\vee}\, (b \,\bar{\vee}\, -c)$$

"If all a is b and some a is not c, then some b is not c";

$$(3) \quad (b \,\bar{\vee}\, -c)(a \,\vee\, -c) \,\bar{\vee}\, (a \,\bar{\vee}\, -b)$$

"If all b is c and some a is not c, then some a is not b".

Also, this method gives a perfectly general formula for the syllogism

$$(a \,\bar{\vee}\, -b)(b \,\bar{\vee}\, c)(a \,\vee\, c) \,\bar{\vee}$$

where the order of the parentheses, and their position relative to the sign $\bar{\vee}$ which stands outside the parentheses, may be altered at will. This single rule covers all the modes and figures of the syllogism, except the illicit particular conclusion drawn from universal premises. We shall revert to this matter in Chapter III.[169]

The copulas $\vee$ and $\bar{\vee}$ have several advantages over their equivalents, $= 0$ and $\neq 0$, or $\subset$ and its negative: (1) $\vee$ and $\bar{\vee}$ are symmetrical relations whose terms can always be interchanged; (2) the operation, mentioned above, of moving $\vee$ and $\bar{\vee}$ with respect to their terms, accomplishes transformations which are less simply performed with other modes of expressing the copula; (3) for various reasons, it is psychologically simpler and more natural to think of logical relations in terms of $\vee$ and $\bar{\vee}$ than in terms of $= 0$ and $\neq 0$. But $\vee$ and $\bar{\vee}$ have one disadvantage as against $=$, $\neq$, and $\subset$,—they do not so readily suggest their mathematical analogues in other algebras. For better or for worse, symbolic logicians have not generally adopted $\vee$ and $\bar{\vee}$.

Of the major contributions since Peirce, the first is that of Ernst Schröder. In his *Operationskreis des Logikkalkuls* (1877), Schröder pointed out that the logical relations expressed in Boole's calculus by subtraction and division were all otherwise expressible, as Peirce had already noted. The meaning of $+$ given by Boole is abandoned in favor of that which it now has, first introduced by Jevons. And the "law of duality", which connects theorems which involve the relation $+$, or $+$ and 1, with corresponding theorems in terms of the logical product $\times$, or $\times$ and 0, is emphasized.

---

[169] See below, pp. 188 *ff.*

(This parallelism of formulae had been noted by Peirce, in his first paper, but not emphasized or made use of.)

The resulting system is the algebra of logic as we know it today. This system is perfected and elaborated in *Vorlesungen über die Algebra der Logik* (1890–95). Volume I of this work covers the algebra of classes; Volume II the algebra of propositions; and Volume III is devoted to the calculus of relations.

The algebra of classes, or as we shall call it, the Boole-Schröder algebra, is the system developed in the next chapter.[170] We have somewhat elaborated the theory of functions, but in all essential respects, we give the algebra as it appears in Schröder. There are two differences of some importance between Schröder's procedure and the one we have adopted. Schröder's assumptions are in terms of the relation of subsumption, $\subset$, instead of the relations of logical product and $=$, which appear in our postulates. And, second, Schröder gives and discusses the various methods of his predecessors, as well as those characteristically his own.

The calculus of propositions (*Aussagenkalkul*) is the extension of the Boole-Schröder algebra to propositions by a method which differs little from that adopted in Chapter IV, Section I, of this book.

The discussion of relations is based upon the work of Peirce. But Peirce's methods are much more precisely formulated by Schröder, and the scope of the calculus is much extended. We summarize the fundamental propositions which Schröder gives for the sake of comparison both with Peirce and with the procedure we shall adopt in Sections II and III of Chapter IV.

1) $A, B, C, D, E \ldots$ symbolize "elements" or individuals.[171] These are distinct from one another and from 0.

2) $1^1 = A + B + C + D + \ldots$

1^1 symbolizes the universe of individuals or the universe of discourse of the first order.

3) i, j, k, l, m, n, p, q represent *any one* of the elements $A, B, C, D, \ldots$ of 1^1.

4) $1^1 = \Sigma_i i$

[170] For an excellent summary by Schröder, see *Abriss der Algebra der Logik*; ed. Dr. Eugen Müller, 1909–10. Parts I and II, covering Vols. I and II of Schröder's *Vorlesungen*, have so far appeared.

[171] The propositions here noted will be found in *Vorlesungen über die Algebra der Logik*, III, 3–42. Many others, and much discussion of theory, have been omitted.

5) $i : j$ represents any two elements, i and j, of 1^1 in a determined order.

6) $(i = j) = (i : j = j : i)$, $(i \neq j) = (i : j \neq j : i)$

           for every i and j.

7) $i : j \neq 0$

Pairs of elements of 1^1 may be arranged in a "block":

8)
$$A : A, \ A : B, \ A : C, \ A : D, \ \ldots$$
$$B : A, \ B : B, \ B : C, \ B : D, \ \ldots$$
$$C : A, \ C : B, \ C : C, \ C : D, \ \ldots$$
$$D : A, \ D : B, \ D : C, \ D : D, \ \ldots$$

$$. \quad . \quad . \quad . \quad . \quad . \quad . \quad . \quad .$$

These are the "individual binary relatives".

9)
$$1^2 = \ \ (A : A) + (A : B) + (A : C) + \ldots$$
$$+ (B : A) + (B : B) + (B : C) + \ldots$$
$$+ (C : A) + (C : B) + (C : C) + \ldots$$
$$+ . \quad . \quad . \quad . \quad . \quad . \quad . \quad .$$

1^2 represents the universe of binary relatives.

10) $1^2 = \Sigma_j \Sigma_i \, (i : j) = \Sigma_i \Sigma_j \, (i : j) = \Sigma_{ij} \, (i : j)$

9) and 10) may be summarized in a simpler notation:

11)
$$1 = \Sigma_{ij} \, i : j = \ \ A : A + A : B + A : C + \ldots$$
$$+ B : A + B : B + B : C + \ldots$$
$$+ C : A + C : B + C : C + \ldots$$
$$+ . \quad . \quad . \quad . \quad . \quad . \quad .$$

12) $i : j : h$ will symbolize an "individual ternary relative".

13) $1^3 \ = \Sigma_h \Sigma_j \Sigma_i \, (i : j : h) = \Sigma_{ijh} \, i : j : h$

Various types of ternary relatives are

14) $A : A : A, \ \ B : A : A, \ \ A : B : A, \ \ A : A : B, \ \ A : B : C$

It is obvious that we may similarly define individual relatives of the fourth, fifth, . . . or any thinkable order.

The general form of a binary relative, a, is

$$a = \Sigma_{ij}\, a_{ij}\, (i : j)$$

where a_{ij} is a coefficient whose value is 1 for those $(i : j)$ pairs in which i has the relation a to j, and is otherwise 0.

$$1 = \Sigma_{ij}\, i : j$$

$0 =$ the null class of individual binary relatives.

$$\boldsymbol{I} = \Sigma_{ij}\, (i = j)(i : j) = \Sigma_i\, (i : i)\ ^{172}$$

$$\boldsymbol{N} = \Sigma_{ij}\, (i \neq j)(i : j)$$

$$(a\, b)_{ij} = a_{ij}\, b_{ij} \qquad\qquad (a + b)_{ij} = a_{ij} + b_{ij}$$

$$-a_{ij} = (-a)_{ij} = -(a_{ij})$$

$$(a\,|\,b)_{ij} = \Sigma_h\, a_{ih}\, b_{hj} \qquad\qquad (a \dagger b)_{ij} = \Pi_h\, (a_{ih} + b_{hj})$$

The general laws which govern propositional functions, or *Aussagenschemata*, such as $(a\, b)_{ij}$, $\Sigma_h\, a_{ih}\, b_{hj}$, $\Pi_h\, (a_{ih} + b_{hj})$, $\Pi_a\, a_{ij}$, $\Sigma_a\, a_{ij}$, etc., are as follows:

A_u symbolizes any statement about u; $\Pi_u A_u$ will have the value 1 in case, and only in case, $A_u = 1$ for every u; $\Sigma_u A_u$ will have the value 1 if there is at least one u such that $A_u = 1$. That is to say, $\Pi_u A_u$ means "A_u for every u", and $\Sigma_u A_u$ means "A_u for some u".

$\alpha)\ \ \Pi_u A_u \subset A_v \subset \Sigma_u A_u, \qquad\qquad -[\Sigma_u A_u] \subset -A_v \subset -[\Pi_u A_u]$

$\beta)\ \ \Pi_u A_u = A_v \Pi_u A_u, \qquad\qquad\quad \Sigma_u A_u = A_v + \Sigma_u A_u$

(The subscript u, in α and β, represents any value of the variable u.)

$\gamma)\ \ -[\Pi_u A_u] = \Sigma_u - A_u, \qquad\qquad -[\Sigma_u A_u] = \Pi_u - A_u$

$\delta)$ If A_u is independent of u, then $\Pi_u A_u = A$, and $\Sigma_u A_u = A$.

$\epsilon)\ \ \Pi_u(A \subset B_u) = (A \subset \Pi_u B_u), \qquad \Pi_u(A_u \subset B) = (\Sigma_u A_u \subset B)$

$\zeta)\ \ \Pi_{u,\,v}$ or $\Pi_u \Pi_v(A_u \subset B_v) = (\Sigma_u A_u \subset \Pi_v B_v)$

$\eta)\ \ \Sigma_u(A_u \subset B) = (\Pi_u A_u \subset B), \qquad \Sigma_u(A \subset B_u) = (A \subset \Sigma_u B_u)$

$\theta)\ \ \Sigma_{u,\,v}$ or $\Sigma_u \Sigma_v(A_u \subset B_v) = (\Pi_u A_u \subset \Sigma_v B_v)$

$\iota)\ \ \begin{cases} \Pi_u(A_u = 1) = (\Pi_u A_u = 1), & \Pi_u(A_u = 0) = (\Sigma_u A_u = 0) \\[1mm] \Sigma_u(A_u = 0) = (\Pi_u A_u = 0), & \Sigma_u(A_u = 1) = (\Sigma_u A_u = 1) \end{cases}$

---

[172] We write $\boldsymbol{I}$ where Schröder has 1'; $\boldsymbol{N}$ where he has 0'; $(a\,|\,b)$ for $(a; b)$; $(a \dagger b)$ for $(a \dagger b)$; $-a$ for a; $\smile a$ for $\breve{a}$.

$$\kappa) \quad \Pi_u(A_u \subset B_u) \subset \left\{ \begin{array}{l} (\Pi_u A_u \subset \Pi_u B_u) \\ (\Sigma_u A_u \subset \Sigma_u B_u) \end{array} \right\} \subset \Sigma_u(A_u \subset B_u)$$

(The reader should note that $\Pi_u(A_u \subset B_u)$ is "formal implication",—in *Principia Mathematica*, $(x) . \varphi x \supset \psi x$.)

$\lambda) \quad A \, \Sigma_u B_u = \Sigma_u A \, B_u,$ $A + \Pi_u B_u = \Pi_u(A + B_u)$

$\mu) \quad (\Sigma_u A_u)(\Sigma_v B_v) = \Sigma_{u,\,v} A_u \, B_v,$ $\Pi_u A_u + \Pi_v B_v = \Pi_{u,\,v}(A_u + B_v)$

$\nu) \quad A \, \Pi_u B_u = \Pi_u A \, B_u,$ $A + \Sigma_u B_u = \Sigma_u(A + B_u)$

$\xi) \quad (\Pi_u A_u)(\Pi_v B_v) = \Pi_{u,\,v} A_u \, B_v = \Pi_u A_u \, B_u,$

$$\Sigma_u A_u + \Sigma_v B_v = \Sigma_{u,\,v}(A_u + B_v) = \Sigma_u(A_u + B_u)$$

$o) \quad \Sigma_u \Pi_v A_{u,\,v} \subset \Pi_v \Sigma_u A_{u,\,v}$

From these fundamental propositions, the whole theory of relations is developed. Though Schröder carries this much further than Peirce, the general outlines are those of Peirce's calculus. Perhaps the most interesting of the new items of Schröder's treatment are the use of "matrices" in the form of the two-dimensional array of individual binary relatives, and the application of the calculus of relatives to Dedekind's theory of "chains", as contained in *Was sind und was sollen die Zahlen*.

Notable contributions to the Boole-Schröder algebra were made by Anton Poretsky in his three papers, *Sept lois fondamentales de la théorie des égalités logiques* (1899), *Quelques lois ultérieures de la théorie des égalités logiques* (1901), and *Théorie des non-égalités logiques* (1904). (With his earlier works, published in Russian, 1881–87, we are not familiar.) Poretsky's Law of Forms, Law of Consequences, and Law of Causes will be given in Chapter II. As Couturat notes, Schröder had been influenced overmuch by the analogies of the algebra of logic to other algebras, and these papers by Poretsky outline an entirely different procedure which, though based on the same fundamental principles, is somewhat more "natural" to logic. Poretsky's method is the perfection of that type of procedure adopted by Jevons and characteristic of the use of the Venn diagrams.

The work of Frege, though intrinsically important, has its historical interest largely through its influence upon Mr. Bertrand Russell. Although the *Begriffsschrift* (1879) and the *Grundlagen der Arithmetik* (1884) both precede Schroder's *Vorlesungen,* Frege is hardly more than mentioned there; and his influence upon Peano and other contributors to the *Formulaire* is surprisingly small when one considers how closely their task is related to his. Frege is concerned explicitly with the logic of mathematics but, in thorough German fashion, he pursues his analyses more and more deeply until we have not only a development of arithmetic of unprecedented rigor but a more or less complete treatise of the logico-metaphysical problems concerning the nature of number, the objectivity of concepts, the relations of concepts, symbols, and objects, and many other subtleties. In a sense, his fundamental problem is the Kantian one of the nature of the judgments involved in mathematical demonstration. Judgments are analytic, depending solely upon logical principles and definitions, or they are synthetic. His thesis, that mathematics can be developed wholly by analytic judgments from premises which are purely logical, is likewise the thesis of Russell's *Principles of Mathematics.* And Frege's *Grundgesetze der Arithmetik,* like *Principia Mathematica,* undertakes to establish this thesis—for arithmetic—by producing the required development.

Besides the precision of notation and analysis, Frege's work is important as being the first in which the nature of rigorous demonstration is sufficiently understood. His proofs proceed almost exclusively by substitution for variables of values of those variables, and the substitution of defined equivalents. Frege's notation, it must be admitted is against him: it is almost diagrammatic, occupying unnecessary space and carrying the eye here and there in a way which militates against easy understanding. It is probably this forbidding character of his medium, combined with the unprecedented demands upon the reader's logical subtlety, which accounts for the neglect which his writings so long suffered. But for this, the revival of logistic proper might have taken place ten years earlier, and dated from Frege's *Grundlagen* rather than Peano's *Formulaire.*

The publication, beginning in 1894, of Peano's *Formulaire de Mathématiques* marks a new epoch in the history of symbolic logic. Heretofore, the investigation had generally been carried on from an interest in exact logic and its possibilities, until, as Schröder remarks, we had an elaborated instrument and nothing for it to do. With Peano and his collaborators, the situation is reversed: symbolic logic is investigated only as the instrument of mathematical proof. As Peano puts it: [173]

"The laws of logic contained in what follows have generally been found

[173] *Formulaire,* I (1901), 9.

by formulating, in the form of rules, the deductions which one comes upon in mathematical demonstrations."

The immediate result of this altered point of view is a new logic, no less elaborate than the old—destined, in fact, to become much more elaborate—but with its elaboration determined not from abstract logical considerations or by any mathematical prettiness, but solely by the criterion of application. De Morgan had said that algebraists and geometers live in "a higher realm of syllogism": it seems to have required the mathematical intent to complete the rescue of logic from its traditional inanities.

The outstanding differences of the logic of Peano from that of Peirce and Schröder are somewhat as follows: [174]

(1) Careful enunciation of definitions and postulates, and of possible alternative postulates, marking an increased emphasis upon rigorous deductive procedure in the development of the system.

(2) The prominence of a new relation, ϵ, the relation of a member of a class to the class.

(3) The prominence of the idea of a propositional function and of "formal implication" and "formal equivalence", as against "material implication" and "material equivalence".

(4) Recognition of the importance of "existence" and of the properties of classes, members of classes, and so on, with reference to their "existence".

(5) The properties of relations in general are not studied, and "relative addition" does not appear at all, but various special relations, prominent in mathematics, are treated of.

The disappearance of the idea of relation in general is a real loss, not a gain.

(6) The increasing use of substitution (for a variable of some value in its range) as the operation which gives proof.

We here recognize those characteristics of symbolic logic which have since been increasingly emphasized.

The publication of *Principia Mathematica* would seem to have determined the direction of further investigation to follow that general direction indicated by the work of Frege and the *Formulaire*. The *Principia* is concerned with the same topics and from the same point of view. But we see here a recognition of difficulties not suggested in the *Formulaire*, a deeper and more lengthy analysis of concepts and a corresponding complexity of procedure. There is also more attention to the details of a rigorous method of proof.

---

[174] All these belong also to the *Logica Mathematica* of C. Burali Forti (Milan, 1894).

The method by which the mathematical logic of *Principia Mathematica* is developed will be discussed, so far as we can discuss it, in the concluding section of Chapter IV. We shall be especially concerned to point out the connection, sometimes lost sight of, between it and the older logic of Peirce and Schröder. And the use of this logic as an instrument of mathematical analysis will be a topic in the concluding chapter.

CHAPTER II

THE CLASSIC, OR BOOLE–SCHRÖDER, ALGEBRA OF LOGIC

I. GENERAL CHARACTER OF THE ALGEBRA. THE POSTULATES AND
THEIR INTERPRETATION

The algebra of logic, in its generally accepted form, is hardly old enough to warrant the epithet "classic". It was founded by Boole and given its present form by Schröder, who incorporated into it certain emendations which Jevons had proposed and certain additions—particularly the relation "is contained in" or "implies"—which Peirce had made to Boole's system. It is due to Schröder's sound judgment that the result is still an algebra, simpler yet more powerful than Boole's calculus. Jevons, in simplifying Boole's system, destroyed its mathematical form; Peirce, retaining the mathematical form, complicated instead of simplifying the original calculus. Since the publication of Schröder's *Vorlesungen über die Algebra der Logik* certain additions and improved methods have been offered, the most notable of which are contained in the studies of Poretsky and in Whitehead's *Universal Algebra*.[1]

But if the term "classic" is inappropriate at present, still we may venture to use it by way of prophecy. As Whitehead has pointed out, this system is a distinct species of the genus "algebra", differing from all other algebras so far discovered by its non-numerical character. It is certainly the simplest mathematical system with any wide range of useful applications, and there are indications that it will serve as the parent stem from which other calculuses of an important type will grow. Already several such have appeared. The term "classic" will also serve to distinguish the Boole-Schröder Algebra from various other calculuses of logic. Some of these, like the system of Mrs. Ladd-Franklin, differ through the use of other relations than $+$, $\times$, $\subset$, and $=$, and are otherwise equivalent—

---

[1] For Poretsky's studies, see *Bibliography;* also p. 114 above. See Whitehead's *Universal Algebra*, Bk. II. Whitehead introduced a theory of "discriminants" and a treatment of existential propositions by means of umbral letters. This last, though most ingenious and interesting, seems to me rather too complicated for use; and I have not made use of "discriminants", preferring to accomplish similar results by a somewhat extended study of the coefficients in functions.

that is to say, with a "dictionary" of equivalent expressions, any theorem of these systems may be translated into a theorem of the Boole-Schröder Algebra, and vice versa. Others are mathematically equivalent as far as they go, but partial. And some, like the calculus of classes in *Principia Mathematica*, are logically but not mathematically equivalent. And, finally, there are systems such as that of Mr. MacColl's *Symbolic Logic* which are neither mathematically nor logically equivalent.

Postulates for the classic algebra have been given by Huntington, by Schröder (in the *Abriss*), by Del Ré, by Sheffer and by Bernstein.[2] The set here adopted represents a modification of Huntington's third set.[3] It has been chosen not so much for economy of assumption as for "naturalness" and obviousness.

Postulated:

A class K of elements a, b, c, etc., and a relation $\times$ such that:

1·1   If a and b are elements in K, then $a \times b$ is an element in K, uniquely determined by a and b.

1·2   For any element a, $a \times a = a$.

1·3   For any elements a and b, $a \times b = b \times a$.

1·4   For any elements a, b, and c, $a \times (b \times c) = (a \times b) \times c$.

1·5   There is a unique element, 0, in K such that $a \times 0 = 0$ for every element a.

1·6   For every element a, there is an element, $-a$, such that

      1·61   If $x \times -a = 0$, then $x \times a = x$,

  and **1·62**   If $y \times a = y$ and $y \times -a = y$, then $y = 0$.

The element 1 and the relations $+$ and $\subset$ do not appear in the above. These may be defined as follows:

1·7 $1 = -0$ Def.

1·8 $a + b = -(-a \times -b)$ Def.

1·9 $a \subset b$ is equivalent to $a \times b = a$ Def.

It remains to be proved that $-a$ is uniquely determined by a, from which it will follow that 1 is unique and that $a + b$ is uniquely determined by a and b.

---

[2] See *Bibl.*

[3] See "Sets of Independent Postulates for the Algebra of Logic", *Trans. Amer. Math. Soc.*, v (1904), 288–309. Our set is got by replacing $+$ in Huntington's set by $\times$, and replacing the second half of G, which involves 1, by its analogue with 0. Thus 1 can be defined, and postulates E and H omitted. Postulate J is not strictly necessary.

The sign of equality in the above has its usual mathematical meaning; i. e., {=} is a relation such that if $x = y$ and $\varphi(x)$ is an unambiguous function in the system, then $\varphi(x)$ and $\varphi(y)$ are equivalent expressions and interchangeable. It follows from this that if $\psi(x)$ is an *ambiguous* function in the system, and $x = y$, every *determined value* of $\psi(x)$, expressible in terms of x, is similarly expressible in terms of y. Suppose, for example, that $-a$, "negative of a", is an ambiguous function of a. Still we may write $-a$ to mean, not the function "negative of a" itself, but to mean some (any) determined value of that function—any one of the negatives of a— and if $-a = b$, then $\varphi(-a)$ and $\varphi(b)$ will be equivalent and interchangeable. This principle is important in the early theorems which involve negatives.

We shall develop the algebra as an abstract mathematical system: the terms, a, b, c, etc., may be any entities which have the postulated properties, and ×, +, and ⊂ may be any relations consistent with the postulates. But for the reader's convenience, we give two possible applications: (1) to the system of all, continuous and discontinuous, regions in a plane, the null-region included, and (2) to the logic of classes.[4]

(1)

For the first interpretation, $a \times b$ will denote the region common to a and b (their overlapping portion or portions), and $a + b$ will denote that which is either a or b or both. $a \subset b$ will represent the *proposition*, "Region a is completely contained in region b (with or without remainder)". 0 will represent the null-region, contained in every region, and 1 the plane itself, or the "sum" {+} of all the regions in the plane. For any region a, $-a$ will be the plane except a, all that is not-a. The postulates will then hold as follows:

1·1 If a and b are regions in the plane, the region common to a and b, $a \times b$, is in the plane. If a and b do not overlap, then $a \times b$ is the null-region, 0.

1·2 For any region a, the region common to a and a, $a \times a$, is a itself.

1·3 The region common to a and b is the region common to b and a.

1·4 The region common to a and $b \times c$ is the region common to $a \times b$ and c—is the region common to all three.

1·5 The region common to any region a and the null-region, 0, is 0.

1·6 For every region a, there is its negative, $-a$, the region outside or

---

[4] Both of these interpretations are more fully discussed in the next chapter.

not contained in a, and this region is such that

1·61 If $-a$ and any region x have only the null-region in common, then the region common to x and a is x itself, or x is contained in a;

and 1·62 If the region common to y and a is y, or y is contained in a, and the region common to y and $-a$ is y, or y is contained in $-a$, then y must be the null-region which is contained in every region.

That the definitions, 1·7, 1·8, and 1·9, hold, will be evident.

(2)

For the second interpretation, a, b, c, etc., will be logical classes, taken in extension—that is, $a = b$ will mean that a and b are classes composed of identically the same members. $a \times b$ will represent the class of those things which are members of a and of b both; $a + b$, those things which are either members of a or members of b or both. $a \subset b$ will be the *proposition* that all members of a are also members of b, or that a is contained in b (with or without remainder). 0 is the null-class or class of no members; and the convention is required that this class is contained in every class. 1 is the "universe of discourse" or the class which contains every entity in the system. For any class a, $-a$ represents the negative of a, or the class of all things which are not members of a. The postulates will hold as follows:

1·1 If a and b are logical classes, taken in extension, the members common to a and b constitute a logical class. In case a and b have no members in common, this class is the null-class, 0.

1·2 The members common to a and a constitute the class a itself.

1·3 The members common to a and b are the same as those common to b and a.

1·4 The members common to a, b, and c, all three, are the same, whether we first find the members common to b and c and then those common to a and this class, or whether we first find the common members of a and b and then those common to this class and c.

1·5 The members common to any class a and the null-class are none, or the null-class.

1·6 For every class a, there is its negative, $-a$, constituted by all members of the "universe of discourse" not contained in a, and such that:

1·61 If $-a$ and any class x have no members in common,

then all members of x are common to x and a, or x is contained in a;

and 1·62   If all members of any class y are common to y and a, and common also to y and $-a$, then y must be null.

1·7   The "universe of discourse", "everything", is the negative of the null-class, "nothing".

1·8   That which is either a or b or both is identical with the negative of that which is both not-a and not-b.

1·9   That "a is contained in b" is equivalent to "The class a is identical with the common members of a and b".

That the postulates are consistent is proved by these interpretations. In the form given, they are not independent, but they may easily be made so by certain alterations in the form of statement.[5]

The following abbreviations and conventions will be used in the statement and proof of theorems:

1. $a \times b$ will generally be abbreviated to $a\,b$ or $a \cdot b$, $a \times (b \times c)$ to $a\,(b\,c)$, $a \times -(b \times -c)$ to $a-(b-c)$ or $a\cdot-(b-c)$, etc.

2. In proofs, we shall sometimes mark a lemma which has been established as (1), or (2), etc., and thereafter in that proof refer to the lemma by this number.   Also, we shall sometimes write "Q.E.D." instead of repeating the theorem to be proved.

3. The principles (postulates, definitions, or previous theorems) by which any step in proof is taken will usually be noted by a reference in square brackets, thus: If $x = 0$, then [1·5] $a\,x = 0$.   Reference to principles whose use is more or less obvious will gradually be omitted as we proceed. Theorems will be numbered decimally, for greater convenience in the insertion of theorems without alteration of other numbers.   The non-decimal part of the number will indicate some major division of theorems, as 1· indicates a postulate or definition.   Theorems which have this digit and the one immediately following the decimal point in common will be different forms of the same principle or otherwise closely related.

II.   Elementary Theorems

2·1   If $a = b$, then $a\,c = b\,c$ and $c\,a = c\,b$.

This follows immediately from the meaning of $=$ and 1·1.

2·2 $a = b$ is equivalent to the pair, $a \subset b$ and $b \subset a$.

If $a = b$, then [1·2] $a\,b = a$ and $b\,a = b$.

─────────

[5] On this point, compare with Huntington's set.

And if $a\,b = a$ and $b\,a = b$, then [1·3] $a = a\,b = b\,a = b$.

But [1·9] $a\,b = a$ is equivalent to $a \subset b$ and $b\,a = b$ to $b \subset a$.

Equality is, then, a reciprocal inclusion relation.

2·3 $a \subset a$.

$a = a$, hence [2·2] Q.E.D.

Every element is "contained in" itself.

2·4 $a - a = 0 = -a\,a$.

[1·2] $a\,a = a$.

Hence [2·1, 1·4, 1·3] $a - a = (a\,a) - a = a\,(a - a) = (a - a)\,a$.

Also [1·2] $-a\,a = -a$.   Hence $a - a = a\,(-a - a) = (a - a) - a$.

But [1·62] if $(a - a)\,a = (a - a) - a = a - a$, then $a - a = 0$.

And [1·3] $-a\,a = a - a$.   Hence also, $-a\,a = 0$.

Thus the product of any element into its negative is 0, and 0 is the modulus of the operation ×.

2·5 $a - b = 0$ is equivalent to $a\,b = a$ and to $a \subset b$.

If $a\,b = a$,   then   [1·4·5, 2·1·4] $a - b = (a\,b) - b = a\,(b - b)$
$= a \cdot 0 = 0$ (1)

And [1·61] if $a - b = 0$, then $a\,b = a$ (2)

By (1) and (2), $a - b = 0$ and $a\,b = a$ are equivalent.

And [1·9] $a\,b = a$ is $a \subset b$.

We shall derive other equivalents of $a \subset b$ later.   The above is required immediately.   In this proof, we have written "1·4·5" and "2·1·4" instead of "1·4, 1·5" and "2·1, 2·4".   This kind of abbreviation in references will be continued.

2·6   If $a \subset 0$, then $a = 0$.

If $a \subset 0$, then [1·9] $a \cdot 0 = a$.   But [1·5] $a \cdot 0 = 0$.

2·7   If $a \subset b$, then $a\,c \subset b\,c$, and $c\,a \subset c\,b$.

If $a \subset b$, then [1·9] $a\,b = a$ and [2·1] $(a\,b)\,c = a\,c$ (1)

But [1·2·3·4] $(a\,b)\,c = (b\,a)\,c = b\,(a\,c) = (a\,c)\,b = [a\,(c\,c)\,b] = [(a\,c)\,c]\,b$
$= (a\,c)(c\,b) = (a\,c)(b\,c)$ (2)

Hence, by (1) and (2), if $a \subset b$, then $(a\,c)(b\,c) = a\,c$ and [1·9] $a\,c \subset b\,c$.

And [1·3] $c\,a = a\,c$ and $c\,b = b\,c$.   Hence also $c\,a \subset c\,b$.

2·8 $-(-a) = a$.

[2·4] $-(-a) \cdot -a = 0$.   Hence [2·5] $-(-a) \subset a$ (1)

By (1), $-[-(-a)] \subset -a$.   Hence [2·7] $a \cdot -[-(-a)] \subset a - a$.

But [2·4] $a - a = 0$. Hence $a \cdot -[-(-a)] \subset 0$.

Hence [2·6] $a \cdot -[-(-a)] = 0$ and [2·5] $a \subset -(-a)$ (2)

[2·2] (1) and (2) are equivalent to $-(-a) = a$.

3·1 $a \subset b$ is equivalent to $-b \subset -a$.

     [2·5] $a \subset b$ is equivalent to $a - b = 0$.

     And [2·8] $a - b = -b\, a = -b - (-a)$.

     And $-b - (-a) = 0$ is equivalent to $-b \subset -a$.

The terms of any relation $\subset$ may be transposed by negating both. If region a is contained in region b, then the portion of the plane not in b is contained in the portion of the plane not in a: if all a's are b's, all non-b's are non-a's. This theorem gives immediately, by 2·8, the two corollaries:

3·12 $a \subset -b$ is equivalent to $b \subset -a$; and

3·13 $-a \subset b$ is equivalent to $-b \subset a$.

3·2 $a = b$ is equivalent to $-a = -b$.

     [2·2] $a = b$ is equivalent to ($a \subset b$ and $b \subset a$).

     [3·1] $a \subset b$ is equivalent to $-b \subset -a$, and $b \subset a$ to $-a \subset -b$.

     Hence $a = b$ is equivalent to ($-a \subset -b$ and $-b \subset -a$), which is equivalent to $-a = -b$.

The negatives of equals are equals. By 2·8, we have also

3·22 $a = -b$ is equivalent to $-a = b$.

Postulate 1·6 does not require that the function "negative of" be unambiguous. There might be more than one element in the system having the properties postulated of $-a$. Hence in the preceding theorems, $-a$ must be read "any negative of a", $-(-b)$ must be regarded as any one of the negatives of any given negative of b, and so on. Thus what has been proved of $-a$, etc., has been proved to hold for every element related to a in the manner required by the postulate. But we can now demonstrate that for every element a there is one and only one element having the properties postulated of $-a$.

3·3 $-a$ is uniquely determined by a.

     By 1·6, there is at least one element $-a$ for every element a. Suppose there is more than one: let $-a_1$ and $-a_2$ represent any two such.

     Then [2·8] $-(-a_1) = a = -(-a_2)$. Hence [3·2] $-a_1 = -a_2$.

Since all functions in the algebra are expressible in terms of a, b, c, etc., the relation $\times$, the negative, and 0, while 0 is unique and $a \times b$ is uniquely determined by a and b, it follows from 3·3 that all functions in the algebra are unambiguously determined when the elements involved are specified. (This would not be true if the inverse operations of "subtraction" and "division" were admitted.)

3·33 The element 1 is unique.

[1·5] 0 is unique, hence [3·3] −0 is unique, and [1·7] 1 = −0.

3·34 −1 = 0.

[1·7] 1 = −0.   Hence [3·2]   Q.E.D.

3·35 If a and b are elements in K, $a + b$ is an element in K uniquely determined by a and b.

The theorem follows from 3.3, 1·1, and 1·8.

3·37 If $a = b$, then $a + c = b + c$ and $c + a = c + b$.

The theorem follows from 3·35 and the meaning of =.

3·4 $-(a + b) = -a - b$.

[1·8] $a + b = -(-a - b)$.

Hence [3·3, 2·8] $-(a + b) = -[-(-a - b)] = -a - b$.

3·41 $-(a b) = -a + -b$.

[1·8, 2·8] $-a + -b = -[-(-a) \cdot -(-b)] = -(a b)$.

3·4 and 3·41 together state De Morgan's Theorem: The negative of a sum is the product of the negatives of the summands; and the negative of a product is the sum of the negatives of its factors. The definition 1·8 is a form of this theorem. Still other forms follow at once from 3·4 and 3·41, by 2·8:

3·42 $-(-a + -b) = a b$.

3·43 $-(a + -b) = -a b$.

3·44 $-(-a + b) = a - b$.

3·45 $-(a - b) = -a + b$.

3·46 $-(-a b) = a + -b$.

From De Morgan's Theorem, together with the principle, 3·2, "The negatives of equals are equals", the definition 1·7, 1 = −0, and theorem 3·34, −1 = 0, it follows that for every theorem in terms of × there is a corresponding theorem in terms of +. If in any theorem, each element be replaced by its negative, and × and + be interchanged, the result is a valid theorem. The negative terms can, of course, be replaced by positive, since we can suppose $x = -a$, $y = -b$, etc. Thus for every valid theorem in the system there is another got by interchanging the negatives 0 and 1 and the symbols $\times$ and $+$. This principle is called the Law of Duality. This law is to be illustrated immediately by deriving from the postulates their correlates in terms of $+$. The correlate of $1\cdot1$ is $3\cdot35$, already proved.

4·2 $a + a = a$.

[1·2] $-a -a = -a$.   Hence [1·8, 3·2, 2·8] $a + a = -(-a -a) = -(-a) = a$.

4·3 $a + b = b + a$.

[1·3] $-a -b = -b -a$.   Hence [3·2] $-(-a -b) = -(-b -a)$.
Hence [1·8] Q.E.D.

4·4 $a + (b + c) = (a + b) + c$.

[1·4] $-a (-b -c) = (-a -b) -c$.
Hence [3·2] $-[-a (-b -c)] = -[(-a -b) -c]$.
But [3·46, 1·8] $-[-a (-b -c)] = a + -(-b -c) = a + (b + c)$.
And [3·45, 1·8] $-[(-a -b) -c] = -(-a -b) + c = (a + b) + c$.

4·5 $a + 1 = 1$.

[1·5] $-a \cdot 0 = 0$.   Hence [3·2] $-(-a \cdot 0) = -0$.
Hence [3·46] $a + -0 = -0$, and [1·7] $a + 1 = 1$.

4·61 If $-x + a = 1$, then $x\, a = x$.

If $-x + a = 1$, then [3·2·34·44] $x -a = -(-x + a) = -1 = 0$.
And [2·5] $x -a = 0$ is equivalent to $x\, a = x$.

4·612 If $-x + a = 1$, then $x + a = a$.

[4·61] If $-a + x = 1$, then $a\, x = a$, and [3·2] $-a + -x = -a$ (1)
By (1) and 2·8, if $-x + a = 1$, $x + a = a$.

4·62 If $y + a = y$ and $y + -a = y$, then $y = 1$.

If $y + a = y$, [3·2] $-y -a = -(y + a) = -y$.
And if $y + -a = y$, $-y\, a = -(y + -a) = -y$.
But [1·62] if $-y\, a = -y$ and $-y -a = -y$, $-y = 0$ and $y = -0 = 1$.

4·8 $a + -a = 1 = -a + a$.   (Correlate of 2·4)

[2·4] $-a\, a = 0$.   Hence [3·2] $a + -a = -(-a\, a) = -0 = 1$.
Thus the modulus of the operation $+$ is 1.

4·9 $-a + b = 1$, $a + b = b$, $a -b = 0$, $a\, b = a$, and $a \subset b$ are all equivalent.

[2·5] $a -b = 0$, $a\, b = a$, and $a \subset b$ are equivalent.
[3·2] $-a + b = 1$ is equivalent to $a -b = -(-a + b) = -1 = 0$.

[4·612] If $-a + b = 1$, $a + b = b$.

And if $a + b = b$, [3·37] $-a + b = -a + (a + b) = (-a + a) + b = 1 + b$
   $= 1$.

Hence $a + b = b$ is equivalent to $-a + b = 1$.

We turn next to further principles which concern the relation $\subset$.

5·1 If $a \subset b$ and $b \subset c$, then $a \subset c$.

   [1·9] $a \subset b$ is equivalent to $a b = a$, and $b \subset c$ to $b c = b$.
   If $a b = a$ and $b c = b$, $a c = (a b) c = a (b c) = a b = a$.
   But $a c = a$ is equivalent to $a \subset c$.

This law of the transitivity of the relation $\subset$ is called the Principle of the Syllogism. It is usually included in any set of postulates for the algebra which are expressed in terms of the relation $\subset$.

5·2 $a b \subset a$ and $a b \subset b$.

   $(a b) a = a (a b) = (a a) b = a b$.
   But $(a b) a = a b$ is equivalent to $a b \subset a$.
   Similarly, $(a b) b = a (b b) = a b$, and $a b \subset b$.

5·21 $a \subset a + b$ and $b \subset a + b$.

   [5·2] $-a -b \subset -a$ and $-a -b \subset -b$.
   Hence [3·12] $a \subset -(-a -b)$ and $b \subset -(-a -b)$.
   But $-(-a -b) = (a + b)$.

Note that 5·2 and 5·21 are correlates by the Law of Duality. In general, having now deduced the fundamental properties of both $\times$ and $+$, we shall give further theorems in such pairs.

A corollary of 5·21 is:

5·22 $a b \subset a + b$.

   [5·1·2·21]

5·3 If $a \subset b$ and $c \subset d$, then $a c \subset b d$.

   [1·9] If $a \subset b$ and $c \subset d$, then $a b = a$ and $c d = c$.
   Hence $(a c)(b d) = (a b)(c d) = a c$, and $a c \subset b d$.

5·31 If $a \subset b$ and $c \subset d$, then $a + c \subset b + d$.

   If $a \subset b$ and $c \subset d$, [3·1] $-b \subset -a$ and $-d \subset -c$.
   Hence [5·3] $-b -d \subset -a -c$, and [3·1] $-(-a -c) \subset -(-b -d)$.
   Hence [1·8] Q.E.D.

By the laws, $a a = a$ and $a + a = a$, 5·3 and 5·31 give the corollaries:

5·32 If $a \subset c$ and $b \subset c$, then $a b \subset c$.

5·33   If $a \subset c$ and $b \subset c$, then $a + b \subset c$.

5·34   If $a \subset b$ and $a \subset c$, then $a \subset b c$.

5·35   If $a \subset b$ and $a \subset c$, then $a \subset b + c$.

5·37   If $a \subset b$, then $a + c \subset b + c$.   (Correlate of 2·7)

   [2·3] $c \subset c$.   Hence [5·31] Q.E.D.

5·4 $a + a b = a$.

   [5·21] $a \subset a + a b$ (1)

   [2·3] $a \subset a$, and [5·2] $a b \subset a$.   Hence [5·33] $a + a b \subset a$ (2)

   [2·2] If (1) and (2), then Q.E.D.

5·41 $a (a + b) = a$.

   [5·4] $-a + -a -b = -a$.   Hence [3·2] $-(-a + -a -b) = -(-a) = a$.
   But [3·4] $-(-a + -a -b) = a \cdot -(-a -b) = a (a + b)$.

5·4 and 5·41 are the two forms of the Law of Absorption.   We have next to prove the Distributive Law, which requires several lemmas.

5·5 $a (b + c) = a b + a c$.

   Lemma 1: $a b + a c \subset a (b + c)$.

   [5·2] $a b \subset a$ and $a c \subset a$.   Hence [5·33] $a b + a c \subset a$ (1)

   [5·2] $a b \subset b$ and $a c \subset c$.   But [5·21] $b \subset b + c$ and $c \subset b + c$.
   Hence [5·1] $a b \subset b + c$ and $a c \subset b + c$.
   Hence [5·33] $a b + a c \subset b + c$ (2)

   [5·34] If (1) and (2), then $a b + a c \subset a (b + c)$.

   Lemma 2:   If $p \subset q$ is false, then there is an element x, $\neq 0$, such that $x \subset p$ and $x \subset -q$.

   $p -q$ is such an element, for [5·2] $p -q \subset p$ and $p -q \subset -q$;   and [4·9] if $p -q = 0$, then $p \subset q$, hence if $p \subset q$ is false, then $p -q \neq 0$. (This lemma is introduced in order to simplify the proof of Lemma 3.)

   Lemma 3: $a (b + c) \subset b + a c$.

   Suppose this false.   Then, by lemma 2, there is an element x, $\neq 0$, such that

$$x \subset a (b + c) \tag{1}$$
$$\text{and} \qquad x \subset -(b + a c) \tag{}$$

   But [3·12] if $x \subset -(b + a c)$, then $b + a c \subset -x$ (2)

   [5·1] If (1), then since [5·2] $a (b + a c) \subset a$, $x \subset a$ (3)

   and also, since $a(b + a c) \subset b + .c$, $x \subset b + c$ (4)

   [5·1] If (2), then since [5·21] $b \subset b + a c$, $b \subset -x$ and [3·12] $x \subset -b$ (5)

   Also [5·1] if (2), then since [5·21] $a c \subset b + a c$, $a c \subset -x$ and [3·12]
   $$x \subset -(a c) \tag{6}$$

From (6) and (3), it follows that $x \subset c$ must be false; for if $x \subset c$ and (3) $x \subset a$, then [5·34] $x \subset a\, c$. But if $x \subset a\, c$ and (6) $x \subset -(a\, c)$, then [1·62] $x = 0$, which contradicts the hypothesis $x \neq 0$.

But if $x \subset c$ be false, then by lemma 2, there is an element y, $\neq 0$, such that

$$y \subset x \tag{7}$$

$$\text{and} \qquad y \subset -c, \qquad \text{or } [3 \cdot 12] \qquad c \subset -y \tag{8}$$

[5·1] If (7) and (5), then $y \subset -b$ and [3·12] $b \subset -y$ $\qquad$ (9)

If (8) and (9), then [5·33] $b + c \subset -y$ and [3·12] $y \subset -(b + c)$ $\qquad$ (10)

If (7) and (4), then [5·1] $y \subset b + c$ $\qquad$ (11)

[1·9] If (11), then $y\,(b + c) = y$, and if (10), $y \cdot -(b + c) = y$ $\qquad$ (12)

But if (12), then [1·62] $y = 0$, which contradicts the condition, $y \neq 0$.

Hence the supposition—that $a(b + c) \subset b + a\, c$ be false—is a false supposition, and the lemma is established.

Lemma 4: $\quad a\,(b + c) \subset a\, b + a\, c.$

By lemma 3, $a\,(b + c) \subset b + a\, c.$

Hence [2·7] $a\,[a\,(b + c)] \subset a\,(b + a\, c).$

But $a\,[a\,(b + c)] = (a\, a)(b + c) = a\,(b + c).$

And $a\,(b + a\, c) = a\,(a\, c + b).$ Hence $a\,(b + c) \subset a\,(a\, c + b).$

But by lemma 3, $a\,(a\, c + b) \subset a\, c + a\, b.$

And $a\, c + a\, b = a\, b + a\, c.$ Hence $a\,(b + c) \subset a\, b + a\, c.$

Proof of the theorem: [2·2] Lemma 1 and lemma 4 are together equivalent to $a\,(b + c) = a\, b + a\, c.$

This method of proving the Distributive Law is taken from Huntington, "Sets of Independent Postulates for the Algebra of Logic". The proof of the long and difficult lemma 3 is due to Peirce, who worked it out for his paper of 1880 but mislaid the sheets, and it was printed for the first time in Huntington's paper.[6]

5·51 $\quad (a + b)(c + d) = (a\, c + b\, c) + (a\, d + b\, d).$

$\qquad$ [5·5] $(a + b)(c + d) = (a + b)\, c + (a + b)\, d = (a\, c + b\, c) + (a\, d + b\, d).$

5·52 $\quad a + b\, c = (a + b)(a + c).$ $\qquad$ (Correlate of 5·5)

$\qquad$ [5·51] $(a + b)(a + c) = (a\, a + b\, a) + (a\, c + b\, c)$

$$= [(a + a\, b) + a\, c] + b\, c.$$

But [5·4] $(a + a\, b) + a\, c = a + a\, c = a.$ Hence Q.E.D.

Further theorems which are often useful in working the algebra and which follow readily from the preceding are as follows:

[6] See "Sets of Independent Postulates, etc.", *loc. cit.*, p. 300, footnote.

5·6 $a \cdot 1 = a = 1 \cdot a.$

> [1·5] $a \cdot 0 = 0.$ Hence $a \cdot -1 = 0.$
> But [1·61] if $a \cdot -1 = 0,$ then $a \cdot 1 = a.$

5·61 $a \subset 1.$

> [1·9] Since $a \cdot 1 = a,$ $a \subset 1.$

5·62 $a + 0 = a = 0 + a.$

> $-a \cdot -0 = -a \cdot 1 = -a.$ Hence [3·2] $a + 0 = -(-a \cdot -0) = -(-a) = a.$

5·63 $0 \subset a.$

> $0 \cdot a = a \cdot 0 = 0.$ Hence [1·9] Q.E.D.

5·64 $1 \subset a$ is equivalent to $a = 1.$

> [2·2] $a = 1$ is equivalent to the pair, $a \subset 1$ and $1 \subset a.$
> But [5·61] $a \subset 1$ holds always. Hence Q.E.D.

5·65 $a \subset 0$ is equivalent to $a = 0.$

> [2·2] $a = 0$ is equivalent to the pair, $a \subset 0$ and $0 \subset a.$
> But [5·63] $0 \subset a$ holds always. Hence Q.E.D.

5·7 If $a + b = x$ and $a = 0,$ then $b = x.$

> If $a = 0,$ $a + b = 0 + b = b.$

5·71 If $a\,b = x$ and $a = 1,$ then $b = x.$

> If $a = 1,$ $a\,b = 1 \cdot b = b.$

5·72 $a + b = 0$ is equivalent to the two equations, $a = 0$ and $b = 0.$

> If $a = 0$ and $b = 0,$ then $a + b = 0 + 0 = 0.$
> And if $a + b = 0,$ $-a\,-b = -(a + b) = -0 = 1.$
> But if $-a\,-b = 1,$ $a = a \cdot 1 = a(-a\,-b) = (a\,-a)\,-b = 0 \cdot -b = 0.$
> And [5·7] if $a + b = 0$ and $a = 0,$ then $b = 0.$

5·73 $a\,b = 1$ is equivalent to the two equations, $a = 1$ and $b = 1.$

> If $a = 1$ and $b = 1,$ then $a\,b = 1 \cdot 1 = 1.$
> And if $a\,b = 1,$ $-a + -b = -(a\,b) = -1 = 0.$ Hence [5·72] $-a = 0$
> and $-b = 0.$
> But [3·2] if $-a = 0,$ $a = 1,$ and if $-b = 0,$ $b = 1.$

5·7 and 5·72 are important theorems of the algebra. 5·7, "Any null term of a sum may be dropped", would hold in almost any system; but 5·72, "If a sum is null, each of its summands is null", is a special law characteristic of this algebra. It is due to the fact that the system contains no inverses with respect to + and 0. a and $-a$ are inverses with respect to $\times$ and 0 and with respect to $+$ and 1. $5 \cdot 71$ and $5 \cdot 73$, the correlates of $5 \cdot 7$ and $5 \cdot 72$, are less useful.

5·8 $a (b + -b) = a b + a -b = a.$

  $[5 \cdot 5]$ $a (b + -b) = a b + a -b.$

  And $[4 \cdot 8]$ $b + -b = 1$.   Hence $a (b + -b) = a \cdot 1 = a.$

5·85 $a + b = a + -a b.$

  $[5 \cdot 8]$ $b = a b + -a b.$

  Hence $a + b = a + (a b + -a b) = (a + a b) + -ab.$

  But $[5 \cdot 4]$ $a + a b = a$.   Hence Q.E.D.

It will be convenient to have certain principles, already proved for two terms or three, in the more general form which they can be given by the use of mathematical induction. Where the method of such extension is obvious, proof will be omitted or indicated only. Since both $\times$ and $+$ are associative, we can dispense with parentheses by the definitions:

5·901 $a + b + c = (a + b) + c$ Def.

5·902 $a b c = (a b) c$ Def.

5·91 $a = a (b + -b)(c + -c)(d + -d) \ldots$

  $[5 \cdot 8]$

5·92 $1 = (a + -a)(b + -b)(c + -c) \ldots$

  $[4 \cdot 8]$

5·93 $a = a + a b + a c + a d + \ldots$

  $[5 \cdot 4]$

5·931 $a = a (a + b)(a + c)(a + d) \ldots$

  $[5 \cdot 41]$

5·94 $a (b + c + d + \ldots) = a b + a c + a d + \ldots$

  $[5 \cdot 5]$

5·941 $a + b c d \ldots = (a + b)(a + c)(a + d) \ldots$

  $[5 \cdot 52]$

5·95 $-(a + b + c + \ldots) = -a -b -c \ldots$

  If the theorem hold for n terms, so that

  $$-(a_1 + a_2 + \ldots + a_n) = -a_1 -a_2 \ldots -a_n$$

  then it will hold for $n + 1$ terms, for by $3 \cdot 4$,

  $$-[(a_1 + a_2 + \ldots + a_n) + a_{n+1}] = -(a_1 + a_2 + \ldots + a_n) \cdot -a_{n+1}$$

  And $[3 \cdot 4]$ the theorem holds for two terms.   Hence it holds for any number of terms.

5·951 $-(a\,b\,c\,d\,\ldots) = -a + -b + -c + -d + \ldots$

Similar proof, using 3·41.

5·96 $1 = a + b + c + \ldots + -a - b - c \ldots$

[4·8, 5·951]

5·97 $a + b + c + \ldots = 0$ is equivalent to the set, $a = 0,\ b = 0,\ c = 0,\ \ldots$

[5·72]

5·971 $a\,b\,c\,d\,\ldots = 1$ is equivalent to the set, $a = 1,\ b = 1,\ c = 1,\ \ldots$

[5·73]

5·98 $a \cdot b\,c\,d\,\ldots = a\,b \cdot a\,c \cdot a\,d \ldots$

[1·2] $a\,a\,a\,a\,\ldots = a$.

5·981 $a + (b + c + d + \ldots) = (a + b) + (a + c) + (a + d) + \ldots$

[4·2] $a + a + a + \ldots = a$.

The extension of De Morgan's Theorem by 5·95 and 5·951 is especially important. 5·91, 5·92, and 5·93 are different forms of the principle by which any function may be expanded into a sum and any elements not originally involved in the function introduced into it. Thus any expression whatever may be regarded as a function of any given elements, even though they do not appear in the expression,—a peculiarity of the algebra. 5·92, the expression of the universe of discourse in any desired terms, or expansion of 1, is the basis of many important procedures.

The theorems 5·91–5·981 are valid only if the number of elements involved be finite, since proof depends upon the principle of mathematical induction.

III. General Properties of Functions

We may use $f(x)$, $\Phi(x, y)$, etc., to denote any expression which involves only members of the class K and the relations $\times$ and $+$. The further requirement that the expression represented by $f(x)$ should involve x or its negative, $-x$, that $\Phi(x, y)$ should involve x or $-x$ and y or $-y$, is unnecessary, for if x and $-x$ do not appear in a given expression, there is an equivalent expression in which they do appear. By 5·91,

$$a = a\,(x + -x) = a\,x + a\,-x = (a\,x + a\,-x)(y + -y)$$
$$= a\,x\,y + a\,x\,-y + a\,-x\,y + a\,-x\,-y, \text{ etc.}$$

$a\,x + a\,-x$ may be called the expansion, or development, of a with reference to x. And any or all terms of a function may be expanded with reference to x, the result expanded with reference to y, and so on for any elements and any number of elements. Hence any expression involving only elements in K and the relations $\times$ and $+$ may be treated as a function of any elements whatever.

If we speak of any a such that $x = a$ as the "value of x", then a value of x being given, the value of any function of x is determined, in this algebra as in any other. But functions of x in this system are of two types: (1) those whose value remains constant, however the value of x may vary, and (2) those such that any value of the *function* being assigned, the value of x is thereby determined, within limits or completely. Any function which is symmetrical with respect to x and $-x$ will belong to the first of these classes; in general, a function which is not completely symmetrical with respect to x and $-x$ will belong to the second. But it must be remembered, in this connection, that a symmetrical function may not *look* symmetrical unless it be completely expanded with reference to each of the elements involved. For example,

$$a + -a\, b + -b$$

is symmetrical with respect to a and $-a$ and with respect to b and $-b$. Expanding the first and last terms, we have

$$a\,(b + -b) + -a\,b + (a + -a)\,-b = a\,b + a\,-b + -a\,b + -a\,-b = 1$$

whatever the value of a or of b. Any function in which an element, x, does not appear, but into which it is introduced by expanding, will be symmetrical with respect to x and $-x$.

The decision what elements a given expression shall be considered a function of is, in this algebra, quite arbitrary except so far as it is determined by the form of result desired. The distinction between coefficients and "variables" or "unknowns" is not fundamental. In fact, we shall frequently find it convenient to treat a given expression first as a function— say—of x and y, then as a function of z, or of x alone. In general, coefficients will be designated by capital letters.

The Normal Form of a Function.—Any function of one variable, $f(x)$, can be given the form

$$A\,x + B\,-x$$

where A and B are independent of x. This is the *normal form* of functions of one variable.

6·1 Any function of one variable, $f(x)$, is such that, for some A and some B which are independent of x,

$$f(x) = A\,x + B\,-x$$

Any expression which involves only elements in the class K and the relations $\times$ and $+$ will consist either of a single term—a single element, or elements related by $\times$—or of a sum of such terms. Only four kinds of such terms are possible: (1) those which involve x, (2) those which involve $-x$, (3) those which involve both, and (4) those which involve neither.[7]

Since the Distributive Law, $5\cdot5$, allows us to collect the coefficients of x, of $-x$ and of $(x-x)$, the most general form of such an expression is

$$p\,x + q\,-x + r\,(x-x) + s$$

where p, q, r, and s are independent of x and $-x$.

But $[2\cdot4]\ r\,(x-x) = r\cdot0 = 0$.

And $[5\cdot9]\ s = s\,x + s\,-x$.

Hence $p\,x + q\,-x + r\,(x-x) + s = (p+s)\,x + (q+s)\,-x$.

Therefore, $A = p+s$, $B = q+s$, gives the required reduction.

The normal form of a function of $n+1$ variables,

$$\Phi(x_1, x_2, \ldots\ x_n, x_{n+1})$$

may be defined as the expansion by the Distributive Law of

$$f(x_1, x_2, \ldots\ x_n)\cdot x_{n+1} + f'(x_1, x_2, \ldots\ x_n)\cdot-x_{n+1}$$

where f and f' are each some function of the n variables, $x_1, x_2, \ldots\ x_n$, and in the normal form. This is a "step by step" definition; the normal form of a function of two variables is defined in terms of the normal form of functions of one variable; the normal form of a function of three variables in terms of the normal form for two, and so on.[8] Thus the normal form of a function of two variables, $\Phi(x, y)$, will be found by expanding

$$(A\,x + B\,-x)\,y + (C\,x + D\,-x)\,-y$$

It will be, $A\,x\,y + B\,-x\,y + C\,x\,-y + D\,-x\,-y$

The normal form of a function of three variables, $\Psi(x, y, z)$, will be

$$A\,x\,y\,z + B\,-x\,y\,z + C\,x\,-y\,z + D\,-x\,-y\,z + E\,x\,y\,-z + F\,-x\,y\,-z$$
$$+ G\,x\,-y\,-z + H\,-x\,-y\,-z$$

And so on. Any function in the normal form will be fully developed with

[7] By a term which "involves" x is meant a term which either *is* x or has x "as a factor". But "factor" seems inappropriate in an algebra in which $h\,x$ is always contained in x, $h\,x \subset x$.

[8] This definition alters somewhat the usual order of terms in the normal form of functions. But it enables us to apply mathematical induction and thus prove theorems of a generality not otherwise to be attained.

reference to each of the variables involved—that is, each variable, or its negative, will appear in every term.

6·11 Any function may be given the normal form.

(*a*) By 6·1, any function of one variable may be given the normal form.

(*b*) If functions of n variables can be given the normal form, then functions of $n + 1$ variables can be given the normal form, for,

Let $\Phi(x_1, x_2, \ldots x_n, x_{n+1})$ be any function of $n + 1$ variables. By definition, its normal form will be equivalent to

$$f(x_1, x_2, \ldots x_n) \cdot x_{n+1} + f'(x_1, x_2, \ldots x_n) \cdot -x_{n+1}$$

where f and f' are functions of $x_1, x_2, \ldots x_n$ and in the normal form.

By the definition of a function, $\Phi(x_1, x_2, \ldots x_n, x_{n+1})$ may be regarded as a function of x_{n+1}. Hence, by 6·1, for some A and some B which are independent of x_{n+1}

$$\Phi(x_1, x_2, \ldots x_n, x_{n+1}) = A\, x_{n+1} + B\, -x_{n+1}$$

Also, by the definition of a function, for some f and some f'

$$A = f(x_1, x_2, \ldots x_n)$$
$$\text{and} \quad B = f'(x_1, x_2, \ldots x_n)$$

Hence, for some f and f' which are independent of x_{n+1}

$$\Phi(x_1, x_2, \ldots x_n, x_{n+1}) = f(x_1, x_2, \ldots x_n) \cdot x_{n+1}$$
$$+ f'(x_1, x_2, \ldots x_n) \cdot -x_{n+1}$$

Therefore, if the functions of n variables, f and f', can be given the normal form, then $\Phi(x_1, x_2, \ldots x_n, x_{n+1})$ can be given the normal form.

(*c*) Since functions of one variable can be given the normal form, and since if functions of n variables can be given the normal form, functions of $n + 1$ variables can be given the normal form, therefore functions of any number of variables can be given the normal form.

The second step, (*b*), in the above proof may seem arbitrary. That it is valid, is due to the nature of functions in this algebra.

6·12 For a function of n variables, $\Phi(x_1, x_2, \ldots x_n)$, the normal form will be a sum of 2^n terms, representing all the combinations of x_1, positive **or** negative, with x_2, positive or negative, with . . . with x_n, positive **or** negative, each term having its coefficient.

(*a*) A normal form function of one variable has two terms, and by definition of the normal form of functions of $n + 1$ variables, if functions of k variables have 2^k terms, a function of $k + 1$ variables will have $2^k + 2^k$, or 2^{k+1}, terms.

(*b*) A normal form function of one variable has the further character described in the theorem; and if normal form functions of k variables have this character, then functions of $k + 1$ variables will have it, since, by definition, the normal form of a function of $k + 1$ variables will consist of the combinations of the $(k + 1)$st variable, positive or negative, with each of the combinations represented in functions of k variables.

Since any coefficient may be 0, the normal form of a function may contain terms which are null. Where no coefficient for a term appears, the coefficient is, of course, 1. The order of terms in the normal form of a function will vary as the order of the variables in the argument of the function is varied. For example, the normal form of $\Phi(x, y)$ is, by definition,

$$A\, x\, y + B -x\, y + C\, x -y + D -x -y$$

and the normal form of $\Psi(y, x)$ is

$$P\, y\, x + Q -y\, x + R\, y -x + S -y -x$$

Except for the coefficients, these differ only in the order of the terms and order of the elements in the terms. And since $+$ and $\times$ are both associative and commutative, such a difference is not material.

6·15 Any two functions of the same variables can differ materially only in the coefficients of the terms.

The theorem follows immediately from 6·12.

In consequence of 6·15, we can, without loss of generality, assume that, for any two normal form functions of the same variables with which we may be concerned, the order of terms and the order of variables in the arguments of the functions is the same. And also, in any function of $n + 1$ variables, $\Phi(x_1, x_2, \ldots x_n, x_{n+1})$, which is equated to

$$f(x_1, x_2, \ldots x_n) \cdot x_{n+1} + f'(x_1, x_2, \ldots x_n) \cdot -x_{n+1}$$

x_{n+1} may be *any chosen one* of the $n + 1$ variables. The convention that it is always the last is consistent with complete generality of the proofs.

6·17 The product of any two terms of a function in the normal form is null.

By 6·12, for any two terms of a function in the normal form, there will be some variable, x_n, such that x_n is positive in one of them and negative in the other; since otherwise the two terms would represent the *same* combination of x_1, positive or negative, with x_2, positive or negative, etc. Consequently, the product of any two terms will involve a factor of the form $x_n -x_n$, and will therefore be null.

Unless otherwise specified, it will be presumed hereafter that any function mentioned is in the normal form.

The Coefficients in a Function.—The coefficients in any function can be expressed in terms of the function itself.

6·21   If $f(x) = A x + B -x$, then $f(1) = A$.

For $f(1) = A \cdot 1 + B \cdot -1 = A + B \cdot 0 = A$.

6·22   If $f(x) = A x + B -x$, then $f(0) = B$.

For $f(0) = A \cdot 0 + B \cdot -0 = 0 + B \cdot 1 = B$.

6·23 $f(x) = f(1) \cdot x + f(0) \cdot -x$.

The theorem follows immediately from 6·1, 6·21 and 6·22.

These laws, first stated by Boole, are very useful in reducing complicated expressions to normal form. For example, if

$$\Psi(x) = a c (d x + -d -x) + (c + x) d$$

reduction by any other method would be tedious. But we have

$$\Psi(1) = a c (d \cdot 1 + -d \cdot 0) + (c + 1) d = a c d + c d + d = d$$

and $$\Psi(0) = a c (d \cdot 0 + -d \cdot 1) + (c + 0) d = a c -d + c d$$

Hence the normal form of $\Psi(x)$ is given by

$$\Psi(x) = d x + (a c -d + c d) -x$$

Laws analogous to 6·23, also stated by Boole, may be given for functions of more than one variable. For example,

$$f(x, y) = f(1, 1) \cdot x y + f(0, 1) \cdot -x y + f(1, 0) \cdot x -y + f(0, 0) \cdot -x -y$$

and $\Phi(x, y, z) = \Phi(1, 1, 1) \cdot x y z + \Phi(0, 1, 1) \cdot -x y z + \Phi(1, 0, 1) \cdot x -y z$

$$+ \Phi(0, 0, 1) \cdot -x -y z + \Phi(1, 1, 0) \cdot x y -z + \Phi(0, 1, 0) \cdot -x y -z$$

$$+ \Phi(1, 0, 0) \cdot x -y -z + \Phi(0, 0, 0) \cdot -x -y -z$$

We can prove that this method of determining the coefficients extends to functions of any number of variables.

6·24   If $C\left\{\begin{array}{cccc} x_1 & x_2 & x_3 \ldots & x_n \\ -x_1 & -x_2 & -x_3 \ldots & -x_n \end{array}\right\}$ be any term of $\Psi(x_1, x_2, x_3, \ldots x_n)$, then

$\Psi\left\{\begin{array}{c} 1, 1, 1, \ldots 1 \\ 0, 0, 0, \ldots 0 \end{array}\right\}$ will be the coefficient, C.

(*a*) By 6·23, the theorem holds for functions of one variable.

(*b*) If the theorem hold for functions of k variables, it will hold for functions of $k + 1$ variables, for,

By 6·11, any function of $k + 1$ variables, $\Phi(x_1, x_2, \ldots x_k, x_{k+1})$, is such that, for some f and some f',

$$\Phi(x_1, x_2, \ldots x_k, x_{k+1}) = f(x_1, x_2, \ldots x_k) \cdot x_{k+1} + f'(x_1, x_2, \ldots x_k) \cdot -x_{k+1}$$

Hence $\Phi\left\{\begin{array}{c} 1, 1, \ldots 1, \\ 0, 0, \ldots 0, \end{array} 1\right\} = f\left\{\begin{array}{c} 1, 1, \ldots 1 \\ 0, 0, \ldots 0 \end{array}\right\} \cdot 1 + f'\left\{\begin{array}{c} 1, 1, \ldots 1 \\ 0, 0, \ldots 0 \end{array}\right\} \cdot 0$

$$= f\left\{\begin{array}{c} 1, 1, \ldots 1 \\ 0, 0, \ldots 0 \end{array}\right\} \tag{1}$$

And $\Phi\left\{\begin{array}{c} 1, 1, \ldots 1, \\ 0, 0, \ldots 0, \end{array} 0\right\} = f\left\{\begin{array}{c} 1, 1, \ldots 1 \\ 0, 0, \ldots 0 \end{array}\right\} \cdot 0 + f'\left\{\begin{array}{c} 1, 1, \ldots 1 \\ 0, 0, \ldots 0 \end{array}\right\} \cdot 1$

$$= f'\left\{\begin{array}{c} 1, 1, \ldots 1 \\ 0, 0, \ldots 0 \end{array}\right\} \tag{2}$$

Therefore, if every term of f be of the form

$$f\left\{\begin{array}{c} 1, 1, \ldots 1 \\ 0, 0, \ldots 0 \end{array}\right\} \cdot \left\{\begin{array}{cccc} x_1 & x_2 \ldots & x_k \\ -x_1 & -x_2 \ldots & -x_k \end{array}\right\}$$

then every term of Φ in which x_{k+1} is positive will be of the form

$$f\left\{\begin{array}{c} 1, 1, \ldots 1 \\ 0, 0, \ldots 0 \end{array}\right\} \cdot \left\{\begin{array}{cccc} x_1 & x_2 \ldots & x_k \\ -x_1 & -x_2 \ldots & -x_k \end{array}\right\} \cdot x_{k+1}$$

and the coefficient of any such term will be $f\left\{\begin{array}{c} 1, 1, \ldots 1 \\ 0, 0, \ldots 0 \end{array}\right\}$, which,

by (1), is $\Phi\left\{\begin{array}{c} 1, 1, \ldots 1, \\ 0, 0, \ldots 0, \end{array} 1\right\}$.

And similarly, if every term of f' be of the form

$$f'\left\{\begin{array}{c} 1, 1, \ldots 1 \\ 0, 0, \ldots 0 \end{array}\right\} \cdot \left\{\begin{array}{cccc} x_1 & x_2 \ldots & x_k \\ -x_1 & -x_2 \ldots & -x_k \end{array}\right\}$$

then every term of Φ in which x_{k+1} is negative will be of the form

$$f'\left\{\begin{array}{c} 1, 1, \ldots 1 \\ 0, 0, \ldots 0 \end{array}\right\} \cdot \left\{\begin{array}{cccc} x_1 & x_2 \ldots & x_k \\ -x_1 & -x_2 \ldots & -x_k \end{array}\right\} \cdot -x_{k+1}$$

and the coefficient of any such term will be $f'\left\{\begin{matrix} 1, 1, \ldots 1 \\ 0, 0, \ldots 0 \end{matrix}\right\}$, which,

by (2), is $\Phi\left\{\begin{matrix} 1, 1, \ldots 1, 0 \\ 0, 0, \ldots 0, 0 \end{matrix}\right\}$.

Hence every term of Φ will be of the form

$$\Phi\left\{\begin{matrix} 1, 1, \ldots 1, 1 \\ 0, 0, \ldots 0, 0 \end{matrix}\right\} \cdot \left\{\begin{matrix} x_1 & x_2 & \ldots & x_k & x_{k+1} \\ -x_1 & -x_2 & \ldots & -x_k & -x_{k+1} \end{matrix}\right\}$$

(c) Since the theorem holds for functions of one variable, and since if it hold for functions of k variables, it will hold for functions of $k + 1$ variables, therefore it holds for functions of any number of variables.

For functions of one variable, further laws of the same type as $6 \cdot 23$— but less useful—have been given by Peirce and Schröder.

If $f(x) = A x + B -x$:

6·25 $\quad f(1) = f(A + B) = f(-A + -B)$.

6·26 $\quad f(0) = f(A \cdot B) = f(-A \cdot -B)$.

6·27 $\quad f(A) = A + B = f(-B) = f(A \cdot -B) = f(A + -B)$
$$= f(1) + f(0) = f(x) + f(-x).$$

6·28 $\quad f(B) = A \cdot B = f(-A) = f(-A \cdot B) = f(-A + B)$
$$= f(1) \cdot f(0) = f(x) \cdot f(-x).$$

The proofs of these involve no difficulties and may be omitted.

In theorems to be given later, it will be convenient to denote the coefficients in functions of the form $\Phi(x_1, x_2, \ldots x_n)$ by $A_1, A_2, A_3, \ldots A_{2^n}$, or by $C_1, C_2, C_3, \ldots$, etc. This notation is perfectly definite, since the order of terms in the normal form of a function is fixed. If the argument of any function be $(x_1, x_2, \ldots x_n)$, then any one of the variables, x_k, will be positive in the term of which C_m is the coefficient in case

$$p \cdot 2^{k-1} < m \leqq (p + 1) \cdot 2^{k-1}$$

where $p = $ any even integer (including 0). Otherwise x_k will be negative in the term. Thus it may be determined, for each of the variables in the function, whether it is positive or negative in the term of which C_m is the coefficient, and the term is thus completely specified. We make no use of this law, except that it validates the proposed notation.

Occasionally it will be convenient to distinguish the coefficients of those terms in a function in which some one of the variables, say x_k, is positive from the coefficients of terms in which x_k is negative. We shall do this by using different letters, as P_1, P_2, P_3, $\ldots$, for coefficients of terms in which x_k is positive, and Q_1, Q_2, Q_3, $\ldots$ for coefficients of terms in which x_k is negative. This notation is perfectly definite, since the number of terms, for a function of n variables, is always 2^n, the number of those in which x_k is positive is always equal to the number of those in which it is negative, and the distribution of the terms in which x_k is positive, or is negative, is determined by the law given above.

The sum of the coefficients, $A_1 + A_2 + A_3 + \ldots$, will frequently be indicated by $\sum A$ or $\sum_h A_h$; the product, $A_1 \cdot A_2 \cdot A_3 \cdot \ldots$ by $\prod A$ or $\prod_h A_h$. Since the number of coefficients involved will always be fixed by the function which is in question, it will be unnecessary to indicate numerically the range of the operators $\sum$ and $\prod$.

The Limits of a Function.—The lower limit of any function is the product of the coefficients in the function, and the upper limit is the sum of the coefficients.

6·3 $A\,B \subset A\,x + B - x \subset A + B.$

$$(A\,B)(A\,x + B - x) = A\,B\,x + A\,B - x = A\,B$$

Hence [1·9] $A\,B \subset A\,x + B - x.$
And $(A\,x + B - x)(A + B) = A\,x + A\,B - x + A\,B\,x + B - x$
$$= (A\,B + A)\,x + (A\,B + B) - x.$$
But [5·4] $A\,B + A = A$, and $A\,B + B = B.$
Hence $(A\,x + B - x)(A + B) = A\,x + B - x,$ and   [1·9] $A\,x + B - x$
$\subset A + B.$

6·31 $f(B) \subset f(x) \subset f(A).$
         [6·3 and 6·26, 6·27]

6·32   If the coefficients in any function, $F(x_1, x_2, \ldots x_n)$, be C_1, C_2, C_3, $\ldots$, then

$$\prod C \subset F(x_1, x_2, \ldots x_n) \subset \sum C$$

(a) By 6·3, the theorem holds for functions of one variable.

(b) Let $\Phi(x_1, x_2, \ldots x_k, x_{k+1})$ be any function of $k + 1$ variables. By 6·11, for some f and some f',

$$\Phi(x_1, x_2, \ldots x_k, x_{k+1}) = f(x_1, x_2, \ldots x_k) \cdot x_{k+1}$$
$$+ f'(x_1, x_2, \ldots x_k) \cdot -x_{k+1} \quad (1)$$

Since this last expression may be regarded as a function of x_{k+1} in which the coefficients are the functions f and f', [6·3]

$$f(x_1, x_2, \ldots x_k) \times f'(x_1, x_2, \ldots x_k) \subset \Phi(x_1, x_2, \ldots x_k, x_{k+1})$$

Let $A_1\{\Phi\}$, $A_2\{\Phi\}$, $A_3\{\Phi\}$, etc., be here the coefficients in Φ; $A_1\{f\}$, $A_2\{f\}$, $A_3\{f\}$, etc., the coefficients in f; and $A_1\{f'\}$, $A_2\{f'\}$, $A_3\{f'\}$, etc., the coefficients in f'.

If $\prod A\{f\} \subset f$ and $\prod A\{f'\} \subset f'$, then [6·3]

$$\prod A\{f\} \times \prod A\{f'\} \subset f \times f'$$

and, by (1), $\prod A\{f\} \times \prod A\{f'\} \subset \Phi$.

But since (1) holds, any coefficient in Φ will be either a coefficient in f or a coefficient in f', and hence

$$\prod A\{f\} \times \prod A\{f'\} = \prod A\{\Phi\}$$

Hence if the theorem hold for functions of k variables, so that

$$\prod A\{f\} \subset f(x_1, x_2, \ldots x_k) \quad \text{and} \quad \prod A\{f'\} \subset f'(x_1, x_2, \ldots x_k),$$

then $\prod A\{\Phi\} \subset \Phi(x_1, x_2, \ldots x_k, x_{k+1})$.

Similarly, since (1) holds, [6·23] $\Phi \subset f + f'$.

Hence if $f \subset \sum A\{f\}$ and $f' \subset \sum A\{f'\}$, then [5·31]

$$\Phi \subset \sum A\{f\} + \sum A\{f'\}$$

But since any coefficient in Φ is either a coefficient in f or a coefficient in f', $\sum A\{f\} + \sum A\{f'\} = \sum A\{\Phi\}$.

Hence $\Phi \subset \sum A\{\Phi\}$.

Thus if the theorem hold for functions of k variables, it will hold for functions of $k + 1$ variables.

(c) Since the theorem holds for functions of one variable, and since if it hold for functions of k variables, it will hold for functions of $k + 1$ variables, therefore it holds generally.

As we shall see, these theorems concerning the limits of functions are the basis of the method by which eliminations are made.

Functions of Functions.—Since all functions of the same variables may be given the same normal form, the operations of the algebra may frequently be performed simply by operating upon the coefficients.

6·4   If $f(x) = A\,x + B\,{-x}$, then $-[f(x)] = -A\,x + -B\,{-x}$.

$$[3·4] \ -(A\,x + B\,{-x}) = -(A\,x) \cdot -(B\,{-x})$$
$$= (-A + -x)(-B + x) = -A\,{-B} + -A\,x + -B\,{-x}$$
$$= (-A\,{-B} + -A)\,x + (-A\,{-B} + -B)\,{-x}$$

But [5·4] $-A\,{-B} + -A = -A$ and $-A\,{-B} + -B = -B$.

Hence $-(A\,x + B\,{-x}) = -A\,x + -B\,{-x}$.

6·41 The negative of any function, in the normal form, is found by replacing each of the coefficients in the function by its negative.

(*a*) By 6·4, the theorem is true for functions of one variable.

(*b*) If the theorem hold for functions of k variables, then it will hold for functions of $k + 1$ variables.

Let $F(x_1, x_2, \ldots x_k, x_{k+1})$ be any function of $k + 1$ variables. Then by 6·11 and 3·2, for some f and some f',

$$-[F(x_1, x_2, \ldots x_k, x_{k+1})] = -[f(x_1, x_2, \ldots x_k) \cdot x_{k+1}$$
$$+ f'(x_1, x_2, \ldots x_k) \cdot -x_{k+1}]$$

But $f(x_1, x_2, \ldots x_k) \cdot x_{k+1} + f'(x_1, x_2, \ldots x_k) \cdot -x_{k+1}$ may be regarded as a function of x_{k+1}.

Hence, by 6·4,

$$-[f(x_1, x_2, \ldots x_k) \cdot x_{k+1} + f'(x_1, x_2, \ldots x_k) \cdot -x_{k+1}]$$
$$= -[f(x_1, x_2, \ldots x_k)] \cdot x_{k+1} + -[f'(x_1, x_2, \ldots x_k)] \cdot -x_{k+1}$$

Hence if the theorem be true for functions of k variables, so that the negative of f is found by replacing each of the coefficients in f by its negative and the negative of f' is found by replacing each of the coefficients in f' by its negative, then the negative of F will be found by replacing each of the coefficients in F by its negative, for, as has just been shown, any term of

$$-[F(x_1, x_2, \ldots x_k, x_{k+1})]$$

in which x_{k+1} is positive is such that its coefficient is a coefficient in

$$-[f(x_1, x_2, \ldots x_k)]$$

and any term of

$$-[F(x_1, x_2, \ldots x_k, x_{k+1})]$$

in which x_{k+1} is negative is such that its coefficient is a coefficient in

$$-[f'(x_1, x_2, \ldots x_k)]$$

(*c*) Since (*a*) and (*b*) hold, therefore the theorem holds generally.

Since a difference in the order of terms is not material, 6·41 holds not only for functions in the normal form but for any function which is completely expanded so that every element involved appears, either positive or negative, in each of the terms. It should be remembered that if any term of an expanded function is missing, its coefficient is 0, and in the negative of the function that term will appear with the coefficient 1.

6·42   The sum of any two functions of the same variables, $\Phi(x_1, x_2, \ldots x_n)$ and $\Psi(x_1, x_2, \ldots x_n)$, is another function of these same variables,

$$F(x_1, x_2, \ldots x_n),$$

such that the coefficient of any term in F is the sum of the coefficients of the corresponding terms in Φ and Ψ.

By 6·15, $\Phi(x_1, x_2, \ldots x_n)$ and $\Psi(x_1, x_2, \ldots x_n)$ cannot differ except in the coefficients of the terms.

Let A_1, A_2, A_3, etc., be the coefficients in Φ; B_1, B_2, B_3, etc., the coefficients of the corresponding terms in Ψ. For any two such corresponding terms, $A_k \left\{ \begin{matrix} x_1 & x_2 & \ldots & x_n \\ -x_1 & -x_2 & \ldots & -x_n \end{matrix} \right\}$ and $B_k \left\{ \begin{matrix} x_1 & x_2 & \ldots & x_n \\ -x_1 & -x_2 & \ldots & -x_n \end{matrix} \right\}$,

$$A_k \left\{ \begin{matrix} x_1 & x_2 & \ldots & x_n \\ -x_1 & -x_2 & \ldots & -x_n \end{matrix} \right\} + B_k \left\{ \begin{matrix} x_1 & x_2 & \ldots & x_n \\ -x_1 & -x_2 & \ldots & -x_n \end{matrix} \right\}$$

$$= (A_k + B_k) \left\{ \begin{matrix} x_1 & x_2 & \ldots & x_n \\ -x_1 & -x_2 & \ldots & -x_n \end{matrix} \right\}$$

And since addition is associative and commutative, the sum of the two functions is equivalent to the sum of the sums of such corresponding terms, pair by pair.

6·43   The product of two functions of the same variables, $\Phi(x_1, x_2, \ldots x_n)$ and $\Psi(x_1, x_2, \ldots x_n)$, is another function of these same variables,

$$F(x_1, x_2, \ldots x_n),$$

such that the coefficient of any term in F is the product of the coefficients of the corresponding terms in Φ and Ψ.

Let $A_k \left\{ \begin{matrix} x_1 & x_2 & \ldots & x_n \\ -x_1 & -x_2 & \ldots & -x_n \end{matrix} \right\}$ and $B_k \left\{ \begin{matrix} x_1 & x_2 & \ldots & x_n \\ -x_1 & -x_2 & \ldots & -x_n \end{matrix} \right\}$ be any two corresponding terms in Φ and Ψ.

$$A_k \left\{ \begin{matrix} x_1 & x_2 & \ldots & x_n \\ -x_1 & -x_2 & \ldots & -x_n \end{matrix} \right\} \times B_k \left\{ \begin{matrix} x_1 & x_2 & \ldots & x_n \\ -x_1 & -x_2 & \ldots & -x_n \end{matrix} \right\}$$

$$= (A_k \times B_k) \left\{ \begin{matrix} x_1 & x_2 & \ldots & x_n \\ -x_1 & -x_2 & \ldots & -x_n \end{matrix} \right\}$$

By 6·15, Φ and Ψ do not differ except in the coefficients, and by 6·17, whatever the coefficients in the normal form of a function, the product of any two terms is null. Hence all the *cross*-products of terms in Φ and Ψ will be null, and the product of the functions will be equivalent to the sum of the products of their corresponding terms, pair by pair.

Since in this algebra two functions in which the variables are not the same may be so expanded as to become functions of the same variables, these theorems concerning functions of functions are very useful.

IV. Fundamental Laws of the Theory of Equations

We have now to consider the methods by which any given element may be eliminated from an equation, and the methods by which the value of an "unknown" may be derived from a given equation or equations. The most convenient form of equation for eliminations and solutions is the equation with one member 0.

Equivalent Equations of Different Forms.—If an equation be not in the form in which one member is 0, it may be given that form by multiplying each side into the negative of the other and adding these two products.

7·1 $a = b$ is equivalent to $a -b + -a\, b = 0$.

[2·2] $a = b$ is equivalent to the pair, $a \subset b$ and $b \subset a$.

[4·9] $a \subset b$ is equivalent to $a -b = 0$, and $b \subset a$ to $-a\, b = 0$.

And [5·72] $a -b = 0$ and $-a\, b = 0$ are together equivalent to $a -b + -a\, b = 0$.

The transformation of an equation with one member 1 is obvious:

7·12 $a = 1$ is equivalent to $-a = 0$.

[3·2]

By 6·41, any equation of the form $f(x_1, x_2, \ldots x_n) = 1$ is reduced to the form in which one member is 0 simply by replacing each of the coefficients in f by its negative.

Of especial interest is the transformation of equations in which both members are functions of the same variables.

7·13   If $\Phi(x_1, x_2, \ldots x_n)$ and $\Psi(x_1, x_2, \ldots x_n)$ be any two functions of the same variables, then

$$\Phi(x_1, x_2, \ldots x_n) = \Psi(x_1, x_2, \ldots x_n)$$

is equivalent to $F(x_1, x_2, \ldots x_n) = 0$, where F is a function such that if A_1, A_2, A_3, etc., be the coefficients in Φ, and B_1, B_2, B_3, etc., be the coefficients of the corresponding terms in Ψ, then the coefficients of the corresponding terms in F will be $(A_1 -B_1 + -A_1 B_1)$, $(A_2 -B_2 + -A_2 B_2)$, $(A_3 -B_3 + -A_3 B_3)$, etc.

By 7·1, $\Phi = \Psi$ is equivalent to $(\Phi \times -\Psi) + (-\Phi \times \Psi) = 0$.

By 6·41, $-\Phi$ and $-\Psi$ are functions of the same variables as Φ and Ψ. Hence, by 6·43, $\Phi \times -\Psi$ and $-\Phi \times \Psi$ will each be functions of these same variables, and by 6·42, $(\Phi \times -\Psi) + (-\Phi \times \Psi)$ will also be a function of these same variables.

Hence Φ, Ψ, $-\Phi$, $-\Psi$, $\Phi \times -\Psi$, $-\Phi \times \Psi$, and $(\Phi \times -\Psi) + (-\Phi \times \Psi)$ are all functions of the same variables and, by 6·15, will not differ except in the coefficients of the terms.

If A_k be any coefficient in Φ, and B_k the corresponding coefficient in Ψ, then by 6·41, the corresponding coefficient in $-\Phi$ will be $-A_k$ and the corresponding coefficient in $-\Psi$ will be $-B_k$.

Hence, by 6·43, the corresponding coefficient in $\Phi \times -\Psi$ will be $A_k -B_k$, and the corresponding coefficient in $-\Phi \times \Psi$ will be $-A_k B_k$.

Hence, by 6·42, the corresponding coefficient in $(\Phi \times -\Psi) + (-\Phi \times \Psi)$ will be $A_k -B_k + -A_k B_k$.

Thus $(\Phi \times -\Psi) + (-\Phi \times \Psi)$ is the function F, as described above, and the theorem holds.

By 7·1, for every equation in the algebra there is an equivalent equation in the form in which one member is 0, and by 7·13 the reduction can usually be made by inspection.

One of the most important additions to the general methods of the algebra which has become current since the publication of Schröder's work is Poretsky's Law of Forms.[9]   By this law, given any equation, an equivalent equation of which one member may be chosen at will can be derived.

7·15 $a = 0$ is equivalent to $t = a -t + -a\, t$.

If $a = 0$, $a -t + -a\, t = 0 \cdot -t + 1 \cdot t = t$.

And if $t = a -t + -a\, t$, then [7·1]

$$(a -t + -a\, t) -t + (a\, t + -a -t)\, t = 0 = a -t + a\, t = a$$

Since t may here be any function in the algebra, this proves that every equation has an unlimited number of equivalents.   The more general form of the law is:

7·16 $a = b$ is equivalent to $t = (a\, b + -a -b)\, t + (a -b + -a\, b) -t$.

[7·1] $a = b$ is equivalent to $a -b + -a\, b = 0$.

And [6·4] $-(a -b + -a\, b) = a\, b + -a -b$.

Hence [7·15] Q.E.D.

The number of equations equivalent to a given equation and expressible

[9] See *Sept lois fondamentales de la théorie des égalités logiques*, Chap. i.

in terms of n elements will be half the number of distinct functions which can be formed from n elements and their negatives, that is, $2^{2^n}/2$.

The sixteen distinct functions expressible in terms of two elements, a and b, are:

a, $-a$, b, $-b$, 0 (i. e., $a -a$, $b -b$, etc.), 1 (i. e., $a + -a$, $b + -b$, etc.), $a\, b$, $a -b$, $-a\, b$, $-a -b$, $a + b$, $a + -b$, $-a + b$, $-a + -b$, $a\, b + -a -b$, and $a -b + -a\, b$.

In terms of these, the eight equivalent forms of the equation $a = b$ are:

$a = b$; $-a = -b$; $0 = a -b + -a\, b$; $1 = a\, b + -a -b$; $a\, b = a + b$; $a -b = -a\, b$; $-a -b = -a + -b$; and $a + -b = -a + b$.

Each of the sixteen functions here appears on one or the other side of an equation, and none appears twice.

For any equation, there is such a set of equivalents in terms of the elements which appear in the given equation. And every such set has what may be called its "zero member" (in the above, $0 = a -b + -a\, b$) and its "whole member" (in the above, $1 = a\, b + -a -b$). If we observe the form of 7·16, we shall note that the functions in the "zero member" and "whole member" are the functions in terms of which the arbitrarily chosen t is determined. Any $t = $ the t which contains the function $\{ = 0\}$ and is contained in the function $\{ = 1\}$. The validity of the law depends simply upon the fact that, for any t, $0 \subset t \subset 1$, i. e., $t = 1 \cdot t + 0 \cdot -t$. It is rather surprising that a principle so simple can yield a law so powerful.

Solution of Equations in One Unknown.—Every equation which is possible according to the laws of the system has a solution for each of the unknowns involved. This is a peculiarity of the algebra. We turn first to equations in one unknown. Every equation in x, if it be possible in the algebra, has a solution in terms of the relation $\subset$.

7·2 $A\, x + B -x = 0$ is equivalent to $B \subset x \subset -A$.

[5·72] $A\, x + B -x = 0$ is equivalent to the pair, $A\, x = 0$ and $B -x = 0$.

[4·9] $B -x = 0$ is equivalent to $B \subset x$.

And $A\, x = 0$ is equivalent to $x -(-A) = 0$, hence to $x \subset -A$.

7·21   A solution in the form $H \subset x \subset K$ is *indeterminate* whenever the equation which gives the solution is symmetrical with respect to x and $-x$.

First, if the equation be of the form $A\, x + A -x = 0$.

The solution then is, $A \subset x \subset -A$.

But if $A\, x + A -x = 0$, then $A = A\,(x + -x) = A\, x + A -x = 0$, and $-A = 1$.

Hence the solution is equivalent to $0 \subset x \subset 1$, which [5·61·63] is satisfied by *every* value of x.

In general, any equation symmetrical with respect to x and $-x$ which gives the solution, $H \subset x \subset K$, will give also $H \subset -x \subset K$. But if $H \subset x$ and $H \subset -x$, then [4·9] $H\,x = H$ and $H\,-x = H$. Hence [1·62] $H = 0$.
And if $x \subset K$ and $-x \subset K$, then [5·33] $x + -x \subset K$, and [4·8, 5·63] $K = 1$.
Hence $H \subset x \subset K$ will be equivalent to $0 \subset x \subset 1$.

It follows directly from 7·21 that if neither x nor $-x$ appear in an equation, then although they may be introduced by expansion of the functions involved, the equation remains indeterminate with respect to x.

7·22 An equation of the form $A\,x + B\,-x = 0$ determines x *uniquely* whenever $A = -B$, $B = -A$.

[3·22] $A = -B$ and $-A = B$ are equivalent; hence either of these conditions is equivalent to both.
[7·2] $A\,x + B\,-x = 0$ is equivalent to $B \subset x \subset -A$.
Hence if $B = -A$, it is equivalent to $B \subset x \subset B$ and to $-A \subset x \subset -A$, and hence [2·2] to $x = B = -A$.

In general, an equation of the form $A\,x + B\,-x = 0$ 'determines x between the limits B and $-A$. Obviously, the solution is unique if, and only if, these limits coincide; and the solution is wholly indeterminate only when they are respectively 0 and 1, the limiting values of variables generally.

7·221 The condition that an equation of the form $A\,x + B\,-x = 0$ be possible in the algebra, and hence that its solution be possible, is $A\,B = 0$.

By 6·3, $A\,B \subset A\,x + B\,-x$. Hence [5·65] if $A\,x + B\,-x = 0$, then $A\,B = 0$.
Hence if $A\,B \neq 0$, then $A\,x + B\,-x = 0$ must be false for all values of x.
And $A\,x + B\,-x = 0$ and the solution $B \subset x \subset -A$ are equivalent.

$A\,B = 0$ is called the "equation of condition" of $A\,x + B\,-x = 0$: it is a necessary, not a sufficient condition. To call it the condition that $A\,x + B\,-x = 0$ *have a solution* seems inappropriate: the solution $B \subset x \subset -A$ is equivalent to $A\,x + B\,-x = 0$, whether $A\,x + B\,-x = 0$ be true, false, or impossible. The sense in which $A\,B = 0$ conditions other forms of the solution of $A\,x + B\,-x = 0$ will be made clear in what follows.

The equation of condition is frequently useful in simplifying the solution.

(In this connection, it should be borne in mind that $A B = 0$ *follows from* $A x + B -x = 0$.) For example, if

$$a b x + (a + b) -x = 0$$

then $(a + b) \subset x \subset -(a b)$. But the equation of condition is

$$a b (a + b) = a b = 0, \qquad \text{or,} \qquad -(a b) = 1$$

Hence the second half of the solution is indeterminate, and the complete solution may be written

$$a + b \subset x$$

However, this simplified form of the solution is *equivalent* to the original equation only on the assumption that the equation of condition is satisfied and $a b = 0$.

Again suppose $\qquad a x + b -x + c = 0$

Expanding c with reference to x, and collecting coefficients, we have

$$(a + c) x + (b + c) -x = 0$$

and the equation of condition is

$$(a + c)(b + c) = a b + a c + b c + c = a b + c = 0$$

The solution is $\qquad b + c \subset x \subset -a -c$

But, by 5·72, the equation of condition gives $c = 0$, and hence $-c = 1$. Hence the complete solution may be written

$$b \subset x \subset -a$$

But here again, the solution $b \subset x \subset -a$ is *equivalent* to the original equation only on the assumption, contained in the equation of condition, that $c = 0$.

This example may also serve to illustrate the fact that in any equation one member of which is 0, any terms which do not involve x or $-x$ may be dropped without affecting the solution for x. If $a x + b -x + c = 0$, then by 5·72, $a x + b -x = 0$, and any addition to the solution by retaining c will be indeterminate. All terms which involve neither the unknown nor its negative belong to the "symmetrical constituent" of the equation—to be explained shortly.

Poretsky's Law of Forms gives immediately a determination of x which is equivalent to the given equation, whether that equation involve x or not.

7·23 $A x + B -x = 0$ is equivalent to $x = -A x + B -x$.

[7·15] $A x + B -x = 0$ is equivalent to

$$x = (A x + B -x) -x + (-A x + -B -x) x = B -x + -A x$$

This form of solution is also the one given by the method of Jevons.[10] Although it is mathematically objectionable that the expression which gives the value of x should involve x and $-x$, this is in reality a useful and logically simple form of the solution. It follows from $7 \cdot 2$ and $7 \cdot 23$ that $x = -A\ x + B\ -x$ is equivalent to $B \subset x \subset -A$.

Many writers on the subject have preferred the form of solution in which the value of the unknown is given in terms of the coefficients and an undetermined (arbitrary) parameter. This is the most "mathematical" form.

7·24 If $A\ B = 0$, as the equation $A\ x + B\ -x = 0$ requires, then $A\ x + B\ -x = 0$ is satisfied by $x = B\ -u + -A\ u$, or $x = B + u\ -A$, where u is arbitrary. And this solution is complete because, for any x such that $A\ x + B\ -x = 0$ there is some value of u such that $x = B\ -u + -A\ u = B + u\ -A$.

(a) By $6 \cdot 4$, if $x = B\ -u + -A\ u$, then $-x = -B\ -u + A\ u$.

Hence if $x = B\ -u + -A\ u$, then

$$A\ x + B\ -x = A\ (B\ -u + -B\ u) + B\ (-B\ -u + A\ u)$$
$$= A\ B\ -u + A\ B\ u = A\ B$$

Hence if $A\ B = 0$ and $x = B\ -u + -A\ u$, then whatever the value of u, $A\ x + B\ -x = 0$.

(b) Suppose x known and such that $A\ x + B\ -x = 0$.

Then if $x = B\ -u + -A\ u$, we have, by $7 \cdot 1$,

$$(B\ -u + -A\ u)\ -x + (-B\ -u + A\ u)\ x$$
$$= (A\ x + -A\ -x)\ u + (B\ -x + -B\ x)\ -u = 0$$

The condition that this equation hold for some value of u is, by $7 \cdot 221$,

$$(A\ x + -A\ -x)(B\ -x + -B\ x) = A\ -B\ x + -A\ B\ -x = 0$$

This condition is satisfied if $A\ x + B\ -x = 0$, for then

$$A\ (B + -B)\ x + (A + -A)\ B\ -x = A\ B + A\ -B\ x + -A\ B\ -x = 0$$

and by $5 \cdot 72$, $A\ -B\ x + -A\ B\ -x = 0$.

(c) If $A\ B = 0$, then $B\ -u + -A\ u = B + u\ -A$, for:

If $A\ B = 0$, then $A\ B\ u = 0$.

Hence $B\ -u + -A\ u = B\ -u + -A\ (B + -B)\ u + A\ B\ u$

$$= B\ -u + (A + -A)\ B\ u + -A\ -B\ u = B\ (-u + u) + -A\ -B\ u$$
$$= B + -A\ -B\ u.$$

But [5·85] $B + -A\ -B\ u = B + u\ -A$.

---

[10] See above, p. 77.

Only the simpler form of this solution, $x = B + u - A$, will be used hereafter.

The above solution can also be verified by substituting the value given for x in the original equation. We then have

$$A (B - u + -A u) + B (-B - u + A u) = A B - u + A B u = A B$$

And if $A B = 0$, the solution is verified for every value of u.

That the solution, $x = B - u + -A u = B + u - A$, means the same as $B \subset x \subset -A$, will be clear if we reflect that the significance of the arbitrary parameter, u, is to determine the limits of the expression.

If $u = 0$, $B - u + -A u = B + u - A = B$.

If $u = 1$, $B - u + -A u = -A$ and $B + u - A = B + -A$. But when

$$A B = 0, \quad B + -A = -A B + -A = -A.$$

Hence $x = B - u + -A u = B + u - A$ simply expresses the fact, otherwise stated by $B \subset x \subset -A$, that the limits of x are B and $-A$.

The equation of condition and the solution for equations of the form $C x + D - x = 1$, and of the form $A x + B - x = C x + D - x$, follow readily from the above.

7·25   The equation of condition that $C x + D - x = 1$ is $C + D = 1$, and the solution of $C x + D - x = 1$ is $-D \subset x \subset C$.

(*a*) By 6·3, $C x + D - x \subset C + D$.

Hence if there be any value of x for which $C x + D - x = 1$, then necessarily $C + D = 1$.

(*b*) If $C x + D - x = 1$, then [6·4] $-C x + -D - x = 0$, and [7·2] $-D \subset x \subset C$.

7·26   If $C + D = 1$, then the equation $C x + D - x = 1$ is satisfied by $x = -D + u C$, where u is arbitrary.

Since [6·4] $C x + D - x = 1$ is equivalent to $-C x + -D - x = 0$, and $C + D = 1$ is equivalent to $-C -D = 0$, the theorem follows from 7·24.

7·27   If $A x + B - x = C x + D - x$, the equation of condition is

$$(A - C + -A C)(B - D + -B D) = 0$$

and the solution is $B - D + -B D \subset x \subset A C + -A -C$, or

$$x = B - D + -B D + u (A C + -A -C), \text{ where } u \text{ is arbitrary.}$$

By 7·13, $A x + B - x = C x + D - x$ is equivalent to

$$(A - C + -A C) x + (B - D + -B d) - x = 0.$$

Hence, by 7·221, the equation of condition is as given above. And by 7·2 and 7·24, the solution is

$$B -D + -B\ D \mathbin{\mathsf{c}} x \mathbin{\mathsf{c}} -(A -C + -A\ C), \qquad \text{or}$$
$$x = B -D + -B\ D + u \cdot -(A -C + -A\ C), \text{ where } u \text{ is arbitrary.}$$

And [6·4] $-(A -C + -A\ C) = A\ C + -A -C.$

The subject of simultaneous equations is very simple, although the clearest notation we have been able to devise is somewhat cumbersome.

7·3 The condition that n equations in one unknown, $A^1 x + B^1 -x = 0$, $A^2 x + B^2 -x = 0$, $\ldots A^n x + B^n -x = 0$, may be regarded as simultaneous, is the condition that

$$\sum_{h,\,k} (A^h\ B^k) = 0$$

And the solution which they give, on that condition, is

$$\sum_k B^k \mathbin{\mathsf{c}} x \mathbin{\mathsf{c}} \prod_k -A^k$$

or $x = \displaystyle\sum_k B^k + u \cdot \prod_k -A^k$, where u is arbitrary.

By 6·42 and 5·72, $A^1 x + B^1 -x = 0$, $A^2 x + B^2 -x = 0$, $\ldots$ $A^n x + B^n -x = 0$, are together equivalent to

$$(A^1 + A^2 + \ldots + A^n)x + (B^1 + B^2 + \ldots + B^n) -x = 0$$
$$\text{or} \qquad \sum_k A^k\, x + \sum_k B^k -x = 0$$

By 7·23, the equation of condition here is

$$\sum_k A^k \times \sum_k B^k = 0$$

But $\displaystyle\sum_k A^k \times \sum_k B^k = (A^1 + A^2 + \ldots + A^n)(B^1 + B^2 + \ldots + B^n)$

$$= A^1\ B^1 + A^1\ B^2 + \ldots + A^1\ B^n + A^2\ B^1 + A^2\ B^2 + \ldots + A^2\ B^n$$
$$+ A^3\ B^1 + A^3\ B^2 + \ldots + A^3\ B^n + \ldots + A^n\ B^1 + \ldots + A^n\ B^n$$
$$= \sum_{h,\,k} (A^h\ B^k).$$

And by 7·2 and 7·24, the solution here is

$$\sum_k B^k \mathbin{\mathsf{c}} x \mathbin{\mathsf{c}} -\{\sum_k A^k\}$$
$$\text{or} \qquad x = \sum_k B^k + u \cdot -\{\sum_k A^k\}$$

And by 5·95, $-\{\displaystyle\sum_k A^k\} = \prod_k -A^k.$

It may be noted that from the solution in this equation, n^2 partial solutions of the form $B^h \subset x \subset -A^j$ can be derived, for

$$B^h \subset \sum_k B^k \quad \text{and} \quad \prod_k -A^k \subset -A^j.$$

Similarly, $2^{2n} - 1$ partial solutions can be derived by taking selections of members of $\sum_k B^k$ and $\prod_k -A^k$.

Symmetrical and Unsymmetrical Constituents of Equations.—Some of the most important properties of equations of the form $A\,x + B\,-x = 0$ are made clear by dividing the equation into two constituents—the most comprehensive constituent which is symmetrical with respect to x and $-x$, and a completely unsymmetrical constituent. For brevity, these may be called simply the "symmetrical constituent" and the "unsymmetrical constituent". In order to get the symmetrical constituent complete, it is necessary to expand each term with reference to every element in the function, coefficients included. Thus in $A\,x + B\,-x = 0$ it is necessary to expand the first term with respect to B, and the second with respect to A.

$$A\,(B + -B)\,x + (A + -A)\,B\,-x = A\,B\,x + A\,B\,-x + A\,-B\,x + -A\,B\,-x = 0$$

By 5·72, this is equivalent to the two equations,

$$A\,B\,(x + -x) = A\,B = 0 \quad \text{and} \quad A\,-B\,x + -A\,B\,-x = 0$$

The first of these is the symmetrical constituent; the second is the unsymmetrical constituent. The symmetrical constituent will always be the equation of condition, while the unsymmetrical constituent will give the solution. But the form of the solution will most frequently be simplified by considering the symmetrical constituent also. The unsymmetrical constituent will always be such that *its* equation of condition is satisfied a priori. Thus the equation of condition of

$$A\,-B\,x + -A\,B\,-x = 0$$

is $(A\,-B)(-A\,B) = 0$, which is an identity.

By this method of considering symmetrical and unsymmetrical constituents, equations which are indeterminate reveal that fact by having no unsymmetrical constituent for the solution. Also, the method enables us to treat even complicated equations by inspection. Remembering that any term in which neither x nor $-x$ appears belongs to the symmetrical constituent, as does also the product of the coefficients of x and $-x$, the separation can be made directly. For example,

$$(c + x)\,d + -c\,-d + (-a + -x)\,b = 0$$

will have as its equation of condition

$$c\,d + -c\,-d + -a\,b + b\,d = 0$$

and the solution will be

$$b \subset x \subset -d$$

Also, as we shall see shortly, the symmetrical constituent is always the complete resultant of the elimination of x.

The method does not readily apply to equations which do not have one member 0. But these can always be reduced to that form. How it extends to equations in more than one unknown will be clear from the treatment of such equations.

Eliminations.—The problem of elimination is the problem, what equations not involving x or $-x$ can be derived from a given equation, or equations, which do involve x and $-x$. In most algebras, one term can, under favorable circumstances, be eliminated from two equations, two terms from three, n terms from $n + 1$ equations. But in this algebra any number of terms (and their negatives) can be eliminated from a single equation; and the terms to be eliminated may be chosen at will. The principles whereby such eliminations are performed have already been provided in theorems concerning the equation of condition.

7·4 $A\,B = 0$ contains all the equations not involving x or $-x$ which can be derived from $A\,x + B\,-x = 0$.

By 7·24, the complete solution of $A\,x + B\,-x = 0$ is

$$x = B\,-u + -A\,u$$

Substituting this value of x in the equation, we have

$$A\,(B\,-u + -A\,u) + B\,(-B\,-u + A\,u) = A\,B\,-u + A\,B\,u = A\,B = 0$$

Hence $A\,B = 0$ is the complete resultant of the elimination of x.

It is at once clear that the resultant of the elimination of x coincides with the equation of condition for solution and with the symmetrical constituent of the equation.

7·41   If n elements, $x_1, x_2, x_3, \ldots x_n$, be eliminated from any equation, $F(x_1, x_2, x_3, \ldots x_n) = 0$, the complete resultant is the equation to 0 of the product of the coefficients in $F(x_1, x_2, x_3, \ldots x_n)$.

    (*a*) By 6·1 and 7·4, the theorem is true for the elimination of one element, x, from any equation, $f(x) = 0$.

    (*b*) If the theorem hold for the elimination of k elements, $x_1, x_2,$

... x_k, from any equation, $\Phi(x_1, x_2, \ldots x_k) = 0$, then it will hold for the elimination of $k + 1$ elements, $x_1, x_2, \ldots x_k, x_{k+1}$, from any equation, $\Psi(x_1, x_2, \ldots x_k, x_{k+1}) = 0$, for:

By 6·11, $\Psi(x_1, x_2, \ldots x_k, x_{k+1}) = f(x_1, x_2, \ldots x_k) \cdot x_{k+1}$
$$+ f'(x_1, x_2, \ldots x_k) \cdot -x_{k+1}.$$

And the coefficients in Ψ will be the coefficients in f and f'. By 7·4, the complete resultant of eliminating x_{k+1} from

$$f(x_1, x_2, \ldots x_k) \cdot x_{k+1} + f'(x_1, x_2, \ldots x_k) \cdot -x_{k+1} = 0$$

is
$$f(x_1, x_2, \ldots x_k) \times f'(x_1, x_2, \ldots x_k) = 0$$

And by 6·43, $f(x_1, x_2, \ldots x_k) \times f'(x_1, x_2, \ldots x_k) = 0$ is equivalent to $\Phi(x_1, x_2, \ldots x_k) = 0$, where Φ is a function such that if the coefficients in f be P_1, P_2, P_3, etc., and the corresponding coefficients in f' be Q_1, Q_2, Q_3, etc., then the corresponding coefficients in Φ will be P_1Q_1, P_2Q_2, P_3Q_3, etc. Hence if the theorem hold for the elimination of k elements, $x_1, x_2, \ldots x_k$, from $\Phi(x_1, x_2, \ldots x_k) = 0$, this elimination will give

$$(P_1Q_1)(P_2Q_2)(P_3Q_3)\ldots = (P_1P_2P_3\ldots Q_1Q_2Q_3\ldots) = 0,$$

where $P_1P_2P_3\ldots Q_1Q_2Q_3\ldots$ is the product of the coefficients in Φ, or in f and f'—i. e., the product of the coefficients in Ψ.

Hence if the theorem hold for the elimination of k elements, $x_1, x_2, \ldots x_k$, from $\Phi(x_1, x_2, \ldots x_k) = 0$, it will hold for the elimination of $k + 1$ elements, $x_1, x_2, \ldots x_k, x_{k+1}$, from $\Psi(x_1, x_2, \ldots x_k, x_{k+1}) = 0$, provided x_{k+1} be the first eliminated.

But since the order of terms in a function is immaterial, and for any order of elements in the argument of a function, there is a normal form of the function, x_{k+1} in the above may be any of the $k + 1$ elements in Ψ, and the order of elimination is immaterial.

(c) Since (a) and (b) hold, therefore the theorem holds for the elimination of any number of elements from the equation to 0 of any function of these elements.

By this theorem, it is possible to eliminate simultaneously any number of elements from any equation, by the following procedure: (1) Reduce the equation to the form in which one member is 0, unless it already have that form; (2) Develop the other member of the equation as a normal-form function of the elements to be eliminated; (3) Equate to 0 the product of the coefficients in this function. This will be the complete elimination resultant.

Occasionally it is convenient to have the elimination resultant in the form of an equation with one member 1, especially if the equation which gives the resultant have that form.

7·42 The complete resultant of eliminating n elements, x_1, x_2, ... x_n, from any equation, $F(x_1, x_2, \ldots x_n) = 1$, is the equation to 1 of the sum of the coefficients in $F(x_1, x_2, \ldots x_n)$.

Let A_1, A_2, A_3, etc., be the coefficients in $F(x_1, x_2, \ldots x_n)$. $F(x_1, x_2, \ldots x_n) = 1$ is equivalent to $-[F(x_1, x_2, \ldots x_n)] = 0$. And by 6·41, $-[F(x_1, x_2, \ldots x_n)]$ is a function, $\Phi(x_1, x_2, \ldots x_n)$, such that if any coefficient in F be A_k, the corresponding coefficient in Φ will be $-A_k$.

Hence, by 7·41, the complete resultant of eliminating x_1, x_2, ... x_n, from $F(x_1, x_2, \ldots x_n) = 1$ is

$$\textstyle\prod -A = 0, \qquad \text{or} \qquad -\{\textstyle\prod -A\} = 1$$

But [5·95] $-\{\textstyle\prod -A\} = \sum A$. Hence Q.E.D.

For purposes of application of the algebra to ordinary reasoning, elimination is a process more important than solution, since most processes of reasoning take place through the elimination of "middle" terms. For example:

If all b is x, $b \subset x$, $b -x = 0$
and no a is x, $a x = 0$,
then $a x + b -x = 0$.   Whence, by elimination, $a b = 0$, or no a is b.

Solution of Equations in more than one Unknown.—The complete solution of any equation in more than one unknown may be accomplished by eliminating all the unknowns except one and solving for that one, repeating the process for each of the unknowns. Such solution will be complete because the elimination, in each case, will give the complete resultant which is independent of the unknowns eliminated, and each solution will be a solution for one unknown, and complete, by previous theorems. However, general formulae of the solution of any equation in n unknowns, for each of the unknowns, can be proved.

7·5 The equation of condition of any equation in n unknowns is identical with the resultant of the elimination of all the unknowns; and this resultant is the condition of the solution with respect to each of the unknowns separately.

(a) If the equation in n unknowns be of the form

$$F(x_1, x_2, \ldots x_n) = 0:$$

Let the coefficients in $F(x_1, x_2, \ldots x_n)$ be A_1, A_2, A_3, etc. Then, by 6·32,

$$\prod A \subset F(x_1, x_2, \ldots x_n)$$

and [5·65] $\prod A = 0$ is a condition of the possibility of

$$F(x_1, x_2, \ldots x_n) = 0$$

And [7·41] $\prod A = 0$ is the resultant of the elimination of x_1, x_2, $\ldots x_n$, from $F(x_1, x_2, \ldots x_n) = 0$.

(b) If the equation in n unknowns have some other form than $F(x_1, x_2, \ldots x_n) = 0$, then by 7·1, it has an equivalent which is of that form, and its equation of condition and its elimination resultant are the equivalents of the equation of condition and elimination resultant of its equivalent which has the form

$$F(x_1, x_2, \ldots x_n) = 0$$

(c) The result of the elimination of all the unknowns is the equation of condition with respect to any one of them, say x_k, because:

(1) The equation to be solved for x_k will be the result of eliminating all the unknowns but x_k from the original equation; and

(2) The condition that this equation, in which x_k is the only unknown, have a solution for x_k is, by (a) and (b), the same as the result of eliminating x_k from it.

Hence the equation of condition with respect to x_k is the same as the result of eliminating, from the original equation, first all the other unknowns and then x_k.

And by 7·41 and (b), the result of eliminating the unknowns is independent of the order in which they are eliminated.

Since this theorem holds, it will be unnecessary to investigate separately the equation of condition for the various forms of equations; they are already given in the theorems concerning elimination.

7·51 Any equation in n unknowns, of the form $F(x_1, x_2, \ldots x_n) = 0$, provided its equation of condition be satisfied, gives a solution for each of the unknowns as follows: Let x_k be any one of the unknowns; let P_1, P_2, P_3, etc., be the coefficients of those terms in $F(x_1, x_2, \ldots x_n)$ in which x_k is positive, and Q_1, Q_2, Q_3, etc., the coefficients of those terms in which x_k is negative. The solution then is

$$\prod Q \subset x_k \subset \sum -P, \quad \text{or} \quad x_k = \prod Q + u \cdot \sum -P, \text{ where } u \text{ is arbitrary.}$$

(a) By 6·11, for some f and some f', $F(x_1, x_2, \ldots x_n) = 0$ is equivalent to $f(x_1, x_2, \ldots x_{n-1}) \cdot x_n + f'(x_1, x_2, \ldots x_{n-1}) \cdot -x_n = 0$. Let the coefficients in f be P_1, P_2, P_3, etc., in f' be Q_1, Q_2, Q_3, etc. Then P_1, P_2, P_3, etc., will be the coefficients of those terms in F in which x_k is positive, Q_1, Q_2, Q_3, the coefficients of terms in F in which x_k is negative.

If $f(x_1, x_2, \ldots x_{n-1}) \cdot x_n$ be regarded as a function of the variables, $x_1, x_2, \ldots x_{n-1}$, its coefficients will be $P_1 x_n$, $P_2 x_n$, $P_3 x_n$, etc.

And if $f'(x_1, x_2, \ldots x_{n-1}) \cdot -x_n$ be regarded as a function of x_1, x_2, $\ldots x_{n-1}$, its coefficients will be $Q_1 -x_n$, $Q_2 -x_n$, $Q_3 -x_n$, etc.

Hence, by 6·42,

$$f(x_1, x_2, \ldots x_{n-1}) \cdot x_n + f'(x_1, x_2, \ldots x_{n-1}) \cdot -x_n = 0$$

is equivalent to $\Psi(x_1, x_2, \ldots x_{n-1}) = 0$, where Ψ is a function in which the coefficients are $(P_1 x_n + Q_1 -x_n)$, $(P_2 x_n + Q_2 -x_n)$, $(P_3 x_n + Q_3 -x_n)$, etc.

And $\Psi(x_1, x_2, \ldots x_{n-1}) = 0$ is equivalent to $F(x_1, x_2, \ldots x_n) = 0$. By 7·41, the complete resultant of the elimination of $x_1, x_2, \ldots x_{n-1}$ from $\Psi(x_1, x_2, \ldots x_{n-1}) = 0$ will be the equation to 0 of the product of its coefficients,—

$$\prod_r (P_r x_n + Q_r -x_n) = 0$$

But any expression of the form $P_r x_n + Q_r -x_n$ is a normal form function of x_n. Hence, by 6·43,

$$\prod_r (P_r x_n + Q_r -x_n) = \prod_r P_r x_n + \prod_r Q_r -x_n$$

By 7·2 and 7·24, the solution of $\prod_r P_r x_n + \prod_r Q_r -x_n = 0$ is

$$\prod Q \subset x_n \subset -\{\prod P\}, \quad \text{or} \quad x_n = \prod Q + u \cdot -\{\prod P\}$$

And [5·951] $-\{\prod P\} = \sum -P$.

(b) Since the order of terms in a function is immaterial, and for any order of the variables in the argument of a function there is a normal form of the function, x_n in the above may be any one of the variables in $F(x_1, x_2, \ldots x_n)$, and $f(x_1, x_2, \ldots x_{n-1})$ and $f'(x_1, x_2, \ldots x_{n-1})$ each some function of the remaining $n - 1$ variables. Therefore, the theorem holds for any one of the variables, x_k.

That a single equation gives a solution for any number of unknowns is another peculiarity of the algebra, due to the fact that from a single equation any number of unknowns may be eliminated.

As an example of the last theorem, we give the solution of the exemplar equation in two unknowns, first directly from the theorem, then by elimination and solution for each unknown separately.

(1) $A \, x \, y + B - x \, y + C \, x - y + D - x - y = 0$ has the equation of condition,

$$A \, B \, C \, D = 0$$

Provided this be satisfied, the solutions for x and y are

$$B \, D \, \mathsf{c} \, x \, \mathsf{c} - A + -C, \qquad \text{or} \qquad x = B \, D + u \, (-A + -C)$$

$$C \, D \, \mathsf{c} \, y \, \mathsf{c} - A + -B, \qquad \text{or} \qquad y = C \, D + u \, (-A + -B)$$

(2) $A \, x \, y + B - x \, y + C \, x - y + D - x - y = 0$ is equivalent to

$$(a) \quad (A \, x + B - x) \, y + (C \, x + D - x) - y = 0$$

and to (b) $\quad (A \, y + C - y) \, x + (B \, y + D - y) - x = 0$

Eliminating y from (a), we have

$$(A \, x + B - x)(C \, x + D - x) = A \, C \, x + B \, D - x = 0$$

The equation of condition with respect to x is, then,

$$(A \, C)(B \, D) = A \, B \, C \, D = 0$$

And the solution for x is

$$B \, D \, \mathsf{c} \, x \, \mathsf{c} - (A \, C), \quad \text{or} \quad x = B \, D + u \cdot -(A \, C). \quad \text{And} \quad -(A \, C) = -A + -C$$

Eliminating x from (b), we have

$$(A \, y + C - y)(B \, y + D - y) = A \, B \, y + C \, D - y = 0$$

The equation of condition with respect to y is, then, $A \, B \, C \, D = 0$. And the solution for y is

$$C \, D \, \mathsf{c} \, y \, \mathsf{c} - (A \, B), \quad \text{or} \quad y = C \, D + v \cdot -(A \, B). \quad \text{And} \quad -(A \, B) = -A + -B$$

Another method of solution for equations in two unknowns, x and y, would be to solve for y and for $-y$ in terms of the coefficients, with x and u as undetermined parameters, then eliminate y by substituting this value of it in the original equation, and solve for x. By a similar substitution, x may then be eliminated and the resulting equation solved for y. This method may inspire more confidence on the part of those unfamiliar with this algebra, since it is a general algebraic method, except that in other algebras more than one equation is required.

The solution of $A \, x \, y + B - x \, y + C \, x - y + D - x - y = 0$ for y is

$$y = (C \, x + D - x) + u \cdot -(A \, x + B - x) = (C + u - A) \, x + (D + u - B) - x$$

The solution for $-y$ is

$$-y = (A\,x + B\,-x) + v\cdot-(C\,x + D\,-x) = (A + v\,-C)\,x + (B + v\,-D)\,-x$$

Substituting these values for y and $-y$ in the original equation,

$$(A\,x + B\,-x)[(C + u\,-A)\,x + (D + u\,-B)\,-x]$$
$$+ (C\,x + D\,-x)[(A + v\,-C)\,x + (B + v\,-D)\,-x]$$
$$= A\,(C + u\,-A)\,x + B\,(D + u\,-B)\,-x + C\,(A + v\,-C)\,x + D\,(B + v\,-D)\,-x$$
$$= A\,C\,x + B\,D\,-x = 0.$$

Hence $$B\,D \subset x \subset -A + -C.$$

Theoretically, this method can be extended to equations in any number of unknowns: practically, it is too cumbersome and tedious to be used at all.

7·52 Any equation in n unknowns, of the form

$$F(x_1, x_2, \ldots x_n) = f(x_1, x_2, \ldots x_n)$$

gives a solution for each of the unknowns as follows: Let x_k be any one of the unknowns; let $P_1, P_2, P_3, \ldots Q_1, Q_2, Q_3, \ldots$ be the coefficients in F, and $M_1, M_2, M_3, \ldots N_1, N_2, N_3, \ldots$ the coefficients of the corresponding terms in f, so that P_r and M_r are coefficients of terms in which x_k is positive, and Q_r and N_r are coefficients of terms in which x_k is negative. The solution for x_k then is

$$\prod_r (Q_r\,-N_r + -Q_r\,N_r) \subset x_k \subset \sum_r (P_r\,M_r + -P_r\,-M_r)$$

or $$x_k = \prod_r (Q_r\,-N_r + -Q_r\,N_r) + u\cdot\sum_r (P_r\,M_r + -P_r\,-M_r)$$

By 7·13, $F(x_1, x_2, \ldots x_n) = f(x_1, x_2, \ldots x_n)$ is equivalent to $\Phi(x_1, x_2, \ldots x_n) = 0$, where Φ is a function such that if A_r and B_r be coefficients of any two corresponding terms in F and f, then the coefficient of the corresponding term in Φ will be $A_r\,-B_r + -A_r\,B_r$. Hence, by 7·51, the solution will be

$$\prod_r (Q_r\,-N_r + -Q_r\,N_r) \subset x_k \subset \sum_r -(P_r\,-M_r + -P_r\,M_r)$$

or $$x_k = \prod_r (Q_r\,-N_r + -Q_r\,N_r) + u\cdot\sum_r -(P_r\,-M_r + -P_r\,M_r)$$

And [6·4] $-(P_r\,-M_r + -P_r\,M_r) = (P_r\,M_r + -P_r\,-M_r)$.

7·53 The condition that m equations in n unknowns, each of the form $F(x_1, x_2, \ldots x_n) = 0$, may be regarded as simultaneous, is as follows: Let the coefficients of the terms in F^1, in the equation $F^1(x_1, x_2, \ldots x_n) = 0$, be $P_1{}^1, P_2{}^1, P_3{}^1, \ldots Q_1{}^1, Q_2{}^1, Q_3{}^1, \ldots$; let the coefficients of the corresponding terms in F^2, in the equation $F^2(x_1, x_2, \ldots x_n) = 0$, be $P_1{}^2$, $P_2{}^2$, $P_3{}^2$, $\ldots$ $Q_1{}^2$, $Q_2{}^2$, $Q_3{}^2$, $\ldots$; the coefficients of the corresponding terms in F^m, in the equation $F^m(x_1, x_2, \ldots x_n) = 0$, be $P_1{}^m$, $P_2{}^m$, $P_3{}^m$, $\ldots$ $Q_1{}^m$, $Q_2{}^m$, $Q_3{}^m$, $\ldots$. The condition then is

$$\prod_r [\sum_h P_r{}^h] \times \prod_r [\sum_h Q_r{}^h] = 0$$

Or if $C_r{}^h$ be any coefficient, whether P or Q, in F^h, the condition is

$$\prod_r [\sum_h C_r{}^h] = 0$$

And the solution which n such equations give, on this condition, for any one of the unknowns, x_k, is as follows: Let $P_1{}^h$, $P_2{}^h$, $P_3{}^h$, $\ldots$ be the coefficients of those terms, in any one of the equations $F^h = 0$, in which x_k is positive, and let $Q_1{}^h$, $Q_2{}^h$, $Q_3{}^h$, $\ldots$ be the coefficients of those terms, in $F^h = 0$, in which x_k is negative. The solution then is

$$\prod_r [\sum_h Q_r{}^h] \subset x_k \subset \sum_r [\prod_h -P_r{}^h]$$

or
$$x_k = \prod_r [\sum_h Q_r{}^h] + u \cdot \sum_r [\prod_h -P_r{}^h]$$

By 6·42, m equations in n unknowns, each of the form $F(x_1, x_2, \ldots x_n) = 0$, are together equivalent to the single equation $\Phi(x_1, x_2, \ldots x_n) = 0$, where each of the coefficients in Φ is the sum of the corresponding coefficients in $F^1, F^2, F^3, \ldots F^m$. That is, if $P_r{}^1$, $P_r{}^2$, $\ldots P_r{}^m$ be the coefficients of corresponding terms in $F^1, F^2, \ldots F^m$, then the coefficient of the corresponding term in Φ will be

$$P_r{}^1 + P_r{}^2 + \ldots + P_r{}^m, \qquad \text{or} \qquad \sum_h P_r{}^h$$

and if $Q_r{}^1$, $Q_r{}^2$, $\ldots Q_r{}^m$ be the coefficients of corresponding terms in $F^1, F^2, \ldots F^m$, then the coefficient of the corresponding term in Φ will be

$$Q_r{}^1 + Q_r{}^2 + \ldots + Q_r{}^m, \qquad \text{or} \qquad \sum_h Q_r{}^h$$

The equation of condition for $\Phi = 0$, and hence the condition that $F^1 = 0$, $F^2 = 0$, $\ldots F^m = 0$ may be regarded as simultaneous, is the equation to 0 of the product of the coefficients in Φ; that is,

$$\sum_h P_1{}^h \times \sum_h P_2{}^h \times \sum_h P_3{}^h \times \ldots \times \sum_h Q_1{}^h \times \sum_h Q_2{}^h \times \sum_h Q_3{}^h \times \ldots = 0$$

or
$$\prod_r [\sum_h P_r{}^h] \times \prod_r [\sum_h Q_r{}^h] = 0$$

And by 7·51, the solution of $\Phi(x_1, x_2, \ldots x_n) = 0$ for x_k is

$$\prod_r [\sum_h Q_r{}^h] \subset x_k \subset \sum_r -[\sum_h P_r{}^h]$$

or
$$x_k = \prod_r \,[\sum_h Q_r{}^h] + u \cdot \sum_r -[\sum_h P_r{}^h]$$

And by 5·95, $-[\sum_h P_r{}^h] = \prod_h -P_r{}^h$.

7·54 The condition that m equations in n unknowns, each of the form

$$F(x_1, x_2, \ldots x_n) = f(x_1, x_2, \ldots x_n)$$

may be regarded as simultaneous, is as follows: Let the coefficients in F^1, in the equation $F^1 = f^1$, be $P_1{}^1, P_2{}^1, P_3{}^1, \ldots Q_1{}^1, Q_2{}^1, Q_3{}^1, \ldots$, and let the coefficients of the corresponding terms in f^1, in the equation $F^1 = f^1$, be $M_1{}^1, M_2{}^1, M_3{}^1, \ldots N_1{}^1, N_2{}^1, N_3{}^1, \ldots$; let the coefficients of the corresponding terms in F^2, in the equation $F^2 = f^2$, be $P_1{}^2, P_2{}^2, P_3{}^2, \ldots Q_1{}^2, Q_2{}^2, Q_3{}^2, \ldots$, and let the coefficients of the corresponding terms in f^2 be $M_1{}^2, M_2{}^2, M_3{}^2, \ldots N_1{}^2, N_2{}^2, N_3{}^2, \ldots$; let the coefficients of the corresponding terms in F^m, in the equation $F^m = f^m$, be $P_1{}^m, P_2{}^m, P_3{}^m, \ldots Q_1{}^m, Q_2{}^m, Q_3{}^m, \ldots$, and let the coefficients of the corresponding terms in f^m be $M_1{}^m, M_2{}^m, M_3{}^m, \ldots N_1{}^m, N_2{}^m, N_3{}^m, \ldots$. The condition then is

$$\prod_r \,[\sum_h (P_r{}^h - M_r{}^h + -P_r{}^h M_r{}^h)] \times \prod_r \,[\sum_h (Q_r{}^h - N_r{}^h + -Q_r{}^h N_r{}^h)] = 0$$

or if $A_r{}^h$ represent any coefficient in F^h, whether P or Q, and $B_r{}^h$ represent the corresponding coefficient in f^h, whether M or N, the condition is

$$\prod_r \,[\sum_h (A_r{}^h - B_r{}^h + -A_r{}^h B_r{}^h)] = 0$$

And the solution which m such equations give, on this condition, for any one of the unknowns, x_k, is as follows: Let $P_r{}^h$ and $M_r{}^h$ be the coefficients of those terms, in any one of the equations $F^h = f^h$, in which x_k is positive, and let $Q_r{}^h$ and $N_r{}^h$ be the coefficients of the terms, in $F^h = f^h$, in which x_k is negative. The solution then is

$$\prod_r \,[\sum_h (Q_r{}^h - N_r{}^h + -Q_r{}^h N_r{}^h)] \subset x_k \subset \sum_r \,[\prod_h (P_r{}^h M_r{}^h + -P_r{}^h -M_r{}^h)]$$

or $\quad x_k = \prod_r \,[\sum_h (Q_r{}^h - N_r{}^h + -Q_r{}^h N_r{}^h)] + u \cdot \sum_r \,[\prod_h (P_r{}^h M_r{}^h + -P_r{}^h -M_r{}^h)]$

By 7·13, $F^h(x_1, x_2, \ldots x_n) = f^h(x_1, x_2, \ldots x_n)$ is equivalent to $\Psi(x_1, x_2, \ldots x_n) = 0$, where Ψ is a function such that if $Q_r{}^h$ and $N_r{}^h$ be coefficients of corresponding terms in F^h and f^h, the coefficient of the corresponding term in Ψ will be $Q_r{}^h - N_r{}^h + -Q_r{}^h N_r{}^h$, and if $P_r{}^h$ and $M_r{}^h$ be coefficients of corresponding terms in F^h and f^h, the coefficient of the corresponding term in Ψ will be $P_r{}^h - M_r{}^h + -P_r{}^h M_r{}^h$. And $-(P_r{}^h - M_r{}^h + -P_r{}^h M_r{}^h) = P_r{}^h M_r{}^h + -P_r{}^h -M_r{}^h$.

Hence the theorem follows from 7·53.

$F(x_1, x_2, \ldots x_n) = f(x_1, x_2, \ldots x_n)$ is a perfectly general equation, since F and f may be any expressions in the algebra, developed as functions of the variables in question. $7 \cdot 54$ gives, then, the condition and the solution of any number of simultaneous equations, in any number of unknowns, for each of the unknowns. This algebra particularly lends itself to generalization, and this is its most general theorem. It is the most general theorem concerning solutions in the whole of mathematics.

Boole's General Problem.—Boole proposed the following as the general problem of the algebra of logic.[11]

Given any equation connecting the symbols x, y, $\ldots$ w, z, $\ldots$. Required to determine the logical expression of any class expressed in any way by the symbols x, y, $\ldots$ in terms of the remaining symbols w, z, $\ldots$. We may express this: Given $t = f(x, y, \ldots)$ and $\Phi(x, y, \ldots) = \Psi(w, z, \ldots)$; to determine t in terms of w, z, $\ldots$. This is perfectly general, since if x, y, $\ldots$ and w, z, $\ldots$ are connected by any number of equations, there is, by $7 \cdot 1$ and $5 \cdot 72$, a single equation equivalent to them all. The rule for solution may be stated: Reduce both $t = f(x, y, \ldots)$ and $\Phi(x, y, \ldots) = \Psi(w, z, \ldots)$ to the form of equations with one member 0, combine them by addition into a single equation, eliminate x, y, $\ldots$, and solve for t. By $7 \cdot 1$, the form of equation with one member 0 is equivalent to the other form. And by $5 \cdot 72$, the sum of two equations with one member 0 is equivalent to the equations added. Hence the single equation resulting from the process prescribed by our rule will contain all the data. The result of eliminating will be the complete resultant which is independent of these, and the solution for t will thus be the most complete determination of t in terms of w, z, $\ldots$ afforded by the data.

Consequences of Equations in General.—A word of caution with reference to the manipulation of equations in this algebra may not be out·of place. As compared with other algebras, the algebra of logic gives more room for choice in this matter. Further, in the most useful applications of the algebra, there are frequently problems of procedure which are not resolved simply by eliminating this and solving for that. The choice of method must, then, be determined with reference to the end in view. But the following general rules are of service:

(1) Get the completest possible expression $= 0$, or the least inclusive possible expression $= 1$.

$a + b + c + \ldots = 0$ gives $a = 0$, $b = 0$, $c = 0$, $\ldots$, $a + b = 0$, $a + c = 0$,

[11]*Laws of Thought*, p. 140.

etc. But $a = 0$ will not generally give $a + b = 0$, etc. Also, $a = 1$ gives $a + b = 1$, $a + \ldots = 1$, but $a + b = 1$ will not generally give $a = 1$.

(2) Reduce any number of equations, with which it is necessary to deal, to a single *equivalent* equation, by first reducing each to the form in which one member is 0 and then adding. The various constituent equations can always be recovered if that be desirable, and the single equation gives other derivatives also, besides being easier to manipulate. Do not forget that it is possible so to combine equations that the result is less general than the data. If we have $a = 0$ and $b = 0$, we have also $a = b$, or $a b = 0$, or $a + b = 0$, according to the mode of combination. But $a + b = 0$ is equivalent to the data, while the other two are less comprehensive.

A general method by which consequences of a given equation, in any desired terms, may be derived, was formulated by Poretsky,[12] and is, in fact, a corollary of his Law of Forms, given above. We have seen that this law may be formulated as the principle that if $a = b$, and therefore $a -b + -a b = 0$ and $a b + -a -b = 1$, then any t is such that $a -b + -a b \subset t$ and $t \subset a b + -a -b$, or any $t =$ the t which contains the "zero member" of the set of equations equivalent to $a = b$, and is contained in the "whole member" of this set. Now if $x \subset t$, $u x \subset t$, for any u whatever, and thus the "zero member" of the Law of Forms may be multiplied by any arbitrarily chosen u which we choose to introduce. Similarly, if $t \subset y$, then $t \subset y + v$, and the "whole member" in the Law of Forms may be increased by the addition of any arbitrarily chosen v. This gives the Law of Consequences.

7·6 If $a = b$, then $t = (a b + -a -b + u) t + v (a -b + -a b) -t$, where u and v are arbitrary.

[7·1·12] If $a = b$, then $a -b + -a b = 0$ and $a b + -a -b = 1$.

Hence $(a b + -a -b + u) t + v (a -b + -a b) -t = (1 + u) t + v \cdot 0 \cdot -t = t$.

This law includes all the possible consequences of the given equation. First, let us see that it is more general than the previous formulae of elimination and solution. Given the equation $A x + B -x = 0$, and choosing $A B$ for t, we should get the elimination resultant.

If $A x + B -x = 0$, then $A B = (-A x + -B -x + u) A B$
$$+ v (A x + B -x)(-A + -B)$$
$$= u A B + v (A -B x + -A B -x).$$

Since u and v are both arbitrary and may assume the value 0, therefore $A B = 0$.

[12] *Sept lois, etc.*, Chap. XII.

But this is only one of the unlimited expressions for $A\,B$ which the law gives. Letting $u = 0$, and $v = 1$, we have

$$A\,B = A\,{-B}\,x\,{+}\,{-A}\,B\,{-x}$$

Letting $u = A$ and $v = B$, we have

$$A\,B = A\,B\,{+}\,{-A}\,B\,{-x}$$

And so on. But it will be found that every one of the equivalents of $A\,B$ which the law gives will be null.

Choosing x for our t, we should get the solution.

If $A\,x + B\,{-x} = 0$, then $x = (-A\,x\,{+}\,{-B}\,{-x}\,{+}\,u)\,x + v\,(A\,x + B\,{-x})\,{-x}$
$$= (-A + u)\,x + v\,B\,{-x}.$$

Since u and v may both assume the value 0,

$$x = -A\,x, \qquad \text{or} \qquad x \subset -A \tag{1}$$

And since u and v may both assume the value 1,

$$x = x + B\,{-x}, \qquad \text{or} \qquad B\,{-x} \subset x$$

But if $B\,{-x} \subset x$, then $B\,{-x} = (B\,{-x})\,x = 0$, or $B \subset x$ (2)
Hence, (1) and (2), $B \subset x \subset -A$.

When $u = 0$ and $v = 1$, the Law of Consequences becomes simply the Law of Forms. For these values in the above,

$$x = -A\,x + B\,{-x}$$

which is the form which Poretsky gives the solution for x.

The introduction of the arbitraries, u and v, in the Law of Consequences extends the principle stated by the Law of Forms so that it covers not only all equivalents of the given equation but also all the non-equivalent inferences. As the explanation which precedes the proof suggests, this is accomplished by allowing the limits of the function equated to t to be expressed in all possible ways. If $a = b$, and therefore, by the Law of Forms,

$$t = (a\,b\,{+}\,{-a}\,{-b})\,t + (a\,{-b}\,{+}\,{-a}\,b)\,{-t}$$

the lower limit of t, 0, is expressed as $a\,{-b}\,{+}\,{-a}\,b$, and the upper limit of t, 1, is expressed as $a\,b\,{+}\,{-a}\,{-b}$. In the Law of Consequences, the lower limit, 0, is expressed as $v\,(a\,{-b}\,{+}\,{-a}\,b)$, that is, in all possible ways which can be derived from its expression as $a\,{-b}\,{+}\,{-a}\,b$; and the upper limit, 1, is expressed as $a\,b\,{+}\,{-a}\,{-b}\,{+}\,u$, that is, in all possible ways which can be derived from its expression as $a\,b\,{+}\,{-a}\,{-b}$. Since an expression of the form

$$t = (a\,b\,{+}\,{-a}\,{-b})\,t + (a\,{-b}\,{+}\,{-a}\,b)\,{-t}$$

or of the form $t = (a\,b + -a\,-b + u)\,t + v\,(a\,-b + -a\,b)\,-t$
determines t only in the sense of thus expressing its limits, and the Law of Consequences covers all possible ways of expressing these limits, it covers all possible inferences from the given equation. The number of such inferences is, of course, unlimited. The number expressible in terms of n elements will be the number of derivatives from an equation with one member 0 and the other member expanded with reference to n elements. The number of constituent terms of this expanded member will be 2^n, and the number of combinations formed from them will be 2^{2^n}. Therefore, since $p_1 + p_2 + p_3 + \ldots = 0$ gives $p_1 = 0$, $p_2 = 0$, $p_3 = 0$, etc., this is the number of consequences of a given equation which are expressible in terms of n elements.

As one illustration of this law, Poretsky gives the sixteen determinations of a in terms of the three elements, a, b, and c, which can be derived from the premises of the syllogism in *Barbara*: [13]

$$\text{If all } a \text{ is } b, \qquad a\,-b = 0,$$
$$\text{and all } b \text{ is } c, \qquad b\,-c = 0,$$
$$\text{then } a\,-b + b\,-c = 0, \text{ and hence,}$$

$$a = a\,(b + -c) = a\,(b + c) = a\,(-b + c) = a + b\,-c = a\,b = a\,(b\,c + -b\,-c)$$
$$= b\,-c + a\,(b\,c + -b\,-c) = a\,c = b\,-c + a\,c = a\,(-b + c) + -a\,b\,-c = a\,b\,c$$
$$= b\,-c + a\,b\,c = a\,(b\,c + -b\,-c) + -a\,b\,-c = a\,c + -a\,b\,-c = a\,b\,c + -a\,b\,-c$$

The Inverse Problem of Consequences.—Just as the Law of Consequences expresses any inference from $a = b$ by taking advantage of the fact that if $a\,-b + -a\,b = 0$, then $(a\,-b + -a\,b)\,v = 0$, and if $a\,b + -a\,-b = 1$, then $a\,b + -a\,-b + u = 1$; so the formula for any equation which will *give the inference $a = b$* can be expressed by taking advantage of the fact that if $v\,(a\,b + -a\,-b) = 1$, then $a\,b + -a\,-b = 1$, and if $a\,-b + -a\,b + u = 0$, then $a\,-b + -a\,b = 0$. We thus get Poretsky's Law of Causes, or as it would be better translated, the Law of Sufficient Conditions.[14]

7·7 If for some value of u and some value of v

$$t = v\,(a\,b + -a\,-b)\,t + (a\,-b + -a\,b + u)\,-t,$$

then $a = b$.

If $t = v\,(a\,b + -a\,-b)\,t + (a\,-b + -a\,b + u)\,-t$, then [7·1, 5·72]

$[v\,(a\,b + -a\,-b)\,t + (a\,-b + -a\,b + u)\,-t]\,-t = 0$

$$= (a\,-b + -a\,b + u)\,-t = (a\,-b + -a\,b)\,-t + u\,-t = 0$$

---

[13] *Ibid.*, pp. 98 *ff.*
[14] *Ibid.*, Chap. XXIII.

Hence $(a -b + -a\, b) -t = 0$ (1)

Hence also [5·7] $t = v\,(a\, b + -a\, -b)\, t$, and [4·9]

$$t\cdot -[v\,(a\, b + -a\, -b)] = 0 = t\,(-v + a\, -b + -a\, b) = t -v + (a\, -b + -a\, b)\, t$$

Hence [5·72] $(a -b + -a\, b)\, t = 0$ (2)

By (1) and (2), $(a -b + -a\, b)(t + -t) = 0 = a -b + -a\, b$.

Hence [7·1] $a = b$.

Both the Law of Consequences and the Law of Sufficient Conditions are more general than the Law of Forms, which may be derived from either.

Important as are these contributions of Poretsky, the student must not be misled into supposing that by their use any desired consequence or sufficient condition of a given equation can be found automatically. The only sense in which these laws give results automatically is the sense in which they make it possible to exhaust the list of consequences or conditions expressible in terms of a given set of elements. And since this process is ordinarily too lengthy for practical purposes, these laws are of assistance principally for testing results suggested by some subsidiary method or by "intuition". One has to discover for himself what values of the arbitraries u and v will give the desired result.

V. Fundamental Laws of the Theory of Inequations

In this algebra, the assertory or copulative relations are $=$ and $\mathbf{c}$. The denial of $a = b$ may conveniently be symbolized in the customary way:

8·01 $a \neq b$ is equivalent to "$a = b$ is false". Def.

We might use a symbol also for "$a \mathbf{c} b$ is false". But since $a \mathbf{c} b$ is equivalent to $a\, b = a$ and to $a -b = 0$, its negative may be represented by $a\, b \neq a$ or by $a -b \neq 0$. It is less necessary to have a separate symbolism for "$a \mathbf{c} b$ is false", since "a is not contained in b" is seldom met with in logic except where a and b are mutually exclusive,—in which case $a\, b = 0$.

For every proposition of the form "If P is true, then Q is true", there is another, "If Q is false, then P is false". This is the principle of the *reductio ad absurdum*,—or the simplest form of it. In terms of the relations $=$ and $\neq$, the more important forms of this principle are:

(1) "If $a = b$, then $c = d$", gives also, "If $c \neq d$, then $a \neq b$".

(2) "If $a = b$, then $c = d$ and $h = k$", gives also, "If $c \neq d$, then $a \neq b$", and "If $h \neq k$, then $a \neq b$".

(3) "If $a = b$ and $c = d$, then $h = k$", gives also, "If $a = b$ and $h \neq k$, then $c \neq d$", and "If $c = d$ and $h \neq k$, then $a \neq b$".

(4) "$a = b$ is equivalent to $c = d$", gives also, "$a \neq b$ is equivalent to $c \neq d$".

(5) "$a = b$ is equivalent to the set, $c = d$, $h = k$, ...," gives also, "$a \neq b$ is equivalent to 'Either $c \neq d$ or $h \neq k$, or ...'". [15]

The general forms of these principles are themselves theorems of the "calculus of propositions"—the application of this algebra to propositions. But the calculus of propositions, as an applied logic, cannot be *derived* from this algebra without a circle in the proof, for the reasoning in demonstration of the theorems *presupposes* the logical laws of propositions at every step. We must, then, regard these laws of the *reductio ad absurdum*, like the principles of proof previously used, as given us by ordinary logic, which mathematics generally presupposes. In later chapters,[16] we shall discuss another mode of developing mathematical logic—the logistic method—which avoids the paradox of assuming the principles of logic in order to prove them. For the present, our procedure may be viewed simply as an application of the *reductio ad absurdum* in ways in which any mathematician feels free to make use of that principle.

Since the propositions concerning inequations follow immediately, for the most part, from those concerning equations, proof will ordinarily be unnecessary.

Elementary Theorems.—The more important of the elementary propositions are as follows:

8·1 If $a c \neq b c$, then $a \neq b$.
    [2·1]

8·12 If $a + c \neq b + c$, then $a \neq b$.
    [3·37]

8·13 $a \neq b$ is equivalent to $-a \neq -b$.
    [3·2]

8·14 $a + b \neq b$, $a b \neq a$, $-a + b \neq 1$, and $a -b \neq 0$ are all equivalent.
    [4·9]

8·15 If $a + b = x$ and $b \neq x$, then $a \neq 0$.
    [5·7]

8·151 If $a = 0$ and $b \neq x$, then $a + b \neq x$.
    [5·7]

8·16 If $a b = x$ and $b \neq x$, then $a \neq 1$.
    [5·71]

---

[15] "Either . . . or . . ." is here to be interpreted as not excluding the possibility that both should be true.

[16] Chap. IV, Sect. VI.

8·161 If $a = 1$ and $b \neq x$, then $ab \neq x$.

[5·71]

8·17 If $a + b \neq 0$ and $a = 0$, then $b \neq 0$.

[5·72]

8·18 If $ab \neq 1$ and $a = 1$, then $b \neq 1$.

[5·73]

8·17 allows us to drop null terms from any sum $\neq 0$. In this, it gives a rule by which an equation and an inequation may be combined. Suppose, for example, $a + b \neq 0$ and $x = 0$.

$a + b = (a + b)(x + -x) = ax + bx + a-x + b-x$.

Hence $ax + bx + a-x + b-x \neq 0$.

But if $x = 0$, then $ax = 0$ and $bx = 0$.

Hence [8·17] $a-x + b-x \neq 0$.

8·2 If $a \neq 0$, then $a + b \neq 0$.

[5·72]

8·21 If $a \neq 1$, then $ab \neq 1$.

[5·73]

8·22 If $ab \neq 0$, then $a \neq 0$ and $b \neq 0$.

[1·5]

8·23 If $a + b \neq 1$, then $a \neq 1$ and $b \neq 1$.

[4·5]

8·24 If $ab \neq x$ and $a = x$, then $b \neq x$.

[1·2]

8·25 If $a \neq 0$ and $a \subset b$, then $b \neq 0$.

[1·9] If $a \subset b$, then $ab = a$.

Hence if $a \neq 0$ and $a \subset b$, then $ab \neq 0$.

Hence [8·22] $b \neq 0$.

8·26 $a + b \neq 0$ is equivalent to "Either $a \neq 0$ or $b \neq 0$ ".

[5·72]

8·261 $a_1 + a_2 + a_3 + \ldots \neq 0$ is equivalent to "Either $a_1 \neq 0$ or $a_2 \neq 0$ or $a_3 \neq 0$, or $\ldots$ ".

8·27 $ab \neq 1$ is equivalent to "Either $a \neq 1$ or $b \neq 1$ ".

[5·73]

8·271 $a_1 a_2 a_3 \ldots \neq 1$ is equivalent to "Either $a_1 \neq 1$ or $a_2 \neq 1$ or $a_3 \neq 1$ or $\ldots$ ".

The difference between 8·26 and 8·27 and their analogues for equations—5·72 $a + b = 0$ is equivalent to the pair, $a = 0$ and $b = 0$, and

5·73 $a\,b = 1$ is equivalent to the pair, $a = 1$ and $b = 1$—points to a necessary difference between the treatment of equations and the treatment of inequations. Two or more equations may always be combined into an equivalent equation; two or more inequations cannot be combined into an *equivalent* inequation. But, by 8·2, $a + b \neq 0$ is a *consequence* of the pair, $a \neq 0$ and $b \neq 0$.

Equivalent Inequations of Different Forms.—The laws of the equivalence of inequations follow immediately from their analogues for equations.

8·3 $a \neq b$ is equivalent to $a\,-b + -a\,b \neq 0$.
  [7·1]

8·31 $a \neq 1$ is equivalent to $-a \neq 0$.
  [7·12]

8·32   If $\Phi(x_1, x_2, \ldots x_n)$ and $\Psi(x_1, x_2, \ldots x_n)$ be any two functions of the same variables, then

$$\Phi(x_1, x_2, \ldots x_n) \neq \Psi(x_1, x_2, \ldots x_n)$$

is equivalent to $F(x_1, x_2, \ldots x_n) \neq 0$, where F is a function of these same variables and such that, if A_1, A_2, A_3, etc., be the coefficients in Φ and B_1, B_2, B_3, etc., be the coefficients of the corresponding terms in Ψ, then the coefficients of the corresponding terms in F will be $A_1\,-B_1 + -A_1\,B_1$, $A_2\,-B_2 + -A_2\,B_2$, $A_3\,-B_3 + -A_3\,B_3$, etc.
  [7·13]

Poretsky's Law of Forms for inequations will be:

8·33 $a \neq 0$ is equivalent to $t \neq a\,-t + -a\,t$.
  [7·15]

Or in more general form:

8·34 $a \neq b$ is equivalent to $t \neq (a\,b + -a\,-b)\,t + (a\,-b + -a\,b)\,-t$.
  [7·16]

Elimination.—The laws governing the elimination of elements from an inequation are not related to the corresponding laws governing equations by the *reductio ad absurdum*. But these laws follow from the same theorems concerning the limits of functions.

8·4   If $A\,x + B\,-x \neq 0$, then $A + B \neq 0$.
  [6·3] $A\,x + B\,-x \subset A + B$.   Hence [8·25] Q.E.D.

8·41   If the coefficients in any function of n variables, $F(x_1, x_2, \ldots x_n)$, be C_1, C_2, C_3, etc., and if $F(x_1, x_2, \ldots x_n) \neq 0$, then

$$\sum C \neq 0$$

[6·32] $\quad F(x_1, x_2, \ldots x_n) \subset C$. Hence [8·25] Q.E.D.

Thus, to eliminate any number of elements from an inequation with one member 0, reduce the other member to the form of a normal function of the elements to be eliminated. The elimination is then secured by putting $\neq 0$ the sum of the coefficients. The form of elimination resultants for inequations of other types follows immediately from the above. It is obvious that they will be analogous to the elimination resultants of equations as follows: To get the elimination resultant of any inequation, take the elimination resultant of the corresponding equation and replace $=$ by $\neq$, and $\times$ by $+$.

A universal proposition in logic is represented by an equation: "All a is b" by $a - b = 0$, "No a is b" by $a\,b = 0$. Since a particular proposition is always the contradictory of some universal, any particular proposition may be represented by an inequation: "Some a is b" by $a\,b \neq 0$, "Some a is not b" by $a - b \neq 0$. The elimination of the "middle" term from an equation which represents the combination of two universal premises gives the equation which represents the universal conclusion. But elimination of terms from *inequations* does not represent an analogous logical process. Two particulars give no conclusion: a particular conclusion requires one universal premise. The drawing of a particular conclusion is represented by a process which combines an equation with an inequation, by 8·17, and then simplifies the result, by 8·22. For example,

All a is b, $\qquad a - b = 0$. $\qquad \therefore\ a - b\,c = 0$.

Some a is c, $\qquad a\,c \neq 0$. $\qquad \therefore\ a\,b\,c + a - b\,c \neq 0$.

$\qquad\qquad\qquad\qquad\qquad\qquad \therefore\ a\,b\,c \neq 0$. $\qquad$ [8·17]

Some b is c. $\qquad\qquad\qquad\quad \therefore\ b\,c \neq 0$. $\qquad$ [8·22]

"Solution" of an Inequation.—An inequation may be said to have a solution in the sense that for any inequation involving x an equivalent inequation one member of which is x can always be found.

8·5 $\quad A\,x + B - x \neq 0$ is equivalent to $x \neq -A\,x + B - x$.

[7·23]

8·51 $\quad A\,x + B - x \neq 0$ is equivalent to "Either $B - x \neq 0$ or $A\,x \neq 0$",— i. e., to "Either $B \subset x$ is false or $x \subset -A$ is false".

[7·2]

Neither of these "solutions" determines x even within limits. "$B \subset x$ is false" does not mean "B is excluded from x"; it means only "B is not wholly within x". "Either $B \subset x$ is false or $x \subset -A$ is false" does not determine either an upper or a lower limit of x; and limits x only by excluding $B + u - A$ from the range of its possible values. Thus "solutions" of inequations are of small significance.

Consequences and Sufficient Conditions of an Inequation.—By Poretsky's method, the formula for any *consequence* of a given *inequation* follows from the Law of Sufficient Conditions for equations.[17] If for some value of u and some value of v,

$$t = v (a b + -a -b) t + (a -b + -a b + u) -t$$

then $a = b$. Consequently, we have by the *reductio ad absurdum*:

8·52 If $a \neq b$, then $t \neq v (a b + -a -b) t + (a -b + -a b + u) -t$, where u and v are arbitrary.

[7·7]

The formula for the *sufficient conditions* of an *inequation* similarly follows from the Law of Consequences for equations. If $a = b$, then

$$t = (a b + -a -b + u) t + v (a -b + -a b) -t$$

where u and v are arbitrary. Consequently, by the *reductio ad absurdum*:

8·53 If for some value of u and some value of v,

$$t \neq (a b + -a -b + u) t + v (a -b + -a b) -t$$

then $a \neq b$.

[7·6]

System of an Equation and an Inequation.—If we have an equation in one unknown, x, and an inequation which involves x, these may be combined in either of two ways: (1) each may be reduced to the form in which one member is 0 and expanded with reference to all the elements involved in either. Then all the terms which are common to the two may, by 8·17, be dropped from the inequation; (2) the equation may be solved for x, and this value substituted for x in the inequation.

8·6 If $A x + B -x = 0$ and $C x + D -x \neq 0$, then $-A C x + -B D -x \neq 0$.

[5·8] If $C x + D -x \neq 0$, then

$$A C x + -A C x + B D -x + -B D -x \neq 0$$

[17] See Poretsky, *Théorie des non-égalités logiques*, Chaps. 71, 76.

[5·72] If $A x + B -x = 0$, then $A x = 0$ and $B -x = 0$, and hence $A C x = 0$ and $B D -x = 0$.

Hence [8·17] $-A C x + -B D -x \neq 0$.

The result here is not equivalent to the data, since—for one reason— the equation $A C x + B D -x = 0$ is not equivalent to $A x + B -x = 0$. Nevertheless this mode of combination is the one most frequently useful.

8·61 The condition that the equation $A x + B -x = 0$ and the inequation $C x + D -x \neq 0$ may be regarded as simultaneous is, $A B = 0$ and $-A C + -B D \neq 0$, and the determination of x which they give is

$$x \neq (-A -C + A -D) x + (B C + -B D) -x$$

[7·23] $A x + B -x = 0$ is equivalent to $x = -A x + B -x$. Substituting this value of x in the inequation,

$$C (-A x + B -x) + D (A x + -B -x) \neq 0$$

or $(-A C + A D) x + (B C + -B D) -x \neq 0$.

[8·4] A condition of this inequation is

$$(-A C + A D) + (B C + -B D) \neq 0,$$

or $(-A + B) C + (A + -B) D \neq 0$.

But the equation $A x + B -x = 0$ requires that $A B = 0$, and hence that $-A + B = -A$ and $-B + A = -B$.

Hence if the equation be possible and $A B = 0$, the condition of the inequation reduces to $-A C + -B D \neq 0$.

[8·4] If the original inequation be possible, then $C + D \neq 0$. But this condition is already present in $-A C + -B D \neq 0$, since $-A C \subset C$ and hence [8·25] if $-A C \neq 0$, then $C \neq 0$, and $-B D \subset D$ and hence if $-B D \neq 0$, then $D \neq 0$, while [8·26] $C + D \neq 0$ is equivalent to "Either $C \neq 0$ or $D \neq 0$", and $-A C + -B D \neq 0$ is equivalent to "Either $-A C \neq 0$ or $-B D \neq 0$".

Hence the entire condition of the system is expressed by

$$A B = 0 \quad \text{and} \quad -A C + -B D \neq 0$$

And [8·5] the solution of the inequation,

$$(-A C + A D) x + (B C + -B D) -x \neq 0, \quad \text{is}$$
$$x \neq (-A -C + A -D) x + (B C + -B D) -x$$

This method gives the most complete determination of x, in the form of an inequation, afforded by the data.

VI. Note on the Inverse Operations, "Subtraction" and
"Division"

It is possible to define "subtraction" $\{-\}$ and "division" $\{:\}$ in the
algebra. Let $a - b$ be x such that $b + x = a$. And let $a : b$ be y such
that $b\,y = a$. However, these inverse operations are more trouble than
they are worth, and should not be admitted to the system.

In the first place, it is not possible to give these relations a general
meaning. We cannot have in the algebra: (1) If a and b are elements
in K, then $a : b$ is an element in K; nor (2) If a and b are elements in K,
then $a - b$ is an element in K. If $a : b$ is an element, y, then for some y
it must be true that $b\,y = a$. But if $b\,y = a$, then, by 2·2, $a \subset b\,y$ and,
by 5·2, $a \subset b$. Thus if a and b be so chosen that $a \subset b$ is false, then $a : b$
cannot be any element in K. To give $a : b$ a general meaning, it would
be required that every element be contained in every element—that is,
that all elements in K be identical. Similarly, if $a - b$ be an element,
x, in K, then for some x, it must be true that $b + x = a$. But if $b + x = a$,
then, by 2·2, $b + x \subset a$ and, by 5·21, $b \subset a$. Thus if a and b be so chosen
that $b \subset a$ is false, then $a - b$ cannot be any element in K.

Again, $a - b$ and $a : b$ are ambiguous. It might be expected that,
since $a + -a = 1$, the value of $1 - a$ would be unambiguously $-a$. But
$1 - a = x$ is satisfied by any x such that $-a \subset x$. For $1 - a = x$ is equivalent to $x + a = 1$, which is equivalent to

$$-(x + a) = -1 = 0 = -a\,-x$$

And $-a\,-x = 0$ is equivalent to $-a \subset x$. Similarly, it might be expected
that, since $a\,-a = 0$, the value of $0 : a$ would be unambiguously $-a$. But
$0 : a = y$, or $a\,y = 0$, is satisfied by any y such that $y \subset -a$. $a\,y = 0$ and
$y \subset -a$ are equivalent.

Finally, these relations can always be otherwise expressed. The value
of $a : b$ is the value of y in the equation, $b\,y = a$. $b\,y = a$ is equivalent to

$$-a\,b\,y + a\,-b + a\,-y = 0$$

The equation of condition here is $a\,-b = 0$. And the solution, on this
condition, is

$$y = a + u\,(a + -b) = a\,b + u\,-a\,-b, \text{ where } u \text{ is undetermined.}$$

The value of $a - b$ is the value of x in the equation, $b + x = a$. $b + x = a$
is equivalent to

$$\cdot\,-a\,b + -a\,x + a\,-b\,-x = 0$$

The equation of condition here is, $-a\,b = 0$. And the solution, on this condition, is

$$x = a - b + v\,a = a - b + v\,a\,b, \text{ where } v \text{ is undetermined.}$$

In each case, the equation of condition gives the limitation of the meaning of the expression, and the solution expresses the range of its possible values.

CHAPTER III

APPLICATIONS OF THE BOOLE–SCHRÖDER ALGEBRA

There are four applications of the classic algebra of logic which are commonly considered: (1) to spatial entities, (2) to the logical relations of classes, (3) to the logical relations of propositions, (4) to the logic of relations.

The application to spatial entities may be made to continuous and discontinuous segments of a line, or to continuous and discontinuous regions in a plane, or to continuous and discontinuous regions in space of any dimensions. Segments of a line and regions in a plane have both been used as diagrams for the relations of classes and of propositions, but the application to regions in a plane gives the more workable diagrams, for obvious reasons. And since it is only for diagrammatic purposes that the application of the algebra to spatial entities has any importance, we shall confine our attention to regions in a plane.

I. Diagrams for the Logical Relations of Classes

For diagrammatic purposes, the elements of the algebra, a, b, c, etc., will denote continuous or discontinuous regions in a given plane, or in a circumscribed portion of a plane. 1 represents the plane (or circumscribed portion) itself. 0 is the null-region which is supposed to be contained in every region. For any given region, a, $-a$ denotes the plane exclusive of a,—i. e., not-a. The "product", $a \times b$ or $a\,b$, is that region which is common to a and b. If a and b do not "overlap", then $a\,b$ is the null-region, 0. The "sum", $a + b$, denotes the region which is either a or b (or both). In determining $a + b$, the common region, $a\,b$, is not, of course, counted twice over.

$$a + b = a -b + a\,b + -a\,b.$$

This is a difference between $+$ in the Boole-Schröder Algebra and the $+$ of arithmetic. The equation, $a = b$, signifies that a and b denote the same region. $a \subset b$ signifies that a lies wholly within b, that a is included or contained in b. It should be noted that whenever $a = b$, $a \subset b$ and $b \subset a$. Also, $a \subset a$ holds always. Thus the relation $\subset$ is analogous not to $<$ in arithmetic but to $\leq$.

While the laws of this algebra hold for regions, thus denoted, however those regions may be distributed in the plane, not every supposition about their distribution is equally convenient as a diagram for the relations of classes. All will be familiar with Euler's diagrams, invented a century earlier than Boole's algebra. "All *a* is *b*" is represented by a circle *a* wholly within a circle *b*; "No *a* is *b*" by two circles, *a* and *b*, which nowhere intersect; "Some *a* is *b*" and "Some *a* is not *b*" by intersecting circles, sometimes with an asterisk to indicate that division of the diagram which represents the proposition. The defects of this style of diagram are obvious:

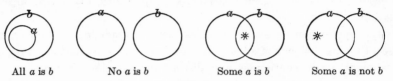

All *a* is *b*   No *a* is *b*   Some *a* is *b*   Some *a* is not *b*

Fig. 1

the representation goes beyond the relation of classes indicated by the proposition. In the case of "All *a* is *b*", the circle *a* falls within *b* in such wise as to suggest that we may infer "Some *b* is not *a*", but this inference is not valid. The representation of "No *a* is *b*" similarly suggests "Some things are neither *a* nor *b*", which also is unwarranted. With these diagrams, there is no way of indicating whether a given region is null. But the general assumption that *no* region of the diagram is null leads to the misinterpretations mentioned, and to others which are similar. Yet Euler's diagrams were in general use until the invention of Venn, and are still doing service in some quarters.

The Venn diagrams were invented specifically to represent the relations of logical classes as treated in the Boole-Schröder Algebra.[1] The principle of these diagrams is that classes be represented by regions in such relation to one another that all the *possible* logical relations of these classes can be indicated in the same diagram. That is, the diagram initially leaves room for any possible relation of the classes, and the actual or given relation can then be specified by indicating that some particular region is null or is not-null. Initially the diagram represents simply the "universe of discourse", or 1. For one element, *a*, $1 = a + -a$.[2] For two elements, *a* and *b*,

$$1 = (a + -a)(b + -b) = a\,b + a\,-b + -a\,b + -a\,-b$$

---

[1] See Venn, *Symbolic Logic*, Chap. v. The first edition of this book appeared before Schröder's *Algebra der Logik*, but Venn adopts the most important alteration of Boole's original algebra—the non-exclusive interpretation of $a + b$.

[2] See above, Chap. ii, propositions 4·8 and 5·92.

For three elements, a, b, and c,

$$1 = (a + -a)(b + -b)(c + -c) = a\,b\,c + a\,b\,-c + a\,-b\,c + -a\,b\,c + a\,-b\,-c$$
$$+ -a\,b\,-c + -a\,-b\,c + -a\,-b\,-c$$

Thus the "universe of discourse" for any number of elements, n, must correspond to a diagram of 2^n divisions, each representing a term in the expansion of 1. If the area within the square in the diagram represent

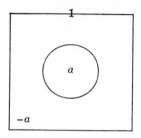
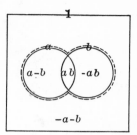

Fig. 2

the universe, and the area within the circle represent the element a, then the remainder of the square will represent its negative, $-a$. If another element, b, is to be introduced into the same universe, then b may be represented by another circle whose periphery cuts the first. The divisions, (1) into a and $-a$, (2) into b and $-b$, will thus be cross-divisions in the universe. If a and b be classes, this arrangement represents all the possible subclasses in the universe;—$a\,b$, those things which are both a and b; $a\,-b$, those things which are a but not b; $-a\,b$, those things which are b but not a; $-a\,-b$, those things which are neither a nor b. The area which represents the product, $a\,b$, will readily be located. We have enclosed by a broken line, in figure 2, the area which represents $a + b$.

The negative of *any* entity is always the plane exclusive of that entity. For example, $-(a\,b + -a\,-b)$, in the above, will be the sum of the other two divisions of the diagram, $a\,-b + -a\,b$.

If it be desired to introduce a third element, c, into the universe, it is necessary to cut each one of the previous subdivisions into two—one part which shall be in c and one part which shall be outside c. This can be be accomplished by introducing a third circle, as in figure 3.

It is not really necessary to draw the square, 1, since the area given to the figure, or the whole page, may as well be taken to represent the universe. But when the square is omitted, it must be remembered that the unenclosed area outside all the lines of the figure is a subdivision of the universe—the entity –*a*, or –*a* –*b*, or –*a* –*b* –*c*, etc., according to the number of elements involved.

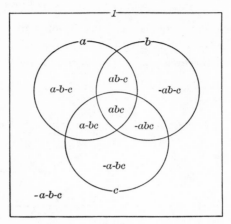

Fig. 3

If a fourth element, *d*, be introduced, it is no longer possible to represent each element by a circle, since a fourth circle could not be introduced in figure 3 so as to cut each previous subdivision into two parts—one part in *d* and one part outside *d*. But this can be done with ellipses.[3] Each

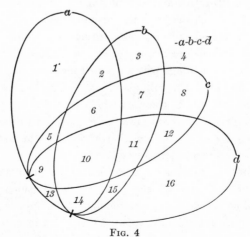

Fig. 4

[3] We have deformed the ellipses slightly and have indicated the two points of junction. This helps somewhat in drawing the diagram, which is most easily done as follows: First, draw the upright ellipse, *a*. Mark a point at the base of it and one on the left. Next,

one of the subdivisions in figure 4 can be "named" by noting whether it is in or outside of each of the ellipses in turn. Thus the area indicated by 6 is $a\,b\,c\,-d$, and the area indicated by 12 is $-a\,-b\,c\,d$. With a diagram of four elements, it requires care, at first, to specify such regions as $a + c$, $a\,c + b\,d$, $b + -d$. These can always be determined with certainty by developing each term of the expression with reference to the missing elements.[4] Thus

$$a\,c + b\,d = a\,c\,(b + -b)(d + -d) + b\,d\,(a + -a)(c + -c)$$

$$= a\,b\,c\,d + a\,b\,c\,-d + a\,-b\,c\,d + a\,-b\,c\,-d + a\,b\,-c\,d + -a\,b\,c\,d + -a\,b\,-c\,d$$

The terms of this sum, in the order given, are represented in figure 4 by the divisions numbered 10, 6, 9, 5, 14, 11, 15. Hence $a\,c + b\,d$ is the region which combines these. With a little practice, one may identify such regions without this tedious procedure. Such an area as $b + -d$ is more easily identified by inspection: it comprises 2, 3, 6, 7, 10, 11, 14, 15, and 1, 4, 5, 8.

Into this diagram for four elements, it is possible to introduce a fifth, e, if we let e be the region *between* the broken lines in figure 5. The principle of the "square diagram" (figure 6) is the same as Venn's: it represents all

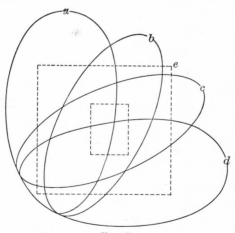

Fig. 5

draw the horizontal ellipse, d, from one of these points to the other, so that the line connecting the two points is common to a and d. Then, draw ellipse b from and *returning to* the base point, and ellipse c from and *returning to* the point on the left. If not done in this way, the first attempts are likely to give twelve or fourteen subdivisions instead of the required sixteen.

4 See Chap. II, 5·91.

the subclasses in a universe of the specified number of elements. No diagram is really convenient for more than four elements, but such are

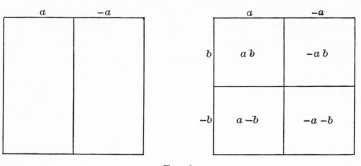

Fig. 6

frequently needed. The most convenient are those made by modifying slightly the square diagram of four terms, at the right in figure 6.[5] Figure 7

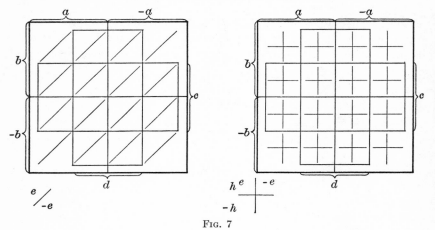

Fig. 7

gives, by this method, the diagrams for five and for six elements. We give also the diagram for seven (figure 8) since this is frequently useful and not easy to make in any other way.

The manner in which any function in the algebra may be specified in a diagram of the proper number of divisions, has already been explained. We must now consider how any asserted relation of elements—any inclu-

[5] See Lewis Carroll, *Symbolic Logic*, for the particular form of the square diagram which we adopt. Mr. Dodgson is able, by this method, to give diagrams for as many as 10 terms, 1024 subdivisions (p. 176).

sion, $a \subset b$, or any equation, $a = b$, or inequation, $a \neq b$—may be represented. Any such relation, or any set of such relations, can be completely specified in these diagrams by taking advantage of the fact that they

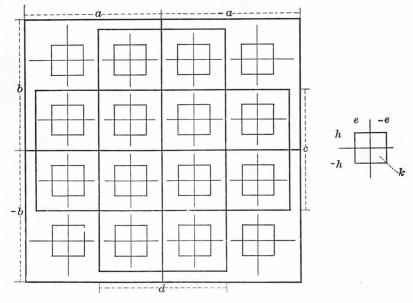

FIG. 8

can always be reduced either to the form of an expression $= 0$ or to the form of an expression $\neq 0$. Any inclusion, $a \subset b$, is equivalent to an equation, $a - b = 0$.[6] And every equation of the form $a = b$ is equivalent to one of the form $a - b + -a \, b = 0$.[7] Thus any inclusion or equation can be represented by some expression $= 0$. Similarly, any inequation of the form $a \neq b$ is equivalent to one of the form $a - b + -a \, b \neq 0$.[8] Thus any asserted relation whatever can be specified by indicating that some region (continuous or discontinuous) either is null, $\{ = 0 \}$, or is not-null, $\{ \neq 0 \}$.

We can illustrate this, and at the same time indicate the manner in which such diagrams are useful, by applying the method to a few syllogisms.

Given: All a is b, $a \subset b$, $a - b = 0$.
    and All b is c, $b \subset c$, $b - c = 0$.

[6] See Chap. II, 4·9.
[7] See Chap. II, 6·4.
[8] See Chap. II, 7·1.

We have here indicated (figure 9) that $a - b$—the a which is not b—is null by striking it out (with horizontal lines). Similarly, we have indicated that all b is c by striking out $b - c$ (with vertical lines). Together, the two operations have eliminated the whole of $a - c$, thus indicating that $a - c = 0$, or "All a is c".

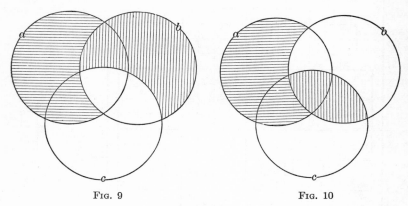

FIG. 9   FIG. 10

For purposes of comparison, we may derive this same conclusion by algebraic processes.[9]

Since $a - b = 0 = a - b (c + -c) = a - b c + a - b - c$,

and $b - c = 0 = b - c (a + -a) = a b - c + -a b - c$,

therefore, $a - b c + a - b - c + a b - c + -a b - c = 0$,

and [5·72] $a b - c + a - b - c = 0 = a - c (b + -b) = a - c$.

The equation in the third line, which combines the two premises, states exactly the same facts which are represented in the diagram. The last equation gives the conclusion, which results from eliminating the middle term, b. Since a diagram will not perform an elimination, we must there "look for" the conclusion.

One more illustration of this kind:

Given: All a is b, $a - b = 0$.

and No b is c, $b c = 0$.

The first premise is indicated (figure 10) by striking out the area $a - b$ (with horizontal lines), the second by striking out $b c$ (with vertical lines). Together, these operations have struck out the whole of $a c$, giving the conclusion $a c = 0$, or "No a is c".

[9] Throughout this chapter, references in square brackets give the number of the theorem in Chap. II by which any unobvious step in proof is taken.

In a given diagram where all the possible classes or regions in the universe are initially represented, as they are by this method of diagramming, we cannot presume that a given subdivision is null or is not-null. The *actual* state of affairs may require that some regions be null, or that some be not-null, or that some be null and others not. Consequently, even when we have struck out the regions which are null, we cannot presume that all the regions *not* struck out are *not*-null. This would be going beyond the premises. All we can say, when we have struck out the null-regions, is that, so far as the premises represented are concerned, any region not struck out *may be* not-null. If, then, we wish to represent the fact that a given region is definitely not-null—that a given class has members, that there is some expression $\neq 0$—we must indicate this by some distinctive mark in the diagram. For this purpose, it is convenient to use asterisks. That $a b \neq 0$, may be indicated by an asterisk in the region $a b$. But here a further difficulty arises. If the diagram involve more than two elements, say, a, b, and c, the region $a b$ will be divided into two parts, $a b c$ and $a b -c$. Now the inequation, $a b \neq 0$, does not tell us that $a b c \neq 0$, and it does not tell us that $a b -c \neq 0$. It tells us only that $a b c + a b -c \neq 0$. If, then, we wish to indicate $a b \neq 0$ by an asterisk in the region $a b$, we shall not be warranted in putting it either inside the circle c or outside c. It belongs in one or the other or both—that is all we know. Hence it is convenient to indicate $a b \neq 0$ by placing an asterisk in *each* of the divisions of $a b$ and connecting them by a broken line, to signify that *at least one* of these regions is not-null (figure 11).

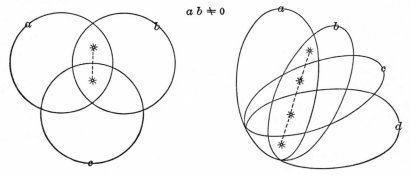

$$a b \neq 0$$

Fig. 11

We shall show later that a particular proposition is best interpreted by an inequation; "Some a is b", the class $a b$ has members, by $a b \neq 0$.

Suppose, then, we have:

Given: All a is b, $a - b = 0$.
    and Some a is c, $a c \neq 0$.

The conclusion, "Some b is c", is indicated (figure 12) by the fact that one of the two connected asterisks must remain—the whole region $a b c$ $+ a - b c$ cannot be null.   But one of them, in $a - b c$, is struck out in indicating the other premise, $a - b = 0$.   Thus $a b c \neq 0$, and hence $a c \neq 0$.

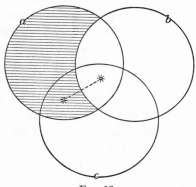

FIG. 12

The entire state of affairs in a universe of discourse may be represented by striking out certain regions, indicating by asterisks that certain regions are not-null, and remembering that any region which is neither struck out nor occupied by an asterisk is in doubt.   Also, the separate subdivisions of a region occupied by *connected* asterisks are in doubt unless all but one of these connected asterisks occupy regions which are struck out.   And any regions which are left in doubt by a given set of premises might, of course, be made specifically null or not-null by an additional premise.

In complicated problems, the use of the diagram is often simpler and more illuminating than the use of transformations, eliminations, and solutions in the algebra.   All the information to be derived from such operations, the diagram gives (for one who can "see" it) at a glance.   Further illustrations will be unnecessary here, since we shall give diagrams in connection with the problems of the next section.

II.   The Application to Classes

The interpretation of the algebra for logical classes has already been explained.[10] a, b, c, etc., are to denote classes taken in extension; that is

---

[10] Chap. II, pp. 121–22.

to say, c signifies, not a class-concept, but the aggregate of all the objects denoted by some class-concept. Thus if $a = b$, the concept of the class a may not be a synonym for the concept of the class b, but the classes a and b must consist of the same members, have the same extension. $a \subset b$ signifies that every member of the class a is also a member of the class b. The "product", $a\,b$, denotes the class of those things which are both members of a and members of b. The "sum", $a + b$, denotes the class of those things which are either members of a or members of b (or members of both). 0 denotes the null-class, or class without members. Various concepts may denote an empty class—"immortal men", "feathered invertebrates", "Julius Caesar's twin," etc.—but all such terms have the same extension; they denote nothing existent. Thus, since classes are taken in extension, there is but one null-class, 0. Since it is a law of the algebra that, for every x, $0 \subset x$, we must accept, in this connection, the convention that the null-class is contained in every class. All the immortal men are members of any class, since there are no such. 1 represents the class "everything", the "universe of discourse", or simply the "universe". This term is pretty well understood. But it may be defined as follows: if a_n be any member of the class a, and X represent the class-concept of the class x, then the "universe of discourse" is the class of all the classes, x, such that "a_n is an X" is either true or false. If "The fixed stars are blind" is neither true nor false, then "fixed stars" and the class "blind" do not belong to the same universe of discourse.

The negative of a, $-a$, is a class such that a and $-a$ have no members in common, and a and $-a$ between them comprise everything in the universe of discourse: $a -a = 0$, "Nothing is both a and not-a", and $a + -a = 1$, "Everything is either a or $-a$".

Since inclusions, $a \subset b$, equations, $a = b$, and inequations, $a \neq b$, represent relations which are asserted to hold between classes, they are capable of being interpreted as logical propositions. And the operations of the algebra—transformations, eliminations, and solutions—are capable of interpretation as processes of reasoning. It would hardly be correct to say that the operations of the algebra represent *the* processes of reasoning from given premises to conclusions: they do indeed represent processes of reasoning, but they seldom attain the result by just those operations which are supposed to characterize the *customary* processes of thinking. In fact, it is the greater generality of the symbolic operations which makes their application to reasoning valuable.

The representation of propositions by inclusions, equations, and inequations, and the interpretation of inclusions, equations, and inequations in the algebra as propositions, offers certain difficulties, due to the fact that the algebra represents relations of extension only, while ordinary logical propositions quite frequently concern relations of intension. In discussing the representation of the four typical propositions, we shall be obliged to consider some of these problems of interpretation.

The universal affirmative, " All a is b ", has been variously represented as,

(1) $a = a\,b$,

(2) $a \subset b$,

(3) $a = v\,b$, where v is undetermined,

(4) $a -b = 0$.

All of these are equivalent.[11] The only possible doubt concerns (3) $a = v\,b$, where v is undetermined. But its equivalence to the others may be demonstrated as follows:

[7·1] $a = v\,b$ is equivalent to $a\cdot-(v\,b) + -a\,v\,b = 0$.
But $a\cdot-(v\,b) + -a\,v\,b = a\,(-v + -b) + -a\,v\,b = a\,-v + a\,-b + -a\,v\,b$.
Hence [5·72] if $a = v\,b$, then $a -b = 0$.
And if $a = a\,b$, then for some value of v (i. e., $v = a$), $a = v\,b$.

These equivalents of " All a is b " would most naturally be read:

(1) The a's are identical with those things which are a's and b's both.

(2) a is contained in b: every member of a is also a member of b.

(3) The class a is identical with some (undetermined) portion of the class b.

(4) The class of those things which are members of a but not members of b is null.

If we examine any one of these symbolic expressions of " All a is b ", we shall discover that not only *may* it hold when $a = 0$, but it *always* holds when $a = 0$. $0 = 0\cdot b$, $0 \subset b$, and $0\cdot-b = 0$, will be true for every element b. And " $0 = v\,b$ for some value of v " is always true—for $v = 0$. Since $a = 0$ means that a has no members, it is thus clear that the algebra requires that " All a is b " be true whenever no members of a exist. The actual use of language is ambiguous on this point. We should hardly say that " All sea serpents have red wings, because there aren't any sea serpents "; yet we understand the hero of the novel who asserts " Whoever

[11] See Chap. ii, 4·9.

enters here must pass over my dead body". This hero does not mean to assert that any one will enter the defended portal over his body: his desire is that the class of those who enter shall be null. The difference of the two cases is this: the *concept* "sea serpent" does not necessarily involve the concept "having red wings", while the concept of "those who enter the portal"—as conceived by the hero—does involve the concept of passing over his body. We readily accept and understand the inclusion of an empty class in some other when the *concept* of the one involves the *concept* of the other—when the relation is one of *intension*. But in this sense, an empty class is not contained in any and every class, but in some only. In order to understand this law of the algebra, "For every x, $0 \subset x$", we must bear in mind two things: (1) that the algebra treats of relations in extension only, and (2) that ordinary language frequently concerns relations of intension, and is usually confined to relations of intension where a null class is involved. The law does *not* accord with the ordinary use of language. This is, however, no observation upon its truth, for it is a necessary law of the relation of classes in extension. It is an immediate consequence of the principle, "For every y, $y \subset 1$", that is, "All members of any class, y, are also members of the class of all things". One cannot accept this last without accepting, by implication, the principle that, in extension, the null-class is contained in every class.

The interpretation of propositions in which no null-class is involved is not subject to any corresponding difficulty, both because in such cases the relations predicated are frequently thought of in extension and because the relation of classes in extension is entirely analogous to their relation in intension except where the class 0 or the class 1 is involved. But the interpretation of the algebra must, in all cases, be confined to extension. In brief: "All a is b" must always be interpreted in the algebra as stating a relation of classes in extension, not of class-concepts, and this requires that, whenever a is an empty class, "All a is b" should be true.

The proposition, "No a is b", is represented by $a\,b = 0$—"Nothing is both a and b", or "Those things which are members of a and of b both, do not exist". Since "No a is b" is equivalent to "All a is not-b", it may also be represented by $a - b = -b$, $a \subset -b$, $b \subset -a$, or $a = v - b$, where v is undetermined. In the case of this proposition, there is no discrepancy between the algebra and the ordinary use of language.

The representation of particular propositions has been a problem to symbolic logicians, partly because they have not clearly conceived the relations of classes and have tried to stretch the algebra to cover traditional relations which hold in intension only. If "Some a is b" be so interpreted that it is false when the class a has no members, then "Some a is b" will not follow from "All a is b", for "All a is b" is true whenever $a = 0$. But on the other hand, if "Some a is b" be *true* when $a = 0$, we have two difficulties: (1) this does not accord with ordinary usage, and (2) "Some a is b" will not, in that case, contradict "No a is b". For whenever there are no members of a (when $a = 0$), "No a is b" ($a\,b = 0$) will be true. Hence if "Some a is b" can be true when $a = 0$, then "Some a is b" and "No a is b" can both be true at once. The solution of the difficulty lies in observing that "Some a is b" as a relation of extension requires that there be some a— that at least one member of the class a exist. Hence, when propositions are interpreted in extension, "Some a is b" *does not follow* from "All a is b", precisely because whenever $a = 0$, "All a is b" will be true. But "Some a is b" does follow from "All a is b, and members of a exist".

To interpret properly "Some a is b", we need only remember that it is the contradictory of "No a is b". Since "No a is b" is interpreted by $a\,b = 0$, "Some a is b" will be $a\,b \neq 0$, that is, "The class of things which are members of a and of b both is not-null".

It is surprising what blunders have been committed in the representation of particular propositions. "Some x is y" has been symbolized by $x\,y = v$, where v is undetermined, and by $u\,x = v\,y$, where u and v are undetermined. Both of these are incorrect, and for the same reason: An "undetermined" element may have the value 0 or the value 1 or any other value. Consequently, both these equations assert precisely nothing at all. They are both of them true a priori, true of every x and y and in all cases. For them to be significant, u and v must not admit the value 0. But in that case they are equivalent to $x\,y \neq 0$, which is much simpler and obeys well-defined laws which are consonant with its meaning.

Since we are to symbolize "All a is b" by $a - b = 0$, it is clear that its contradictory, "Some a is not b", will be $a - b \neq 0$.

To sum up, then: the four typical propositions will be symbolized as follows:

A. All a is b, $a - b = 0$.
E. No a is b, $a\,b = 0$.
I. Some a is b, $a\,b \neq 0$.
O. Some a is not b, $a - b \neq 0$.

Each of these four has various equivalents:[12]

[12] See Chap. II, 4·9 and 8·14.

A. $a - b = 0$, $a = a\,b$, $-a + b = 1$, $-a + -b = -a$, $a \subset b$, and $-b \subset -a$ are all equivalent.

E. $a\,b = 0$, $a = a - b$, $-a + -b = 1$, $-a + b = -a$, $a \subset -b$, and $b \subset -a$ are all equivalent.

I. $a\,b \neq 0$, $a \neq a - b$, $-a + -b \neq 1$, and $-a + b \neq -a$ are all equivalent.

O. $a - b \neq 0$, $a \neq a\,b$, $-a + b \neq 1$, and $-a + -b \neq -a$ are all equivalent.

The reader will easily translate these equivalent forms for himself.

With these symbolic representations of A, E, I and O, let us investigate the relation of propositions traditionally referred to under the topics, "The Square of Opposition", and "Immediate Inference".

That the traditional relation of the two pairs of contradictories holds, is at once obvious. If $a - b = 0$ is true, then $a - b \neq 0$ is false; if $a - b = 0$ is false, then $a - b \neq 0$ is true. Similarly for the pair, $a\,b = 0$ and $a\,b \neq 0$.

The relation of contraries is defined: Two propositions such that both may be false but both cannot be true are "contraries". This relation is traditionally asserted to hold between A and E. It does not hold in extension: it fails to hold in the algebra precisely whenever the subject of the two propositions is a null-class. If $a = 0$, then $a - b = 0$ and $a\,b = 0$.[13] That is to say, if no members of a exist, then from the point of view of extension, "All a is b" and "No a is b" are both true. But if it be assumed or stated that the class a has members ($a \neq 0$), then the relation holds.

$a = a\,(b + -b) = a\,b + a - b$.

Hence if $a \neq 0$, then $a\,b + a - b \neq 0$.

[8·17] If $a\,b + a - b \neq 0$ and $a - b = 0$, then $a\,b \neq 0$. (1)

And if $a\,b + a - b \neq 0$ and $a\,b = 0$, then $a - b \neq 0$. (2)

We may read the last two lines:

(1) If there are members of the class a and all a is b, then "No a is b" is false.

(2) If there are members of the class a and no a is b, then "All a is b" is false.

By tradition, the particular affirmative should follow from the universal affirmative, the particular negative from the universal negative. As has been pointed out, this relation fails to hold when $a = 0$. But it holds whenever $a \neq 0$. We can read $a\,b \neq 0$, in (1) above, as "Some a is b" instead of "'No a is b' is false", and $a - b \neq 0$, in (2), as "Some a is not b" instead of "'All a is b' is false". We then have:

[13] See Chap. II, 1·5.

(1) If there are members of a, and all a is b, then some a is b.

(2) If there are members of a, and no a is b, then some a is not b.

"Subcontraries" are propositions such that both cannot be false but both may be true. Traditionally "Some a is b" and "Some a is not b" are subcontraries. But whenever $a = 0$, $a\,b \neq 0$ and $a\,{-}b \neq 0$ are both false, and the relation fails to hold. When $a \neq 0$, it holds. Since $a\,b = 0$ is "'Some a is b' is false", and $a\,{-}b = 0$ is "'Some a is not b' is false", we can read (1) and (2) above:

(1) If there are members of a, and "Some a is b" is false, then some a is not b.

(2) If there are members of a and "Some a is not b" is false, then some a is b.

To sum up, then: the traditional relations of the "square of opposition" hold in the algebra whenever the subject of the four propositions denotes a class which has members. When the subject denotes a null-class, only the relation of the contradictories holds. The two universal propositions are, in that case, both true, and the two particular propositions both false.

The subject of immediate inference is not so well crystallized by tradition, and for the good reason that it runs against this very difficulty of the class without members. For instance, the following principles would all be accepted by some logicians:

"No a is b"	gives	"No b is a".
"No b is a"	gives	"All b is not-a".
"All b is not-a"	gives	"Some b is not-a".
"Some b is not-a"	gives	"Some not-a is b".
Hence "No a is b"	gives	"Some not-a is b".

"No cows (a) are inflexed gasteropods (b)" implies "Some non-cows are inflexed gasteropods": "No mathematician (a) has squared the circle (b)" implies "Some non-mathematicians *have* squared the circle". These inferences are invalid precisely because the class b—inflexed gasteropods, successful circle-squarers—is an empty class; and because it was presumed that "All b is not-a" gives "Some b is not-a". Those who consider the algebraic treatment of null-classes to be arbitrary will do well to consider the logical situation just outlined with some care. The inference of *any* particular proposition from the corresponding universal requires the assumption that either the class denoted by the subject of the particular proposition or the class denoted by its predicate ("not-b" regarded as the predicate of "Some a is not b") is a class which has members.

The "conversion" of the universal negative and of the particular affirmative is validated by the law $a\,b = b\,a$. "No a is b", $a\,b = 0$, gives $b\,a = 0$, "No b is a". And "Some a is b", $a\,b \neq 0$, gives $b\,a \neq 0$, "Some b is a". Also, "Some a is not b", $a\,{-}b \neq 0$, gives $-b\,a \neq 0$, "Some not-b is a". The "converse" of the universal affirmative is simply the "converse" of the corresponding particular, the inference of which from the universal has already been discussed.

What are called "obverses"—i. e., two equivalent propositions with the same subject and such that the predicate of one is the negative of the predicate of the other—are merely alternative readings of the same equation, or depend upon the law, $-(-a) = a$[14]. Since $x\,y = 0$ is "No x is y", $a\,{-}b = 0$, which is "All a is b", is also "No a is not-b". And since $a\,b = 0$ is equivalent to $a\,{-}(-b) = 0$, "No a is b" is equivalent to "All a is not-b".

A convenient diagram for immediate inferences can be made by putting S (subject) and P (predicate) in the *center* of the circles assigned to them, $-S$ between the two divisions of $-S$, and $-P$ between its two constituent divisions. The eight arrows indicate the various ways in which the dia-

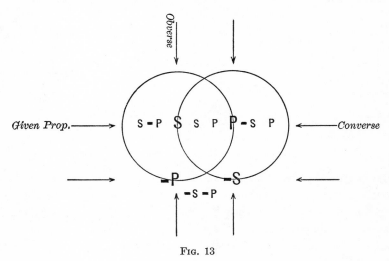

Fɪɢ. 13

gram may be read, and thus suggest all the immediate inferences which are valid. For example, the arrow marked "converse" indicates the two terms which will appear in the converse of the given proposition and the order in which they occur. *In* this diagram, we must specify the null and

[14] See Chap. ɪɪ, 2·8.

not-null regions indicated by the given proposition. And we may—if we wish—add the qualification that the classes, S and P, have members.

If "No S is P", and S and P have members:

$$S P = 0, \qquad S \neq 0, \qquad P \neq 0$$

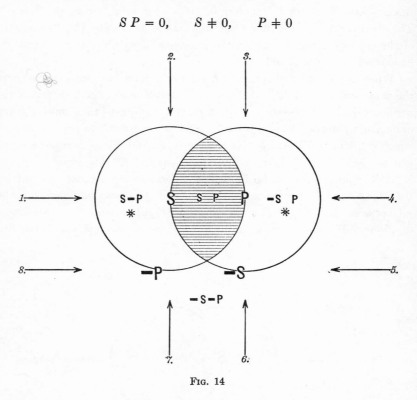

Fig. 14

Reading the diagram of figure 14 in the various possible ways, we have:

1. No S is P,   and 1. Some S is not P.   (According as we read what is indicated by the fact that $S P$ is null, or what is indicated by the fact that $S -P$ is not-null.)

2. All S is not-P,   and 2. Some S is not-P.

3. All P is not-S,   and 3. Some P is not-S.

4. No P is S,   and 4. Some P is not-S.

5. Wanting.

6. Some not-S is P.

7. Some not-P is S.

8. Wanting.

Similarly, if "All S is P", and S and P have members:

$$S - P = 0, \qquad S \neq 0, \qquad P \neq 0$$

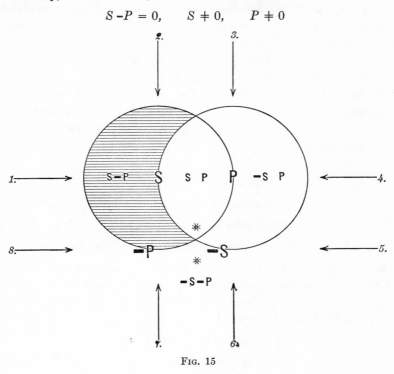

Fig. 15

Reading from the diagram (figure 15), we have:

1. All S is P, and 1. Some S is P.
2. No S is not-P.
3. Wanting.
4. Some P is S.
5. Some not-S is not-P.
6. Wanting.
7. No not-P is S.
8. All not-P is not-S, and 8. Some not-P is not-S.

The whole subject of immediate inference is so simple as to be almost trivial. Yet in the clearing of certain difficulties concerning null-classes the algebra has done a real service here.

The algebraic processes which give the results of syllogistic reasoning have already been illustrated. But in those examples we carried out the operations at unnecessary lengths in order to illustrate their connection with the diagrams.   The premises of any syllogism give information which concerns, altogether, three classes.   The object is to draw a conclusion which gives as much of this information as can be stated independently of the "middle" term.   This is exactly the kind of result which elimination gives in the algebra.   And elimination is very simple.   The result of eliminating x from $A\,x + B\,{-}x = 0$ is $A\,B = 0$.[15]   Whenever the conclusion of a syllogism is universal, it may be obtained by combining the premises in a single equation one member of which is 0, and eliminating the "middle" term.   For example:

$$\text{No } x \text{ is } y, \qquad x\,y = 0.$$

$$\text{All } z \text{ is } x, \qquad z\,{-}x = 0.$$

$$\text{Combining these, } x\,y + z\,{-}x = 0.$$

$$\text{Eliminating } x, \qquad y\,z = 0.$$

Hence the valid conclusion is "No y is z", or "No z is y".

Any syllogism with a universal conclusion may also be symbolized so that the conclusion follows from the law, "If $a \subset b$ and $b \subset c$, then $a \subset c$". By this method, the laws, $-(-a) = a$ and "If $a \subset b$, then $-b \subset -a$", are sometimes required also.[16]   For example:

$$\text{No } x \text{ is } y, \qquad x \subset -y.$$

$$\text{All } z \text{ is } x, \qquad z \subset x.$$

Hence $z \subset -y$, or "No z is y", and $y \subset -z$, or "No y is z".

There is no need to treat further examples of syllogisms with universal conclusions: they are all alike, as far as the algebra is concerned.   Of course, there are other ways of representing the premises and of getting the conclusion, but the above are the simplest.

When a syllogism has a particular premise, and therefore a particular conclusion, the process is somewhat different.   Here we have given one equation $\{ = 0\}$ and one inequation $\{ \neq 0\}$.   We proceed as follows: (1) expand the inequation by introducing the third element; (2) multiply the equation by the element not appearing in it; (3) make use of the principle, "If $a + b \neq 0$ and $a = 0$, then $b \neq 0$", to obtain an inequation with only one term in the literal member; (4) eliminate the element representing the "middle term" from this inequation.   Take, for example, $A\,I\,I$ in

---

[15] See Chap. II, 7·4.
[16] See Chap. II, 2·8 and 3·1.

the third figure:

$$\text{All } x \text{ is } z, \qquad x - z = 0.$$

$$\text{Some } x \text{ is } y, \qquad x \, y \neq 0.$$

$x \, y = x \, y \, (z + -z) = x \, y \, z + x \, y -z.$ Hence, $x \, y \, z + x \, y -z \neq 0.$

[1·5] Since $x -z = 0$, $x \, y -z = 0$.

[8·17] Since $x \, y \, z + x \, y -z \neq 0$ and $x \, y -x = 0$, therefore $x \, y \, z \neq 0$.

Hence [8·22] $y \, z \neq 0$, or "Some y is z".

An exactly similar process gives the conclusion for every syllogism with a particular premise.

We have omitted, so far, any consideration of syllogisms with both premises universal and a particular conclusion—those with "weakened" conclusions, and *A A I* and *E A O* in the third and fourth figures. These are all invalid as general forms of reasoning. They involve the difficulty which is now familiar: a universal does not give a particular without an added assumption that some class has members. If we add to the premises of such syllogisms the assumption that the class denoted by the middle term is a class with members, this makes the conclusion valid. Take, for example, *A A I* in the third figure:

$$\text{All } x \text{ is } y, \qquad x -y = 0, \qquad \text{and } x \text{ has members}, \qquad x \neq 0.$$

$$\text{All } x \text{ is } z, \qquad x -z = 0.$$

Since $x \neq 0$, $x \, y + x -y \neq 0$, and since $x -y = 0$, $x \, y \neq 0$.

Hence $x \, y \, z + x \, y -z \neq 0.$ (1)

Since $x -z = 0$, $x \, y -z = 0$.   (2)

By (1) and (2), $x \, y \, z \neq 0$, and hence $y \, z \neq 0$, or "Some y is z".

Syllogisms of this form are generally considered valid because of a tacit assumption that we are dealing with things which exist. In symbolic reasoning, or any other which is rigorous, any such assumption must be made explicit.

An alternative treatment of the syllogism is due to Mrs. Ladd-Franklin.[17] If we take the two premises of any syllogism and the *contradictory* of its conclusion, we have what may be called an "inconsistent triad"—three propositions such that if any two of them be true, the third must be false. For if the two premises be true, the conclusion must be true and its con-

---

[17] See "On the Algebra of Logic", in *Studies in Logic by members of Johns Hopkins University*, ed. by Peirce; also articles listed in *Bibl.* We do not follow Mrs. Franklin's symbolism but give her theory in a modified form, due to Josiah Royce.

tradictory false. And if the contradictory of the conclusion be true, i. e., if the conclusion be false, and either of the premises true, then the other premise must be false. As a consequence, every inconsistent triad corresponds to three valid syllogisms. Any two members of the triad give the contradictory of the third as a conclusion. For example:

Inconsistent Triad

1. All x is y
2. All y is z
3. Some x is not z.

Valid Syllogisms

1. All x is y	1. All x is y	2. All y is z
2. All y is z	3. Some x is not z	3. Some x is not z
∴. All x is z.	∴. Some y is not z.	∴. Some x is not y.

Omitting the cases in which two universal premises are supposed to give a particular conclusion, since these really have *three* premises and are not syllogisms, the inconsistent triad formed from *any* valid syllogism will consist of two universals and one particular. For two universals will give a universal conclusion, whose contradictory will be a particular; while if one premise be particular, the conclusion will be particular, and its contradictory will be the second universal. Representing universals and particulars as we have done, this means that if we symbolize *any* inconsistent triad, we shall have two equations $\{= 0\}$ and one inequation $\{\neq 0\}$. And the two universals $\{= 0\}$ must give the contradictory of the particular as a conclusion. This means that the contradictory of the particular must be expressible as the elimination resultant of an equation of the form $a\,x + b\,{-x} = 0$, because we have found all conclusions from two universals to be thus obtainable. Hence the two universals of any inconsistent triad will be of the form $a\,x = 0$ and $b\,{-x} = 0$ respectively. The elimination resultant of $a\,x + b\,{-x} = 0$ is $a\,b = 0$, whose contradictory will be $a\,b \neq 0$. Hence every inconsistent triad will have the form:

$$a\,x = 0, \qquad b\,{-x} = 0, \qquad a\,b \neq 0$$

where a and b are any terms whatever positive or negative, and x is any positive term.

The validity of any syllogism may be tested by expressing its propositions in the form suggested, contradicting its conclusion by changing it from $\{= 0\}$ to $\{\neq 0\}$ or the reverse, and comparing the resulting triad with the above form.   And the conclusion of any syllogism may be got by considering how the triad must be completed to have the required form. Thus, if the two premises are

$$\text{No } x \text{ is } y, \qquad x\,y = 0$$
$$\text{and} \quad \text{All not-}z \text{ is } y, \quad -z\,-y = 0$$

the conclusion must be universal.   The particular required to complete the triad is $x\,-z \neq 0$.   Hence the conclusion is $x\,-z = 0$, or "All x is z". (Incidentally it may be remarked that this valid syllogism is in no one of the Aristotelian moods.)   Again, if the premises should be $x\,y = 0$ and $y\,z = 0$, no conclusion is possible, because these two cannot belong to the same inconsistent triad.

We can, then, frame a single canon for all strictly valid syllogistic reasoning: The premises and the contradictory of the conclusion, expressed in symbolic form, $\{ = 0\}$ or $\{ \neq 0\}$, must form a triad such that

(1) There are two universals $\{ = 0\}$ and one particular $\{ \neq 0\}$.

(2) The two universals have a term in common, which is once positive and once negative.

(3) The particular puts $\neq 0$ the product of the coefficients of the common term in the two universals.

A few experiments with traditional syllogisms will make this matter clear to the reader.   The validity of this canon depends solely upon the nature of the syllogism—three terms, three propositions—and upon the law of elimination resultants, "If $a\,x + b\,-x = 0$, then $a\,b = 0$".

Reasoning which involves conditional propositions—hypothetical arguments, dilemmas, etc.—may be treated by the same process, if we first reduce them to syllogistic form.   For example, we may translate "If A is B, then C is D" by "All x is y", where x is the class of cases in which A is B, and y the class of cases in which C is D—i. e., "All cases in which A is B are cases in which C is D".   And we may translate "But A is B" by "All z is x", where z is the case or class of cases under discussion.   Thus the hypothetical argument: "If A is B, C is D.   But A is B.   Therefore, C is D", is represented by the syllogism:

"All cases in which A is B are cases in which C is D.

"But all the cases in question are cases in which A is B.

"Hence all the cases in question are cases in which C is D."

And all other arguments of this type are reducible to syllogisms in some similar fashion.   Thus the symbolic treatment of the syllogism extends to them also. But conditional reasoning is more easily and simply treated by another interpretation of the algebra—the interpretation for propositions.

The chief value of the algebra, as an instrument of reasoning, lies in its liberating us from the limitation to syllogisms, hypothetical arguments, dilemmas, and the other modes of traditional logic. Many who object to the narrowness of formal logic still do not realize how arbitrary (from the logical point of view) its limitations are. The reasons for the syllogism, etc., are not logical but *psychological*. It may be worth while to exemplify this fact. We shall offer two illustrations designed to show, each in a different way, a wide range of logical possibilities undreamt of in formal logic. The first of these turns upon the properties of a triadic relation whose significance was first pointed out by Mr. A. B. Kempe.[18]

It is characteristically human to think in terms of dyadic relations: we habitually break up a triadic relation into a pair of dyads. In fact, so ingrained is this disposition that some will be sure to object that a triadic relation *is* a pair of dyads. It would be exactly as logical to maintain that all dyadic relations are triads with a null member. Either statement is correct enough: the difference is simply one of point of view—psychological preference. If there should be inhabitants of Mars whose logical sense coincided with our own, so that any conclusion which seemed valid to us would seem valid to them, and vice versa, but whose psychology otherwise differed from ours, these Martians might have an equally fundamental prejudice in favor of triadic relations. We can point out one such which they might regard as *the* elementary relation of logic—as we regard equality or inclusion. In terms of this triadic relation, all their reasoning might be carried out with complete success.

Let us symbolize by (ac/b), $a -b\,c + -a\,b -c = 0$. This relation may be diagrammed as in figure 16, since $a -b\,c + -a\,b -c = 0$ is equivalent to $a\,c \subset b \subset (a + c)$. (Note that (ac/b) and (ca/b) are equivalent, since $a -b\,c + -a\,b -c$ is symmetrical with respect to a and c.)

This relation (ac/b) represents precisely the information which we habitually discard in drawing a syllogistic conclusion from two universal premises. If all a is b and all b is c, we have

$$a -b = 0 \qquad \text{and} \qquad b -c = 0$$

$$\text{Hence } a -b\,(c + -c) + (a + -a)\,b -c = 0,$$

---

[18] See his paper "On the Relation of the Logical Theory of Classes and the Geometrical Theory of Points", *Proc. London Math. Soc.*, XXI, 147–82. But the use we here make of this relation is due to Josiah Royce.

Or, $a -b c + a -b -c + a b -c + -a b -c = 0$.

[5·72] This equation is equivalent to the pair,

(1) $a -b -c + a b -c = a -c (b + -b) = a -c = 0$,

and (2) $a -b c + -a b -c = 0$.

(1) is the syllogistic conclusion, "All a is c"; (2) is (ac/b). Perhaps most of us would feel that a syllogistic conclusion states all the information given by the premises: the Martians might equally well feel that precisely

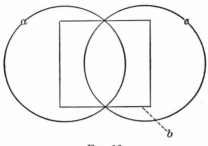

Fig. 16

what we overlook is the only thing worth mentioning. And yet with this curious "illogical" prejudice, they would still be capable of understanding and of getting for themselves any conclusion which a syllogism or a hypothetical argument can give, and many others which are only very awkwardly stateable in terms of our formal logic. Our relation, $a \subset b$, or "All a is b", would be, in their terms, $(0b/a)$. $(0b/a)$ is equivalent to

$$1 \cdot a -b + 0 \cdot -a b = 0 = a -b$$

Hence the syllogism in *Barbara* would be " $(0b/a)$ and $(0c/b)$, hence $(0c/a)$ ". This would, in fact, be only a special case of a more general principle which is one of those we may suppose the Martians would ordinarily rely upon for inference: "If (xb/a) and (xc/b), then (xc/a) ". That this general principle holds, is proved as follows:

$$(xb/a) \text{ is } -x a -b + x -a b = 0$$
$$(xc/b) \text{ is } -x b -c + x -b c = 0$$

These two together give:

$$-x a -b (c + -c) + x -a b (c + -c) + -x b -c (a + -a) + x -b c (a + -a) = 0,$$

or, $-x a -b c + -x a -b -c + x -a b c + x -a b -c + -x a b -c + -x -a b -c$
$$+ x a -b c + x -a -b c = 0.$$

[5·72] This equation is equivalent to the pair,

(1) $-x\,a\,b\,-c\,+\,-x\,a\,-b\,-c\,+\,x\,-a\,b\,c\,+\,x\,-a\,-b\,c$
$$= -x\,a\,-c\,(b\,+\,-b)\,+\,x\,-a\,c\,(b\,+\,-b)$$
$$= -x\,a\,-c\,+\,x\,-a\,c\,=\,0.$$

(2) $x\,-a\,b\,-c\,+\,-x\,-a\,b\,-c\,+\,x\,a\,-b\,c\,+\,-x\,a\,-b\,c$
$$= -a\,b\,-c\,(x\,+\,-x)\,+\,a\,-b\,c\,(x\,+\,-x)$$
$$= -a\,b\,-c\,+\,a\,-b\,c\,=\,0.$$

(1) is (xc/a), of which our syllogistic conclusion is a special case; (2) is a similar valid conclusion, though one which we never draw and have no language to express.

Thus these Martians could deal with and understand our formal logic by treating our dyads as triads with one member null. In somewhat similar fashion, hypothetical propositions, the relation of equality, syllogisms with a particular premise, dilemmas, etc., are all capable of statement in terms of the relation (ac/b). As a fact, this relation is much more powerful than any dyad for purposes of reasoning. Anyone who will trouble to study its properties will be convinced that the only sound reason for not using it, instead of our dyads, is the psychological difficulty of keeping in mind at once two triads with two members in common but differently placed, and a third member which is different in the two. Our attention-span is too small. But the operations of the algebra are independent of such purely psychological limitations—that is to say, a process too complicated for us in any other form becomes sufficiently simple to be clear in the algebra. The algebra has a generality and scope which "formal" logic cannot attain.

This illustration has indicated the possibility of entirely valid nontraditional *modes* of reasoning. We shall now exemplify the fact that by modes which are not so remote from familiar processes of reasoning, any number of non-traditional *conclusions* can be drawn. For this purpose, we make use of Poretsky's Law of Forms:[19]

$$x = 0 \text{ is equivalent to } t = t\,-x\,+\,-t\,x$$

This law is evident enough: if $x = 0$, then for any t, $t\,-x = t\cdot 1 = t$, and $-t\,x = -t\cdot 0 = 0$, while $t + 0 = t$. Let us now take the syllogistic premises, "All a is b" and "All b is c", and see what sort of results can be derived from them by this law.

$$\text{All } a \text{ is } b, \qquad a\,-b\,=\,0.$$
$$\text{All } b \text{ is } c, \qquad b\,-c\,=\,0.$$

[19] See Chap. ii, 7·15 and 7·16.

Combining these, $a - b + b - c = 0$.

And $[3 \cdot 4 \cdot 41]$ $-(a - b + b - c) = -(a - b) \cdot -(b - c) = (-a + b)(-b + c)$
$$= -a - b + -a\,c + b\,c.$$

Let us make substitutions, in terms of a, b, and c, for the t of this formula.

$$a + b = (a + b)(-a - b + -a\,c + b\,c) + -a - b\,(a - b + b - c)$$
$$= a\,b\,c + -a\,b\,c + b\,c = b\,c$$

What is either a or b is identical with that which is both b and c. This is a non-syllogistic conclusion from "All a is b and all b is c". Other such conclusions may be got by similar substitutions in the formula.

$$a + c = (a + c)(-a - b + -a\,c + b\,c) + -a - c\,(a - b + b - c)$$
$$= a\,b\,c + -a - b\,c + -a\,c + b\,c + -a\,b - c = a\,b\,c + -a\,(b + c).$$

What is either a or c is identical with that which is a, b, and c, all three, or is not a and either b or c.

$$-b\,c = -b\,c\,(-a - b + -a\,c + b\,c) + (b + -c)(a - b + b - c)$$
$$= -a - b\,c + b - c + a - b - c = -a - b\,c + (a + b) - c$$

That which is c but not b is identical with what is c but neither a nor b or is either a or b but not c. The number of such conclusions to be got from the premises, "All a is b" and "All b is c", is limited only by the number of functions which can be formed with a, b, and c, and the limitation to substitutions in terms of these is, of course, arbitrary. By this method, the number of conclusions which can be drawn from given premises is entirely unlimited.

In concluding this discussion of the application of the algebra to the logic of classes, we may give a few examples in which problems more involved than those usually dealt with by formal logic are solved. The examples chosen are mostly taken from other sources, and some of them, like the first, are fairly historic.

Example 1.[20]

A certain club has the following rules: (*a*) The financial committee shall be chosen from among the general committee; (*b*) No one shall be a member both of the general and library committees unless he be also on the financial committee; (*c*) No member of the library committee shall be on the financial committee.

Simplify the rules.

[20] See Venn, *Symbolic Logic*, ed. 2, p. 331.

Let f = member of financial committee.

g =   "   " general   "   .

l =   "   " library   "   .

The premises then become:

(a) $f \subset g$,   or $f - g = 0$.

(b) $(g\,l) \subset f$,   or $-f\,g\,l = 0$.

(c) $f\,l = 0$.

We can discover by diagramming whether there is redundancy here. In figure 17, (a) is indicated by vertical lines, (b) by horizontal, (c) by oblique.

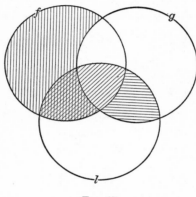

Fig. 17

(a) and (c) both predicate the non-existence of $f - g\,l$. To simplify the rules, unite (a), (b), and (c) in a single equation:

$$f - g + -f\,g\,l + f\,l = 0$$

Hence, $f - g + -f\,g\,l + f\,l\,(g + -g) = f - g + -f\,g\,l + f\,g\,l + f - g\,l$

[5·91] $= f - g + (-f + f)\,g\,l = f - g + g\,l = 0.$

And [5·72] this is equivalent to the pair, $f - g = 0$ and $g\,l = 0$.

Thus the simplified rules will be:

(a') The financial committee shall be chosen from among the general committee.

(b') No member of the general committee shall be on the library committee.

Example 2.[21]

The members of a certain collection are classified in three ways—as a's or not, as b's or not, and as c's or not. It is then found that the class b is made up precisely of the a's which are not c's and the c's which are not a's. How is the class c constituted?

Given: $b = a-c + -a\,c$. To solve for c.[22]

$b = b\,(c + -c) = b\,c + b\,-c.$

Hence, $b\,c + b\,-c = a\,-c + -a\,c.$

Hence $[7\cdot27]$ $a\,-b + -a\,b \subset c \subset a\,-b + -a\,b.$

Or $[2\cdot2]$ $c = a\,-b + -a\,b.$

The c's comprise the a's which are not b's and the b's which are not a's.

Another solution of this problem would be given by reducing $b = a-c + -a\,c$ to the form $\{ = 0\}$ and using the diagram.

$[7\cdot1]$ $b = a-c + -a\,c$ is equivalent to

$$b\cdot-(a-c + -a\,c) + -b\,(a-c + -a\,c) = 0$$

And $[6\cdot4]$ $-(a-c + -a\,c) = a\,c + -a\,-c.$

Hence, $a\,b\,c + -a\,b\,-c + a\,-b\,-c + -a\,-b\,c = 0.$

We observe here (figure 18) not only that $c = a\,-b + -a\,b$, but that the

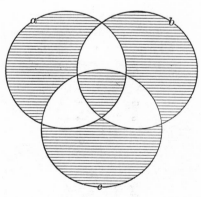

Fig. 18

relation of a, b, and c, stated by the premise is totally symmetrical, so that we have also $a = b\,-c + -b\,c.$

---

[21] Adapted from one of Venn's, first printed in an article on "Boole's System of Logic", *Mind*, I (1876), p. 487.

[22] This proof will be intelligible if the reader understands the solution formula referred to.

Example 3.[23]

If x that is not a is the same as b, and a that is not x is the same as c, what is x in terms of a, b, and c?

Given: $b = -a\,x$ and $c = a-x$. To solve for x.

[7·1] $b = -a\,x$ is equivalent to

$$-(-a\,x)\,b + -a\,-b\,x = 0 = (a + -x)\,b + -a\,-b\,x$$
$$= a\,b + b\,-x + -a\,-b\,x = 0 \quad (1)$$

And $c = a-x$ is equivalent to

$$-(a-x)\,c + a-c\,-x = 0 = (-a+x)\,c + a-c\,-x$$
$$= -a\,c + c\,x + a-c\,-x = 0 \quad (2)$$

Combining (1) and (2),

$$a\,b + -a\,c + (-a\,-b+c)\,x + (b+a-c)\,-x = 0 \quad (3)$$

Hence [5·72] $(-a\,-b+c)\,x + (b+a-c)\,-x = 0 \quad (4)$

[7·221] This gives the equation of condition,

$$(-a\,-b+c)(b+a-c) = b\,c = 0 \quad (5)$$

[7·2] The solution of (4) is

$$(b+a-c) \subset x \subset -(-a\,-b+c)$$

And by (5),

$$-(-a\,-b+c) = -(-a\,-b+c) + b\,c = (a+b)\,-c + b\,c$$
$$= a-c + b\,(c + -c) = b+a-c$$

Hence [2·2] $x = b+a-c$.

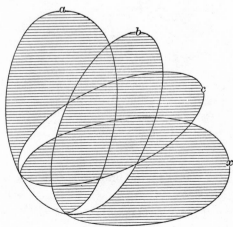

Fig. 19

[23] See Lambert, *Logische Abhandlungen*, i, 14.

This solution is verified by the diagram (figure 19) of equation (3), which combines all the data. Lambert gives the solution as

$$x = (a+b) -c$$

This also is verified by the diagram.

Example 4.[24]

What is the precise point at issue between two disputants, one of whom, *A*, asserts that space should be defined as three-way spread having points as elements, while the other, *B*, insists that space should be defined as three-way spread, and admits that space has points as elements.

$$\text{Let } s = \text{space},$$
$$t = \text{three-way spread},$$
$$p = \text{having points as elements}.$$

A asserts: $s = t\,p$. *B* states: $s = t$ and $s \subset p$.

$s = t\,p$ is equivalent to

$$s \cdot -(t\,p) + -s\,t\,p = 0 = s -t + s -p + -s\,t\,p = 0 \tag{1}$$
$$s \subset p \text{ is equivalent to } s -p = 0 \tag{2}$$
$$\text{And } s = t \text{ is equivalent to } s -t + -s\,t = 0 \tag{3}$$

(2) and (3) together are equivalent to

$$s -t + s -p + -s\,t = 0 \tag{4}$$

(1) represents *A*'s assertion, and (4) represents *B*'s. The difference between

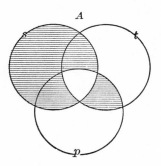
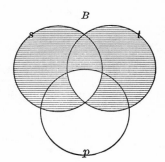

F ɪ ɢ. 20

the two is that between $-s\,t\,p = 0$ and $-s\,t = 0$. (See figure 20.)

$$-s\,t = -s\,t\,p + -s\,t -p$$

[24] Quoted from Jevons by Mrs. Ladd-Franklin, *loc. cit.*, p. 52.

The difference is, then, that B asserts $-s\,t\,-p = 0$, while A does not. It would be easy to misinterpret this issue. $-s\,t\,-p = 0$ is $t\,-p \subset s$, "Three-way spread not having points as elements, is space". But B cannot significantly assert this, for he has denied the existence of *any* space not having points as elements. *Both* assert $s = t\,p$. The real difference is this: B definitely asserts that all three-way spread has points as elements and is space, while A has left open the possibility that there should be three-way spread not having points as elements which should not be space.

Example 5.

Amongst the objects in a small boy's pocket are some bits of metal which he regards as useful. But all the bits of metal which are not heavy enough to sink a fishline are bent. And he considers no bent object useful unless it is either heavy enough to sink a fishline or is not metal. And the only objects heavy enough to sink a fishline, which he regards as useful, are bits of metal that are bent. Specifically what has he in his pocket which he regards as useful?

Let x = bits of metal,
$\quad\;\; y$ = objects he regards as useful,
$\quad\;\; z$ = things heavy enough to sink a fishline,
$\quad\;\; w$ = bent objects.

Symbolizing the propositions in the order stated, we have

$$x\,y \neq 0$$
$$x\,-z \subset w, \qquad \text{or} \qquad x\,-z\,-w = 0$$
$$y\,w \subset (z\,+\,-x), \qquad \text{or} \qquad x\,y\,-z\,w = 0$$
$$z\,y \subset x\,w, \qquad \text{or} \qquad -x\,y\,z\,+\,y\,z\,-w = 0$$

Expanding the inequation with reference to z and w,

$$x\,y\,z\,w\,+\,x\,y\,z\,-w\,+\,x\,y\,-z\,w\,+\,x\,y\,-z\,-w \neq 0$$

Combining the equations,

$$x\,-z\,-w\,(y\,+\,-y)\,+\,x\,y\,-z\,w\,+\,-x\,y\,z\,(w\,+\,-w)\,+\,y\,z\,-w\,(x\,+\,-x) = 0$$

or $\quad x\,y\,-z\,-w\,+\,x\,-y\,-z\,-w\,+\,x\,y\,-z\,w\,+\,-x\,y\,z\,w\,+\,-x\,y\,z\,-w\,+\,x\,y\,z\,-w = 0$

All the terms of the inequation appear also in this equation, with the exception of $x\,y\,z\,w$. Hence, by $8 \cdot 17$, $x\,y\,z\,w \neq 0$. The small boy has some bent bits of metal heavy enough to sink a fishline, which he considers useful. This appears in the diagram (figure 21) by the fact that while

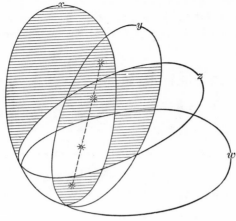

FIG. 21

some subdivision of $x\,y$ must be not-null, all of these but $x\,y\,z\,w$ is null. It appears also that anything else he may have which he considers useful may or may not be bent but is not metal.

Example 6.[25]

The annelida consist of all invertebrate animals having red blood in a double system of circulating vessels. And all annelida are soft-bodied, and either naked or enclosed in a tube. Suppose we wish to obtain the relation in which soft-bodied animals enclosed in tubes are placed (by virtue of the premises) with respect to the possession of red blood, of an external covering, and of a vertebral column.

Let a = annelida,
s = soft-bodied animals,
n = naked,
t = enclosed in a tube,
i = invertebrate,
r = having red blood, etc.

Given: $a = i\,r$ and $a \subset s\,(n + t)$, with the implied condition, $n\,t = 0$. To eliminate a and find an expression for $s\,t$.

[25] See Boole, *Laws of Thought*, pp. 144–46.

$a = i\, r$ is equivalent to

$$-(i\, r)\, a + -a\, i\, r = a -i + a -r + -a\, i\, r = 0 \tag{1}$$

$a \subset s\, (n + t)$ is equivalent to $a \cdot -(s\, n + s\, t) = 0$.

$-(s\, n + s\, t) = -(s\, n) \cdot -(s\, t) = (-s + -n)(-s + -t) = -s + -n\, -t$.

Hence,　　　　　　　$a -s + a -n\, -t = 0 \tag{2}$

Combining (1) and (2) and $n\, t = 0$,

$$a -i + a -r + -a\, i\, r + a -s + a -n\, -t + n\, t = 0 \tag{3}$$

Eliminating a, by 7·4,

$$(-i + -r + -s + -n\, -t + n\, t)(i\, r + n\, t) = n\, t + i\, r -s + i\, r -n\, -t = 0$$

The solution of this equation for s is[26] $i\, r \subset s$.

And its solution for t is $i\, r -n \subset t \subset -n$.

Hence [5·3] $i\, r -n \subset s\, t \subset -n$, or $s\, t = i\, r -n + u \cdot -n$, where u is undetermined.

The soft-bodied animals enclosed in a tube consist of the invertebrates

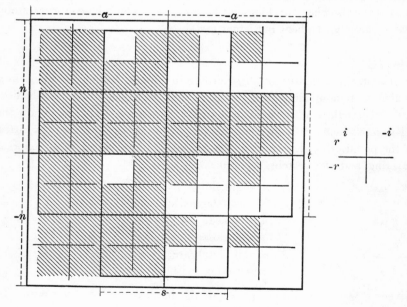

Fig. 22

[26] See Chap. ii, Sect. iv, "Symmetrical and Unsymmetrical Constituents of an Equation".

which have red blood in a double system of circulating vessels and a body covering, together with an undetermined additional class (which may be null) of other animals which have a body covering. This solution may be verified by the diagram of equation (3) (figure 22). In this diagram, $s\,t$ is the square formed by the two crossed rectangles. The lower half of this inner square exhibits the solution. Note that the qualification, $-n$, in $i\,r\,-n\,c\,s\,t$, is necessary. In the top row is a single undeleted area representing a portion of $i\,r\,(n)$ which is not contained in $s\,t$.

Example 7.[27]

Demonstrate that from the premises "All a is either b or c", and "All c is a", no conclusion can be drawn which involves only two of the classes, a, b, and c.

Given: $a \subset (b+c)$ and $c \subset a$.

To prove that the elimination of any one element gives a result which is either indeterminate or contained in one or other of the premises.

$a \subset (b+c)$ is equivalent to $a\,-b\,-c = 0$.

And $c \subset a$ is equivalent to $-a\,c = 0$.

Combining these, $a\,-b\,-c\,+-a\,c = 0$.

Eliminating a [7·4], $(-b\,-c)\,c = 0$, which is the identity, $0 = 0$.

Eliminating c, $(a\,-b)\,-a = 0$, or $0 = 0$.

Eliminating b, $(-a\,c+a\,-c)\,-a\,c = -a\,c = 0$, which is the second premise.

Example 8.

A set of balls are all of them spotted with one or more of the colors, red, green, and blue, and are numbered. And all the balls spotted with red are also spotted with blue. All the odd-numbered blue balls, and all the even numbered balls which are not both red and green, are on the table. Describe the balls not on the table.

Let e = even-numbered, $-e$ = odd-numbered,
  r = spotted with red,
  b = spotted with blue,
  g = spotted with green,
  t = balls on the table.

Given: (1) $-r\,-b\,-g = 0$.

[27] See De Morgan, *Formal Logic*, p. 123.

(2) $r - b = 0.$

(3) $[-e\,b + e -(r\,g)] \subset t,$ or $(-e\,b + e -r + e -g) -t = 0.$

To find an expression, x, such that $-t \subset x$, or $-t\,x = -t.$ Such an expression should be as brief as possible. Consequently we must develop $-t$ with respect to e, r, b, and g, and eliminate all null terms. (An alternative method would be to solve for $-t$, but the procedure suggested is briefer.)

$$-t = -t\,(e + -e)(r + -r)(b + -b)(g + -g)$$

$$= -t\,(e\,r\,b\,g + e\,r\,b -g + e\,r -b\,g + e -r\,b\,g + -e\,r\,b\,g + e\,r\,b -g$$

$$+ e -r\,b -g + -e\,r\,b -g + e -r -b\,g + -e -r\,b\,g + -e\,r -b\,g$$

$$+ e -r -b -g + -e\,r -b -g + -e -r\,b -g + -e -r -b\,g + -e -r -b -g) \quad (4)$$

From (1), (2), and (3),

$$-t\,(-e\,b + e -r + e -g + r -b + -r -b -g) = 0 \quad (5)$$

Eliminating from (4) terms involved in (5),

$$-t = -t\,(e\,r\,b\,g + -e -r -b\,g),\quad \text{or}\quad -t \subset (e\,r\,b\,g + -e -r -b\,g)$$

All the balls not on the table are even-numbered and spotted with all three colors or odd-numbered and spotted with green only.

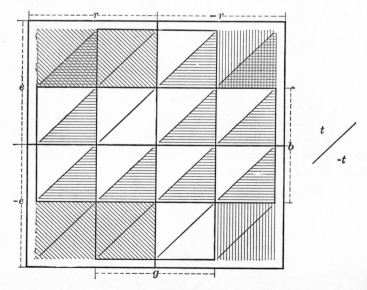

Fig. 23

In the diagram (figure 23), equation (1) is indicated by vertical lines, (2) by oblique, (3) by horizontal.

Example 9.[28]

Suppose that an analysis of the properties of a particular class of substances has led to the following general conclusions:

1st. That wherever the properties a and b are combined, either the property c, or the property d, is present also; but they are not jointly present.

2d. That wherever the properties b and c are combined, the properties a and d are either both present with them, or both absent.

3d. That wherever the properties a and b are both absent, the properties c and d are both absent also; and vice versa, where the properties c and d are both absent, a and b are both absent also.

Let it then be required from the above to determine what may be concluded in any particular instance from the presence of the property a with respect to the presence or absence of the properties b and c, paying no regard to the property d.

Given: (1) $a\,b \subset (c\,{-d} + {-c}\,d)$.

      (2) $b\,c \subset (a\,d + {-a}\,{-d})$.

      (3) ${-a}\,{-b} = {-c}\,{-d}$.

To eliminate d and solve for a.

(1) is equivalent to $a\,b \cdot {-}(c\,{-d} + {-c}\,d) = 0$.

(2) is equivalent to $b\,c \cdot {-}(a\,d + {-a}\,{-d}) = 0$.

But $[6\cdot4]$ $-(c\,{-d} + {-c}\,d) = c\,d + {-c}\,{-d}$,

and $-(a\,d + {-a}\,{-d}) = {-a}\,d + a\,{-d}$.

Hence we have, $a\,b\,(c\,d + {-c}\,{-d}) = a\,b\,c\,d + a\,b\,{-c}\,{-d} = 0$ (4)

and $b\,c\,({-a}\,d + a\,{-d}) = {-a}\,b\,c\,d + a\,b\,c\,{-d} = 0$ (5)

(3) is equivalent to

$$-a\,{-b}\,(c + d) + (a + b)\,{-c}\,{-d}$$
$$= {-a}\,{-b}\,c + {-a}\,{-b}\,d + a\,{-c}\,{-d} + b\,{-c}\,{-d} = 0 \quad (6)$$

Combining (4), (5), and (6), and giving the result the form of a function of d,

$$(-a\,{-b}\,c + {-a}\,{-b} + a\,b\,c + {-a}\,b\,c)\,d$$
$$+ ({-a}\,{-b}\,c + a\,{-c} + b\,{-c} + a\,b\,{-c} + a\,b\,c)\,{-d} = 0$$

[28] See Boole, *Laws of Thought*, pp. 118–20. For further problems, see Mrs. Ladd-Franklin, *loc. cit.*, pp. 51–61, Venn, *Symbolic Logic*, Chap. xiii, and Schröder, *Algebra der Logik:* Vol. i, *Dreizehnte Vorlesung.*

Or, simplifying, by 5·4 and 5·91,

$$(-a\,-b\,+\,b\,c)\,d\,+\,(-a\,-b\,c\,+\,a\,-c\,+\,b\,-c\,+\,a\,b\,c)\,-d\,=\,0$$

Hence [7·4] eliminating d,

$$(-a\,-b\,+\,b\,c)(-a\,-b\,c\,+\,a\,-c\,+\,b\,-c\,+\,a\,b\,c)\,=\,-a\,-b\,c\,+\,a\,b\,c\,=\,0$$

Solving this equation for a [7·2], $-b\,c\,\subset\,a\,\subset\,(-b\,+\,-c)$.

The property a is always present when c is present and b absent, and whenever a is present, either b is absent or c is absent.

The diagram (figure 24) combines equations (4), (5), and (6).

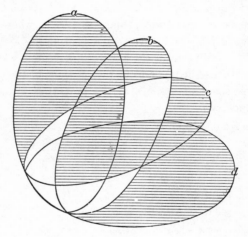

Fig. 24

As Boole correctly claimed, the most powerful application of this algebra is to problems of probability. But for this, additional laws which do not belong to the system are, of course, required. Hence we omit it. Something of what the algebra will do toward the solution of such problems will be evident if the reader imagine our Example 8 as giving numerically the proportion of balls spotted with red, with blue, and with green, and the *quaesitum* to be "If a ball not on the table be chosen at random, what is the probability that it will be spotted with all three colors? that it will be spotted with green?" The algebra alone, without any additional laws, answers the last question. As the reader will observe from the solution, all the balls not on the table are spotted with green.

III. The Application to Propositions

If, in our postulates, a, b, c, etc., represent propositions, and the "product", $a\,b$, represent the proposition which asserts a and b both, then we have another interpretation of the algebra. Since $a + b$ is the negative of $-a\,-b$, $a + b$ will represent "It is false that a and b are both false", or "At least one of the two, a and b, is true". It has been customary to read $a + b$, "Either a or b", or "Either a is true or b is true". But this is somewhat misleading, since "Either . . . or . . ." frequently denotes, in ordinary use, a relation which is to be understood in intension, while this algebra is incapable of representing relations of intension. For instance, we should hardly affirm "Either parallels meet at finite intervals or all men are mortal". We might well say that the "Either . . . or . . ." relation here predicated fails to hold because the two propositions are irrelevant. But at least one of the two, "Parallels meet at finite intervals" and "All men are mortal", is a true proposition. The relation denoted by $+$ in the algebra holds between them. Hence, if we render $a + b$ by "Either a or b", we must bear in mind that no *necessary* connection of a and b, no relation of "relevance" or "logical import", is intended.

The negative of a, $-a$, will be its contradictory, or the proposition "a is false". It might be thought that $-a$ should symbolize the "contrary" of a as well,—that if a be "All men are mortal", then "No men are mortal" should be $-a$. But if the contrary as well as the contradictory be denoted by $-a$, then $-a$ will be an ambiguous function of a, whereas the algebra requires that $-a$ be unique. [29]

The interpretation of 0 and 1 is most easily made clear by considering the connection between the interpretation of the algebra for propositions and its interpretation for classes. The propositional sign, a, may equally well be taken to represent the class of cases in which the proposition a is true. $a\,b$ will then represent the class of cases in which a and b are both true; $-a$, the class of cases in which a is false, and so on. The "universe", 1, will be the class of all cases, or all "actual" cases, or the universe of facts. Thus $a = 1$ represents "The cases in which a is true are all cases", or "a is true in point of fact", or simply "a is true". Similarly 0 is the class of no cases, and $a = 0$ will mean "a is true in no case", or "a is false".

It might well be asked: May not a, b, c, etc., represent statements which are sometimes true and sometimes false, such as "Today is Monday" or "The die shows an ace"? May not a symbolize the cases in which a is

[29] See Chap. II, 3·3.

true, and these be not all but only some of the cases? And should not $a = 1$ be read "*a* is always true", as distinguished from the less comprehensive statement, "*a* is true"? The answer is that the interpretation thus suggested can be made and that Boole actually made it in his chapters on "Secondary Propositions".[30] But symbolic logicians have come to distinguish between assertions which are sometimes true and sometimes false and *propositions*. In the sense in which "Today is Monday" is sometimes true and sometimes false, it is called a propositional function and not a proposition. There are two principal objections to interpreting the Boole-Schröder Algebra as a logic of propositional functions. In the first place, the logic of propositional functions is much more complex than this algebra, and in the second place, it is much more useful to restrict the algebra to *propositions* by the additional law "If $a \neq 0$, then $a = 1$, and if $a \neq 1$, then $a = 0$", and avoid any confusion of propositions with assertions which are sometimes true and sometimes false. In the next chapter, we shall investigate the consequences of this law, which holds for propositions but not for classes or for propositional functions. We need not presume this law at present: the Boole-Schröder Algebra, exactly as presented in the last chapter, is applicable throughout to propositions. But we shall remember that a *proposition* is either always true or never true: if a proposition is true at all, it is always true. Hence in the interpretation of the algebra for propositions, $a = 1$ means "*a* is true" or "*a* is always true" indifferently—the two are synonymous. And $a = 0$ means either "*a* is false" or "*a* is always false".

The relation $a \subset b$, since it is equivalent to $a - b = 0$, may be read "It is false that '*a* is true and *b* is false'", or loosely, "If *a* is true, then *b* is true". But $a \subset b$, like $a + b$, is here a relation which does not signify "relevance" or a connection of "logical import". Suppose $a =$ "$2 + 2 = 4$" and $b =$ "Christmas is a holiday". We should hardly say "If $2 + 2 = 4$, then Christmas is a holiday". Yet it is false that "$2 + 2 = 4$ and Christmas *is not* a holiday": in this example $a - b = 0$ is true, and hence $a \subset b$ will hold. This relation, $a \subset b$, is called "material implication"; it is a relation of extension, whereas we most frequently interpret "implies" as a relation of intension. But $a \subset b$ has one most important property in common with our usual meaning of "*a* implies *b*"—when $a \subset b$ is true, the case in which *a* is true but *b* is false does not occur. If $a \subset b$ holds, and *a* is true, then *b* will not be false, though it may be irrelevant. Thus "material

---

[30] *Laws of Thought*, Chaps. XI–XIV.

implication" is a relation which covers more than the "implies" of ordinary logic: $a \subset b$ holds whenever the usual "a implies b" holds; it also holds in some cases in which "a implies b" does not hold.[31]

The application of the algebra to propositions is so simple, and so resembles its application to classes, that a comparatively few illustrations will suffice. We give some from the elementary logic of conditional propositions, and conclude with one taken from Boole.

Example 1.

    If A is B, C is D.   (1)

    And A is B.   (2)

Let $x = A$ is B; $y = C$ is D.

        The two premises then are:

            (1) $x \subset y$, or [4·9] $-x + y = 1$.

            (2) $x = 1$, or $-x = 0$.

        [5·7] Since $-x + y = 1$ and $-x = 0$, $y = 1$.

$y = 1$ is the conclusion "C is D".

Example 2.

    (1) If A is B, C is D.

    (2) But C is not D.

Let $x = A$ is B; $y = C$ is D.

        (1) $x \subset y$, or $-x + y = 1$.

        (2) $y = 0$.

        [5·7] Since $-x + y = 1$ and $y = 0$, $-x = 1$.

$-x = 1$ is the conclusion "A is B is false", or "A is not B".

Example 3.

    (1) If A is B, C is D; and (2) if E is F, G is H.

    (3) But either A is B or C is D.

Let $w = A$ is B; $x = C$ is D; $y = E$ is F; $z = G$ is H.

        (1) $w \subset x$, or [4·9] $w x = w$.

        (2) $y \subset z$, or $y z = y$.

        (3) $w + y = 1$.

---

[31] "Material implication" is discussed more at length in Chap. IV, Sect. I.

Since $w + y = 1$, and $w\,x = w$ and $y\,z = y$, $w\,x + y\,z = 1$.
Hence [4·5] $w\,x + -w\,x + y\,z + -y\,z = 1 + -w\,x + -y\,z = 1$.
Hence $x\,(w + -w) + z\,(y + -y) = x + z = 1$.

$x + z = 1$ is the conclusion "Either C is D or G is H". This dilemma may be diagrammed if we put our equations in the equivalent forms (1) $w - x = 0$, (2) $y - z = 0$, (3) $-w - y = 0$. In figure 25, $w - x$ is struck

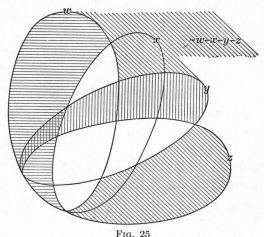

Fig. 25

out with horizontal lines, $y - z$ with vertical, $-w - y$ with oblique. That everything which remains is either x or z is evident.

Example 4.

    (1) Either A is B or C is not D.
    (2) Either C is D or E is F.
    (3) Either A is B or E is not F.

Let $x = A$ is B; $y = C$ is D; $z = E$ is F.

    (1) $x + -y = 1$.
    (2) $y + z = 1$, or $-y - z = 0$.
    (3) $x + -z = 1$, or $-x\,z = 0$.
    By (1), $x + -y\,(z + -z) = x + -y\,z + -y - z = 1$.
    Hence by (2), $x + -y\,z = 1 = x + -y\,z\,(x + -x) = x + x - y\,z + -x - y\,z$.
    And by (3), $-x - y\,z = 0$. Hence $x + x - y\,z = x = 1$.

Thus these three premises give the categorical conclusion "A is B", indicating the fact that the traditional modes of conditional syllogism are by no means exhaustive.

Example 5.[32]

Assume the premises:

1. If matter is a necessary being, either the property of gravitation is necessarily present, or it is necessarily absent.

2. If gravitation is necessarily absent, and the world is not subject to any presiding intelligence, motion does not exist.

3. If gravitation is necessarily present, a vacuum is necessary.

4. If a vacuum is necessary, matter is not a necessary being.

5. If matter is a necessary being, the world is not subject to a presiding intelligence.

Let x = Matter is a necessary being.

y = Gravitation is necessarily present.

z = The world is not subject to a presiding intelligence.

w = Motion exists.

t = Gravitation is necessarily absent.

v = A vacuum is necessary.

The premises then are:

(1) $x \subset (y + t)$, or $x -y -t = 0$.

(2) $t z \subset -w$, or $t z w = 0$.

(3) $y \subset v$, or $y -v = 0$.

(4) $v \subset -x$, or $v x = 0$.

(5) $x \subset z$, or $x -z = 0$.

And since gravitation cannot be both present and absent,

(6) $y t = 0$.

Combining these equations:

$$x -y -t + t z w + y -v + v x + x -z + y t = 0 \qquad (7)$$

From these premises, let it be required, first, to discover any conection between x, "Matter is a necessary being", and y, "Gravitation is necessarily present". For this purpose, it is sufficient to discover whether any one of the four, $x y = 0$, $x -y = 0$, $-x y = 0$, or $-x -y = 0$, since these are the relations which state any implication which holds between x, or $-x$, and y, or $-y$. This can always be done by collecting the coefficients of $x y$, $x -y$, $-x y$, and $-x -y$, in the comprehensive expression of the data, such as equation (7), and finding which of them, if any, reduce to 1. But

[32] See Boole, *Laws of Thought*, Chap. XIV. The premises assumed are supposed to be borrowed from Clarke's metaphysics.

sometimes, as in the present case, this lengthy procedure is not necessary, because the inspection of the equation representing the data readily reveals such a relation.

From (7), [5·72] $v\,x + -v\,y = 0$.

Hence [1·5] $v\,x\,y + -v\,x\,y = (v + -v)\,x\,y = x\,y = 0$, or $x \subset -y,\ y \subset -x$. If matter is a necessary being, then gravitation is not necessarily present; if gravitation is necessarily present, matter is not a necessary being.

Next, let any connection between x and w be required. Here no such relation is easily to be discovered by inspection. Remembering that if $a = 0$, then $a\,b = 0$ and $a - b = 0$;

From (7), $(-y - t + t\,z + y - v + v + -z + y\,t)\,w\,x$

$$+ (t\,z + y - v + y\,t)\,w - x$$
$$+ (-y - t + y - v + v + -z + y\,t)\,-w\,x$$
$$+ (y - v + y\,t)\,-w\,-x = 0 \qquad (8)$$

Here the coefficient of $w\,x$ reduces to 1, for [5·85],

$$y - v + v = y + v, \qquad \text{and} \qquad t\,z + -z = t + -z$$

and hence the coefficient is $-y - t + y + t + v + -z + y\,t$.

But [5·96] $(-y - t + y + t) + v + -z + y\,t = 1 + v + -z + y\,t = 1$.

Hence $w\,x = 0$, or $w \subset -x,\ x \subset -w$.

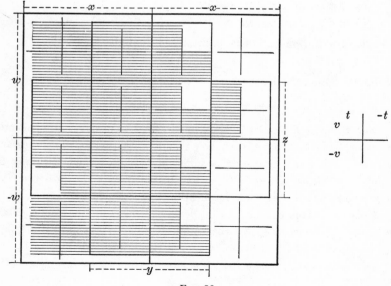

Fig. 26

None of the other coefficients in (8) reduces to 1. Hence the conclusion which connects x and w is: "If motion exists, matter is not a necessary being; if matter is a necessary being, motion does not exist".

Further conclusions, relating other terms, might be derived from the same premises. All such conclusions are readily discoverable in the diagram of equation (7). In fact, the diagram is more convenient for such problems than the transformation of equations in the algebra.

Another method for discovering the implications involved in given data is to state the data entirely in terms of the relation $\subset$, and, remembering that "If $a \subset b$ and $b \subset c$, then $a \subset c$", as well as "$a \subset b$ is equivalent to $-b \subset -a$", to seek directly any connection thus revealed between the propositions which are in question. Although by this method it is possible to overlook a connection which exists, the danger is relatively small.

IV. THE APPLICATION TO RELATIONS

The application of the algebra to relations is relatively unimportant, because the logic of relations is immensely more complex than the Boole-Schröder Algebra, and requires more extensive treatment in order to be of service. We shall, consequently, confine our discussion simply to the explanation of this interpretation of the algebra.

A relation, taken in *extension*, is the class of all couples, triads, or tetrads, etc., which *have the property* of being so related. That is, the relation "father of" is the class of all those couples, $(x; y)$, such that x is father of y: the dyadic relation R is the class of all couples $(x; y)$ such that x has the relation R to y, $x R y$. The *extension* of a relation is the class of things which have the relation. We must distinguish between the class of couples $(x; y)$ and the class of couples $(y; x)$, since not all relations are symmetrical and $x R y$ commonly differs from $y R x$. Since the properties of relations, so far as the laws of this algebra apply to them, are the same whether they are dyadic, triadic, or tetradic, etc., the discussion of dyadic relations will be sufficient.

The "product", $R \times S$, or $R S$, will represent the class of all those couples $(x; y)$ such that $x R y$ and $x S y$ are both true. The "sum", $R + S$, will be the class of all couples $(x; y)$ such that at least one of the two, $x R y$ and $x S y$, holds. The negative of R, $-R$, will be the class of couples $(x; y)$ for which $x R y$ is *false*.

The null-relation, 0, will be the null-class of couples. If the class of couples $(t; u)$ for which $t R u$ is true, is a class with no members, and the class of couples $(v; w)$ for which $v\,S\,w$ is true is also a class with no members, then R and S have the same extension. It is this extension which 0 represents. Thus $R = 0$ signifies that there are no two things, t and u, such that $t\,R\,u$ is true—that nothing has the relation R to anything. Similarly, the universal-relation, 1, is the class of *all* couples (in the universe of discourse).

The inclusion, $R \subset S$, represents the assertion that every couple $(x; y)$ for which $x\,R\,y$ is true is also such that $x\,S\,y$ is true; or, to put it otherwise, that the class of couples $(x; y)$ for which $x\,R\,y$ is true is included in the class of couples $(u; v)$ for which $u\,S\,v$ is true. Perhaps the most satisfactory reading of $R \subset S$ is "The presence of the relation R implies the presence of the relation S". $R = S$, being equivalent to the pair, $R \subset S$ and $S \subset R$, signifies that R and S have the same extension—that the class of couples $(x; y)$ for which $x\,R\,y$ is true is identically the class of couples $(u; v)$ for which $u\,S\,v$ is true.

It is obvious that all the postulates, and hence all the propositions, of the Boole-Schröder Algebra hold for relations, so interpreted.

1·1 If R and S are relations (that is, if there is a class of couples $(x; y)$ such that $x\,R\,y$ is true, and a class of couples $(u; v)$ such that $u\,S\,v$ is true), then $R \times S$ is a relation (that is, there is a class of couples $(w; z)$ such that $w\,R\,z$ and $w\,S\,z$ are both true). If R and S be such that there is no couple $(w; z)$ for which $w\,R\,z$ and $w\,S\,z$ both hold, then $R \times S$ is the null-relation, 0 —i. e., the null-class of couples.

1·2 The class of couples $(x; y)$ for which $x\,R\,y$ and $x\,R\,y$ both hold is simply the class of couples for which $x\,R\,y$ holds.

1·3 The class of couples denoted by $R \times S$ is the same as that denoted by $S \times R$—namely, the class of couples $(x; y)$ such that $x\,R\,y$ and $x\,S\,y$ are both true.

1·4 The class of couples $(x; y)$ for which $x\,R\,y$, $x\,S\,y$, and $x\,T\,y$ all hold is identically the same in whatever order the relations be combined— i. e., $R \times (S \times T) = (R \times S) \times T$.

1·5 $R \times 0 = 0$—i. e., the product of the class of couples for which $x\,R\,y$ holds and the null-class of couples is the null-class of couples.

1·6 For every relation, R, there is a relation $-R$, the class of couples for which $x\,R\,y$ is false, and $-R$ is such that:

1·61 If the relation $R \times -S$ is null (that is, if there is no couple such that $x\,R\,y$ is true and $x\,S\,y$ is false), then $R \times S = R$ (that is, the class of couples for which $x\,R\,y$ is true is identically the class of couples for which $x\,R\,y$ and $x\,S\,y$ are both true); and

1·62 If $R \times S = R$ and $R \times -S = R$, then $R = 0$—i. e., if the class of couples for which $x \, R \, y$ and $x \, S \, y$ are both true is identically the class of couples for which $x \, R \, y$ is true, and if also the class of couples for which $x \, R \, y$ is true and $x \, S \, y$ is *false* is identically the class of couples for which $x \, R \, y$ is true, then the class of couples for which $x \, R \, y$ is true is null.

1·7 $1 = -0$—i. e., the universal class of couples is the negative of the null-class of couples, within the universe of discourse of couples.

1·8 $R + S = -(-R \times -S)$—i. e., the class of couples $(x; y)$ such that at least one of the two, $x \, R \, y$ and $x \, S \, y$, is true is the negative of the class of couples for which $x \, R \, y$ and $x \, S \, y$ are both false.

1·9 $R \times S = R$ is equivalent to $R \subset S$—i. e., if the class of couples $(x; y)$ for which $x \, R \, y$ and $x \, S \, y$ are both true is identical with the class of couples for which $x \, R \, y$ is true, then the presence of R implies the presence of S; and if the presence of R implies the presence of S, then the class of couples $(x; y)$ for which $x \, R \, y$ is true is identical with the class of couples for which $x \, R \, y$ and $x \, S \, y$ are both true.[33]

[33] For a further discussion of the logic of relations, see Chap. IV, Sect. V.

CHAPTER IV

SYSTEMS BASED ON MATERIAL IMPLICATION

We are concerned, in the present chapter, with the "calculus of propositions" or calculus of "material implication", and with its extension to propositional functions. We shall discover here two distinct modes of procedure, and it is part of our purpose to set these two methods side by side.

The first procedure takes the Boole-Schröder Algebra as its foundation, interprets the elements of this system as propositions, and adds to it a postulate which holds for propositions but not for logical classes. The result is what has been called the "Two-Valued Algebra", because the additional postulate results in the law: For any x, if $x \neq 1$, then $x = 0$, and if $x \neq 0$, then $x = 1$. This Two-Valued Algebra is one form of the calculus of propositions. The extension of the Two-Valued Algebra to propositions of the form φx_n, where x_n is an individual member of a class composed of x_1, x_2, x_3, etc., gives the calculus of propositional functions. Π and Σ functions have a special significance in this system, and the relation of "formal implication", $\Pi_x(\varphi x \subset \psi x)$, is particularly important. In terms of it, the logical properties of relations—including the properties treated in the last chapter but going beyond them—can be established. This is the type of procedure used by Peirce and Schröder.

The second method—that of *Principia Mathematica*—begins with the calculus of propositions, or calculus of material implication, in a form which is simpler and otherwise superior to the Two-Valued Algebra, then proceeds from this to the calculus of propositional functions and formal implication, and upon this last bases not only the treatment of relations but also the "calculus of classes".

It is especially important for the comprehension of the whole subject of symbolic logic that the *agreement in results* and the *difference of method*, of these two procedures, should be understood. Too often they appear to the student simply unrelated.

I. The Two-Valued Algebra[1]

If the elements a, b, ... p, q, etc., represent propositions, and $a \times b$ or $a\,b$ represent the joint assertion of a and b, then the assumptions of the

[1] See Schröder, *Algebra der Logik:* II, especially *Fünfzehnte Vorlesung.* An excellent summary is contained in Schröder's *Abriss* (ed. Müller), *Teil* II.

Boole-Schröder Algebra will all be found to hold for propositions, as was explained in the last chapter.[2] As was there made clear, $p = 0$ will represent "p is false", and $p = 1$, "p is true". Since 0 and 1 are unique, it follows that any two propositions, p and q, such that $p = 0$ and $q = 0$, or such that $p = 1$ and $q = 1$, are also such that $p = q$. $p = q$, in the algebra, represents a relation of extension or "truth value", not an equivalence of content or meaning.

$-p$ symbolizes the contradictory or denial of p.

The meaning of $p + q$ is readily determined from its definition,

$$p + q = -(-p -q)$$

$p + q$ is the denial of "p is false and q is false", or it is the proposition "At least one of the two, p and q, is true". $p + q$ may be read loosely, "Either p is true or q is true". The possibility that both p and q should be true is not excluded.

$p \subset q$ is equivalent to $p q = p$ and to $p -q = 0$. $p \subset q$ is the relation of material implication. We shall consider its properties with care later in the section. For the present, we may note simply that $p \subset q$ means exactly "It is false that p is true and q false". It may be read "If p is true, q is true", or "p (materially) implies q".

With the interpretations here given, all the postulates of the Boole-Schröder Algebra are true for propositions. Hence all the theorems will also be true for propositions. But there is an additional law which holds for propositions:

$$p = (p = 1)$$

"The proposition, p, is equivalent to 'p is true'". It follows immediately from this that

$$-p = (-p = 1) = (p = 0)$$

"$-p$ is equivalent to 'p is false'". It also follows that $-p = -(p = 1)$, and hence

$$-(p = 1) = (p = 0), \quad \text{and} \quad -(p = 0) = (p = 1)$$

"'$p = 1$ is false' is equivalent to $p = 0$", and "'$p = 0$ is false' is equivalent to $p = 1$". Thus the calculus of propositions is a *two-valued* algebra: every proposition is either $= 0$ or $= 1$, either true or false. We may, then, proceed as follows: All the propositions of the Boole-Schröder Algebra

---

[2] However, many of the theorems, especially those concerning functions, eliminations, and solutions, are of little or no importance in the calculus of propositions.

which were given in Chapter II may be regarded as already established in the Two-Valued Algebra. We may, then, simply add another division of propositions—the *additional* postulate of the Two-Valued Algebra and the *additional* theorems which result from it. Since the last division of theorems in Chapter II was numbered 8·, we shall number the theorems of this section 9·.

The additional postulate is:

9·01 For every proposition p, $p = (p = 1)$.

And for convenience we add the convention of notation:

9·02 $-(p = q)$ is equivalent to $p \neq q$.

As a consequence of 9·01, we shall have such expressions as $-(p = 1)$ and $-(p = 0)$. 9·02 enables us to use the more familiar notation, $p \neq 1$ and $p \neq 0$.

It follows immediately from 9·01 that the Two-Valued Algebra cannot be viewed as a wholly abstract mathematical system. For whatever p and 1 may be, $p = 1$ is a proposition. Hence the postulate asserts that any element, p, in the system, is a proposition. But even a *necessary* interpretation may be abstracted from in one important sense—no step in proof need be allowed to depend upon this interpretation. This is the procedure we shall follow, though it is not the usual one. It will appear shortly that the validity of the interpretations can be *demonstrated* within the system itself.

In presenting the consequences of 9·01 and 9·02, we shall indicate previous propositions by which any step in proof is taken, by giving the number of the proposition in square brackets. Theorems of Chapter II may, of course, be used exactly as if they were repeated in this chapter.

9·1 $-p = (p = 0)$.

[9·01] $-p = (-p = 1)$. And [3·2] $-p = 1$ is equivalent to $p = 0$.

9·12 $-p = (p \neq 1)$.

[9·01] $p = (p = 1)$. Hence [3·2] $-p = -(p = 1) = (p \neq 1)$.

9·13 $(p \neq 1) = (p = 0)$.

[9·1·12]

9·14 $(p \neq 0) = (p = 1)$.

[9·13, 3·2]

9·13 and 9·14 together express the fact that the algebra is two-valued. Every proposition is either true or false.

Up to this point—that is, throughout Chapter II—we have written the logical relations "If . . . , then . . .", "Either . . . or . . .", "Both . . . and . . .", etc., not in the symbols of the system but just as they would be written in arithmetic or geometry or any other mathematical system. We have had no right to do otherwise. That ". . . $\subset$ . . ." is *by interpretation* "If . . . , then . . .", and ". . . $+$ . . ." is by interpretation "Either . . . or . . .", does not warrant us in identifying the theorem "If $a \subset b$, then $-b \subset -a$" with "$(a \subset b) \subset (-b \subset -a)$". We have had no more reason to identify "If . . . , then . . ." in theorems with ". . . $\subset$ . . ." than a geometrician would have to identify the period at the end of a theorem with a geometrical point. The framework of logical relations in terms of which theorems are stated must be distinguished from the *content* of the system, even when that content is logic.

But we can *now prove* that we have a right to interchange the joint assertion of p and q with $p \times q$, "If p, then q", with $p \subset q$, etc. We can demonstrate that if p and q are members of the class K, then $p \subset q$ is a member of K, and that "If p, then q", is *equivalent to* $p \subset q$. And we can demonstrate that this is true not merely as a matter of interpretation but by the necessary laws of the system itself. We can thus prove that writing the logical relations involved in the theorems—"Either . . . or . . .," "Both . . . and . . .," "If . . . , then . . ."—in terms of $+$, $\times$, $\subset$, etc., is a valid procedure.

The theorems in which these things are proved are never needed hereafter, except in the sense of validating this interchange of symbols and their interpretation. Consequently we need not give them any section number.

(1) If p is an element in K, $p = 1$ and $p = 0$ are elements in K.

[9·01] If p is an element in K, $p = 1$ is an element in K.   [1·6] If p is an element in K, $-p$ is an element in K, and hence [9·1] $p = 0$ is an element in K.

(2) The two, p and q, are together equivalent to $p \times q$, or $p\,q$.

[9·01] $p\,q = (p\,q = 1)$.   [5·73] $p\,q = 1$ is equivalent to the pair, $p = 1$ and $q = 1$, and hence [9·01] to the pair, p and q.

(3) If p and q are elements in K, then $p \subset q$ is an element in K.

[4·9] $p \subset q$ is equivalent to $p - q = 0$, and hence [9·1] to $-(p - q)$. But if p and q are elements in K, [1·6, 1·1] $-(p - q)$ is an element in K.

(4) $-p$ is equivalent to "p is false".

[9·12] $-p = (p \neq 1)$, and [8·01] $p \neq 1$ is equivalent to "$p = 1$ is false", and hence [9·01] to "p is false".

(5) $p \subset q$ is equivalent to "If p, then q".

[5·64] $p \subset q$ gives "If $p = 1$, then $q = 1$", and hence [9·01] "If p, then q".

And "If p, then q" gives $p \subset q$, for [9·01] it gives "If $p = 1$, then $q = 1$", and

(*a*) Suppose as a fact $p = 1$. Then, by hypothesis, $q = 1$, and [2·2] $p \subset q$.

(*b*) Suppose that $p \neq 1$. Then [9·14] $p = 0$, and [5·63] $p \subset q$.

(6) If p and q are elements in K, then $p = q$ is an element in K.

[7·1] $p = q$ is equivalent to $p -q + -p\, q = 0$, and hence [9·1] to $-(p -q + -p\, q)$. Hence [1·6, 1·1, 3·35] Q.E.D.

(7) $p = q$ is equivalent to "p is equivalent to q".

[2·2] $p = q$ is equivalent to "$p \subset q$ and $q \subset p$". By (5) above, "$p \subset q$ and $q \subset p$" is equivalent to "If p, then q, and if q, then p". And this is equivalent to "p is equivalent to q".

(8) If p and q are elements in K, then $p \neq q$ is an element in K.

[9·02] $(p \neq q) = -(p = q)$.

Hence, by (6) above and 1·6, Q.E.D.

(9) $p \neq q$ is equivalent to "p is not equivalent to q".

By (4) and (2) above, Q.E.D.

(10) $p + q$ is equivalent to "At least one of the two, p and q, is true.

[1·8] $p + q = -(-p -q)$.

By (4) and (2) above, $-(-p -q)$ is equivalent to "It is false that (p is false and q is false)". And this is equivalent to "At least one of the two, p and q, is true".

In consideration of the above theorems, we can henceforth write "... $\subset$ ..." for "If ..., then ...", "... $=$ ..." for "... is equivalent to ...", "... $+$ ..." for "Either ... or ...", etc., for we have proved that not only all expressions formed from elements in K and the relations $\times$ and $+$ are elements in K, but also that expressions which involve $\subset$, and $=$, and $\neq$ are elements in the system of the Two-Valued Algebra. The equivalence of "If ..., then ..." with "... $\subset$ ...", of "Both ... and ..." with "... $\times$ ...", etc., is no longer a matter of interpretation but a *consequence* of 9·01, $p = (p = 1)$. Also, we can go back over the theorems of Chapter II and, *considering them as propositions of the Two-Valued Algebra*, we can replace "If ..., then ...", etc., by the symbolic equivalents.   Each theorem not wholly in symbols gives a corresponding theorem which is wholly in symbols.   But when we consider the Boole-Schröder Algebra, without the additional postulate, 9·01, this procedure is not valid.   It is valid only where 9·01 is one of the postulates— i. e., only in the system of the Two-Valued Algebra.

Henceforth we shall write all our theorems with $p \subset q$ for "If p, then q", $p = q$ for "p is equivalent to q", etc.   But in the *proofs* we shall frequently use "If . . . , then . . ." instead of ". . . $\subset$ . . . ", etc., because the symbolism sometimes renders the proof obscure and makes hard reading. (That this is the case is due to the fact that the Two-Valued Algebra does not have what we shall hereafter explain as the true "logistic" form.)

9·15 $0 \neq 1$.

$0 = 0$.   Hence [9·13] $0 \neq 1$.

9·16 $(p \neq q) = (-p = q) = (p = -q)$.

(1) If $p \neq q$ and $p = 1$, then $q \neq 1$ and [9·13] $q = 0$. And if $p = 1$, [3·2] $-p = 0$.   Hence $-p = q$.

(2) If $p \neq q$ and $p \neq 1$, then [9·13] $p = 0$, and [3·2] $-p = 1$. Hence if $p \neq q$, then $q \neq 0$, and [9·14] $q = 1 = -p$.

(3) If $-p = q$ and $q = 1$, then $-p = 1$, and [3·2] $p = 0$. Hence [9·15] $p \neq q$.

(4) If $-p = q$ and $q \neq 1$, then $-p \neq 1$, and [9·13] $-p = 0$. Hence [3·2] $p = 1$, and $p \neq q$.

By (1) and (2), if $p \neq q$, then $-p = q$.   And by (3) and (4), if $-p = q$, then $p \neq q$.   Hence $p \neq q$ and $-p = q$ are equivalent.

And [3·2] $(-p = q) = (p = -q)$.

This theorem illustrates the meaning of the relation, $=$, in the calculus of material implication.   If $p \neq q$, then either $p = 1$ and $q = 0$ or $p = 0$ and $q = 1$.   But if $p = 1$, then $-p = 0$, and if $p = 0$, then $-p = 1$.   Hence the theorem.   Let p represent "Caesar died", and q represent "There is no place like home".   If "Caesar died" is not equivalent to "There is no place like home", then "Caesar did not die" is equivalent to "There is no place like home".   The equivalence is one of *truth values*—$\{ = 0\}$ or $\{ = 1\}$—not of content or logical significance.

9·17 $p = (p = 1) = (p \neq 0) = (-p = 0) = (-p \neq 1)$.

[$9·01·13·14·16$]

9·18 $-p = (p = 0) = (p \neq 1) = (-p = 1) = (-p \neq 0)$.

[$9·1·13·14·16$]

9·2 $(p = 1)(p = 0) = 0.$

[2·4] $p -p = 0$.   And [9·01] $p = (p = 1)$; [9·1] $-p = (p = 0)$.
No proposition is both true and false.

9·21 $(p \neq 1)(p \neq 0) = 0.$

[2·4] $-p \, p = 0$.   And [9·18] $-p = (p \neq 1)$; [9·17] $p = (p \neq 0)$.

9·22 $(p = 1) + (p = 0) = 1.$

[4·8] $p + -p = 1$.   Hence [9·01·1] Q. E. D.
Every proposition is either true or false.

9·23 $(p \neq 1) + (p \neq 0) = 1.$

[4·8, 9·01·1]

Theorems of the same sort as the above, the proofs of which are obvious, are the following:

9·24 $(p \, q) = (p \, q = 1) = (p \, q \neq 0) = (p = 1)(q = 1) = (p \neq 0)(q \neq 0)$
$= (p \neq 0)(q = 1) = (p = 1)(q \neq 0) = -(-p + -q)$
$= (-p + -q = 0) = [(p = 0) + (q = 0) = 0]$
$= [(p \neq 1) + (q \neq 1) = 0],$ etc., etc.

9·25 $(p + q) = (p + q = 1) = (p + q \neq 0) = (p = 1) + (q = 1)$
$= (p \neq 0) + (q \neq 0) = -(-p -q) = [(p = 0)(q = 0) = 0]$
$= [(p \neq 1)(q \neq 1) \neq 1],$ etc., etc.

These theorems illustrate the variety of ways in which the same logical relation can be expressed in the Two-Valued Algebra. This is one of the defects of the system—its redundancy of forms. In this respect, the alternative method, to be discussed later, gives a much neater calculus of propositions.

We turn now to the properties of the relation **c**. We shall include here some theorems which do not require the additional postulate, 9·01, for the sake of bringing together the propositions which illustrate the meaning of "material implication".

9·3 $(p \subset q) = (-p + q) = (p -q = 0).$

[4·9] $(p \subset q) = (p -q = 0) = (-p + q = 1)$.
[9·01] $(-p + q = 1) = (-p + q)$.

"p materially implies q" is equivalent to "Either p is false or q is true", and to "It is false that p is true and q false".

Since $p \subset q$ has been proved to be an element in the system, "It is false that p materially implies q" may be symbolized by $-(p \subset q)$.

9·31 $-(p \subset q) = (-p + q = 0) = (p - q).$

   $[3·4]$ $-(-p + q) = p - q.$ And $[9·3]$ $-(p \subset q) = -(-p + q).$

   $[9·02]$ $-(-p + q) = (-p + q = 0).$

"p does not materially imply q" is equivalent to "It is false that either p is false or q is true", and to "p is true and q false".

9·32 $(p = 0) \subset (p \subset q).$

   $[5·63]$ $0 \subset q.$ Hence Q.E.D.

If p is false, then for any proposition q, p materially implies q. This is the famous—or notorious—theorem: "A false proposition implies any proposition".

9·33 $(q = 1) \subset (p \subset q).$

   $[5·61]$ $p \subset 1.$ Hence Q.E.D.

This is the companion theorem: "A true proposition is implied by any proposition".

9·34 $-(p \subset q) \subset (p = 1).$

   The theorem follows from 9·32 by the *reductio ad absurdum*, since if $-(p \subset q)$, then $[9·32]$ $p \neq 0$, and $[9·14]$ $p = 1.$

If there is any proposition, q, which p does not materially imply, then p is true. This is simply the inverse of 9·32.   A similar consequence of 9·33 is:

9·35 $-(p \subset q) \subset (q = 0).$

   If $-(p \subset q)$, then $[9·33]$ $q \neq 1$, and $[9·13]$ $q = 0.$

If p does not materially imply q, then q is false.

9·36 $-(p \subset q) \subset (p \subset -q);$ $-(p \subset q) \subset (-p \subset q);$ $-(p \subset q) \subset (-p \subset -q).$

   $[9·34·35]$ If $-(p \subset q)$, then $p = 1$ and $q = 0.$

   $[3·2]$ If $p = 1,$ $-p = 0,$ and if $q = 0,$ then $-q = 1.$

   $[9·32]$ If $-p = 0,$ then $-p \subset q$ and $-p \subset -q.$

   $[9·33]$ If $-q = 1,$ then $p \subset -q.$

If p does not materially imply q, then p materially implies the negative, or denial, of q, and the negative of p implies q, and the negative of p implies the negative of q. If "Today is Monday" does not materially imply "The moon is made of green cheese", then "Today is Monday" implies "The moon *is not* made of green cheese", and "Today *is not* Monday" implies "The moon is made of green cheese", and "Today *is not* Monday" implies "The moon *is not* made of green cheese".

   Some of the peculiar properties of material implication are due to the fact that the relations of the algebra were originally devised to represent the system of logical classes. But 9·36 exhibits properties of material implication which have no analogy amongst the relations of classes. 9·36 is a consequence of the additional postulate, $p = (p = 1)$. For classes, c represents "is contained in": but if a is not contained in b, it does not follow that a is contained in not-b—a may be partly in and partly outside of b.

9·37 $-(p \subset q) \subset (q \subset p)$.

[9·36] If $-(p \subset q)$, then $-p \subset -q$, and hence [3·1] $q \subset p$.

Of any two propositions, p and q, if p does not materially imply q, then q materially implies p.

9·38 $(p\,q) \subset [(p \subset q)(q \subset p)]$.

[9·24] $p\,q = (p = 1)(q = 1)$.   Hence [9·33] Q.E.D.

If p and q are both true, then each materially implies the other.

9·39 $(-p\,-q) \subset [(p \subset q)(q \subset p)]$.

[9·24] $-p\,-q = (-p = 1)(-q = 1) = (p = 0)(q = 0)$.
Hence [9·32] Q.E.D.

If p and q are both false, then each materially implies the other.

For any pair of propositions, p and q, there are four possibilities:

1) $p = 1$, $q = 1$: p true, q true.
2) $p = 0$, $q = 0$: p false, q false.
3) $p = 0$, $q = 1$: p false, q true.
4) $p = 1$, $q = 0$: p true, q false.

Now in the algebra, $0 \subset 0$, $1 \subset 1$, and $0 \subset 1$; but $1 \subset 0$ is false. Hence in the four cases, above, the material implications and equivalences are as follows:

1) $p \subset q$, $q \subset p$, $p = q$.
2) $p \subset q$, $q \subset p$, $p = q$.
3) $p \subset q$, $-(q \subset p)$, $p \neq q$.
4) $-(p \subset q)$, $q \subset p$, $p \neq q$.

This summarizes theorems 9·31–9·39. These relations hold regardless of the content or meaning of p and q. Thus $p \subset q$ and $p = q$ are not the "implication" and "equivalence" of ordinary logic, because, strictly speaking, p and q in the algebra are not "propositions" but simply the "truth values" of the propositions represented. In other words, material implication and material equivalence are relations of the *extension* of propositions, whereas the "implication" and "equivalence" of ordinary logic are relations of intension or meaning. But, as has been mentioned, the material implication, $p \subset q$, has one most important property in common with "q can be inferred from p" in ordinary logic; if p is true and q false, $p \subset q$ does not hold. And the relation of material equivalence, $p = q$, never connects a true proposition with a false one.

These theorems should make as clear as it can be made the exact meaning and character of material implication. This is important, since many theorems whose significance would otherwise be very puzzling follow from the unusual character of this relation.

Two more propositions, of some importance, may be given:

9·4 $(p \, q \subset r) = (q \, p \subset r) = [p \subset (q \subset r)] = [q \subset (p \subset r)].$

$\quad\quad$ [1·3] $p \, q = q \, p.$ Hence [3·2] $-(p \, q) = -(q \, p),$ and $[-(p \, q) + r]$
$\quad = [-(q \, p) + r].$
$\quad\quad$ But [9·3] $[-(p \, q) + r] = (p \, q \subset r),$ and $[-(q \, p) + r] = (q \, p \subset r).$
$\quad\quad$ And [3·41] $[-(p \, q) + r] = [(-p + -q) + r] = [-p + (-q + r)] = [p \subset (q \subset r)]$
$\quad\quad$ Similarly, $[-(q \, p) + r] = [q \subset (p \subset r)].$

This theorem contains Peano's Principle of Exportation,

$$[(p \, q) \subset r] \subset [p \subset (q \subset r)]$$

"If $p \, q$ implies r, then p implies that q implies r"; and his Principle of Importation,

$$[p \subset (q \subset r)] \subset [(p \, q) \subset r]$$

"If p implies that q implies r, then if p and q are both true, r is true."

9·5 $[(p \, q) \subset r] = [(p \, -r) \subset -q] = [(q \, -r) \subset -p].$

$\quad\quad$ [9·3] $[(p \, q) \subset r] = [-(p \, q) + r] = [(-p + -q) + r] = [(-p + r) + -q]$
$\quad\quad\quad\quad = [(-q + r) + -p] = [-(p \, -r) + -q] = [-(q \, -r) + -p].$
$\quad\quad$ [9·3] $[-(p \, -r) + -q] = [(p \, -r) \subset -q],$ and
$\quad\quad\quad\quad\quad\quad\quad\quad [-(q \, -r) + -p] = [(q \, -r) \subset -p].$

If p and q together imply r, then if p is true but r is false, q must be false, and if q is true but r is false, p must be false. This is a principle first stated by Aristotle, but especially important in Mrs. Ladd-Franklin's theory of the syllogism.

We have now given a sufficient number of theorems to characterize the Two-Valued Algebra—to illustrate the consequences of the additional postulate $p = (p = 1)$, and the properties of $p \subset q$. Any further theorems of the system will be found to follow readily from the foregoing.

A convention of notation which we shall make use of hereafter is the following: A sign $=$, unless enclosed in parentheses, takes precedence over any other sign; a sign $\subset$, unless enclosed in parentheses, takes precedence over any $+$ or $\times$; and the sign $+$, unless enclosed in parentheses, takes precedence over a relation $\times$. This saves many parentheses and brackets.

II. The Calculus of Propositional Functions. Functions of One Variable

The calculus of propositional functions is an extension of the Two-Valued Algebra to propositions which involve the values of variables. Following Mr. Russell,[3] we may distinguish propositions from propositional functions as follows: A proposition is any expression which is either true or false; a propositional function is an expression, containing one or more variables, which becomes a proposition when each of the variables is replaced by some one of its values.

There is one meaning of "Today is Monday" for which 'today' denotes ambiguously Jan. 1, or Jan. 2, or . . . , etc. For example, when we say "'Today is Monday' implies 'Tomorrow is Tuesday'", we mean that if Jan. 1 is Monday, then Jan. 2 is Tuesday; if Jan. 2 is Monday, then Jan. 3 is Tuesday; if July 4 is Monday, then July 5 is Tuesday, etc. 'Today' and 'tomorrow' are here variables, whose values are Jan. 1, Jan. 2, Jan. 3, etc., that is, all the different actual days. When 'today' is used in this variable sense, "Today is Monday" is sometimes true and sometimes false, or more accurately, it is true *for some values* of the variable 'today', and false for other values. "Today is Monday" is here a *propositional function*.

There is a quite different meaning of "Today is Monday" for which 'today' is not a variable but denotes just one thing—Jan. 22, 1916. In *this* sense, if "Today is Monday" is true it is always true. It is either simply true or simply false: its meaning and its truth or falsity cannot change. For this meaning of 'today', "Today is Monday" is a *proposition*. 'Today,' meaning Jan. 16, 1916, is one value of the *variable* 'today'. When this value is substituted for the variable, then the propositional function is turned into a proposition.

---

[3] See *Principles of Mathematics*, Chap. VII, and *Principia Mathematica*, I, p. 15. Mr. Russell carries out this distinction in ways which we do not follow. But so far as is here in question, his view is the one we adopt. *Principia Mathematica* is cited hereafter as *Principia*.

We may use φx, $\psi(x, y)$, $\zeta(x, y, z)$, etc., to represent propositional functions, in which the variable terms are x, or x and y, or x, y, and z, etc. These *propositional* functions must be carefully distinguished from the functions discussed in Chapter II. We there used f, F, and the Greek *capitals*, Φ, Ψ, etc., to indicate functions; here we use only Greek *small letters*. Also, for any function of one variable, we here omit any parenthesis around the variable—φx, ψy, ζx.

$f(x)$, $\Psi(x, y)$, etc., in Chapter II are confined to representing such expressions as can be formed from elements in the class K and the relations $\times$ and $+$. If x and y in $\Psi(x, y)$ are logical classes, then $\Psi(x, y)$ is some logical class, such as $x + y$ or $a x + b - y$. Or if x in $f(x)$ is a proposition, then $f(x)$ is some proposition such as $a x$ or $-x + b$. The *propositional* functions, φx, $\psi(x, y)$, $\zeta(x, y, z)$, etc., are subject to no such restriction. φx *becomes* a proposition when x is replaced by one of its values, but it does not necessarily become any such proposition as $a x$ or $-x + b$. 'x is Monday,' 'x is a citizen of y,' 'y is between x and z'—these are typical propositional functions. They are neither true nor false, but they become either true or false as soon as terms denoting individual things are substituted for the variables x, y, etc. All the functions in this chapter are such propositional functions, or expressions derived from them.

A fundamental conception of the theory of propositional functions is that of the "range of significance". The range of significance of a function is determined by the extent of the class, or classes, of terms which are values of its variables. All the terms which can be substituted for x, in φx, and 'make sense', constitute the range of φx. If φx be 'x is mortal', the range of this function is the aggregate of all the individual terms for which 'x is mortal' is *either true or false*. Thus the "range of significance" is to propositional functions what the "universe of discourse" is to class terms. Two propositional functions, φx and ψy, may be such that the class of values of x in φx, or the range of φx, is identical with the class of values of y in ψy, or the range of ψy. Or the two functions may have different ranges of significance. 'x is a man' and 'x is a poet' will have the same *range*, though the values of x for which they are *true* will differ. Any x for which 'x is a man' is either true or false, is also such that 'x is a poet' is either true or false. But some x's for which 'x is a poet' is either true or false are such that 'x precedes $x+1$' is nonsense. 'x is a poet' and 'x precedes $x+1$' have different ranges.[4] It is important to note that the

[4] According to Mr. Russell's "theory of types" (see *Principia*, I, pp. 41–42), the one fundamental restriction of the range of a propositional function is the principle that nothing

range of φx is determined, not by x, but by φ. φx and φy are the same function.

If we have a propositional function of two variables, say 'x is a citizen of y', we must make two substitutions in order to turn it into a proposition which is either true or false. And we conceive of two aggregates or classes— the class of values of the first variable, x, and the class of values of the second variable, y. These two classes may, for a given function, be identical, or they may be different. It depends upon the function. "John Jones is a citizen of Turkey" is either true or false; "Turkey is a citizen of John Jones" is nonsense. But "3 precedes 5" is either true or false, as is also "5 precedes 3". The range of x and of y in $\psi(x, y)$ depends upon ψ, not upon x and y.

A convenient method of representing the values of x in φx is by x_1, x_2, x_3, etc. This is not to presume that the number of such values of x in φx is finite, or even denumerable. Any sort of tag which would distinguish these values as individual would serve all the uses which we shall make of x_1, x_2, x_3, etc., equally well. If x_1, x_2, x_3, etc., are individuals,[5] then φx_1, φx_2, φx_3, etc., will be *propositions;* and φx_n will be a proposition. φx_3 is a proposition about a specified individual; φx_n is a proposition about 'a certain individual' which is not specified.[6] Similarly, if the values of x in $\psi(x, y)$ be x_1, x_2, x_3, etc., and the values of y be y_1, y_2, y_3, etc., then $\psi(x_2, y_3)$, $\psi(x_2, y_n)$, $\psi(x_m, y_n)$, etc., are propositions.

We shall now make a new use of the operators Π and Σ, giving them a meaning similar to, but not identical with, the meaning which they had in Chapter II. To emphasize this difference in use, the operators are here set in a different style of type. We shall let $\Sigma_x \varphi x$ represent $\varphi x_1 + \varphi x_2 + \varphi x_3 + \ldots$ to as many terms as there are distinct values of x in φx. And $\Pi_x \varphi x$ will represent $\varphi x_1 \times \varphi x_2 \times \varphi x_3 \times \ldots$ to as many terms as there are distinct values of x in φx. (We have heretofore abbreviated $a \times b$ to $a\,b$ or $a \cdot b$. But where propositional functions are involved, the form of expressions is

that presupposes the function, or a function of the same range, can be a value of the function. It seems to us that there are other restrictions, not derived from this, upon the range of a function. But, fortunately, it is not necessary to decide this point here.

[5] "Individuals" in the sense of being distinct values of x in φx—which is the only conception of "individual" which we require.

[6] It may be urged that φx_n is not a proposition but a propositional function. The question is most difficult, and we cannot enter upon it. But this much may be said: Whenever, and in whatever sense, statements about an unspecified individual can be *asserted*, φx_n is a proposition. If any object to this, we shall reply "A certain gentleman is confused". Peirce has discussed this question most acutely. (See above, pp. 93–94.)

likely to be complex. Consequently we shall, in this chapter, always write "products" with the sign ×.)

The fact that there might be an infinite set of values of x in φx does not affect the theoretical adequacy of our definitions. For nothing here depends upon the order of φx_m, φx_n, φx_p, and it is only required that the values of x which are distinct should be identifiable or "tagable". The objection that the values of x might not be even denumerable is more serious, but the difficulty may be met by a device to be mentioned shortly.

Since φx_1, φx_2, φx_3, etc., are propositions, $\varphi x_1 + \varphi x_2 + \varphi x_3 + \ldots$ is a proposition—the proposition, "Either φx_1 or φx_2 or φx_3 or ... etc.". Thus $\Sigma_x \varphi x$ represents "For some value of x (at least one), φx is true". And $\Sigma_x \varphi x$ is a proposition. Similarly, $\varphi x_1 \times \varphi x_2 \times \varphi x_3 \times \ldots$ is the joint assertion of φx_1 and φx_2 and φx_3, etc. Thus $\Pi_x \varphi x$ represents the proposition "For all values of x, φx is true". We may translate $\Sigma_x \varphi x$ loosely by "φx is *sometimes* true", and $\Pi_x \varphi x$ loosely by "φx is *always* true". This translation fails of literal accuracy inasmuch as the variations of x in φx may not be confined to differences of *time*.

The conception of a propositional function, φx, and of the class of values of the variable in this function, thus give us the new types of proposition, φx_3, φx_n, $\Sigma_x \varphi x$, and $\Pi_x \varphi x$. Since the laws of the Two-Valued Algebra hold for propositions generally, all the theorems of that system will be true when propositions such as the above are substituted for a, b, ... p, q, etc. (We must, of course, remember that while a, b, ... p, q, etc., in the Two-Valued Algebra represent propositions, x in φx, etc., is *not* a proposition but a variable whose values are individual things. In the theorems to follow, we shall sometimes need a symbol for propositions in which no variables are specified. To avoid any possible confusion, we shall represent such propositions by a capital letter, P.) We may, then, *assume as already proved* any theorem which can be got by replacing a, b, ... p, q, etc., in any proposition of the Two-Valued Algebra, by φx_3, φx_n, $\Sigma_x \varphi x$, or $\Pi_x \varphi x$. *Additional* theorems, which can be proved for propositions involving values of variables, will be given below. These are to be proved by reference to earlier theorems, in Chapter II and in Section I of this chapter. As before, the number of the theorem by which any step in proof is taken will be given in square brackets. Since the previous theorems are numbered up to 9·, the additional theorems of this section will be numbered beginning with 10·.

One additional assumption, beyond those of the Two-Valued Algebra, will be needed. The propositions which have been proved in sufficiently general form to be used where sums and products of more than three terms are in question all require for their demonstration the principle of mathematical induction.   If, then, we wish to use those theorems in the proofs of this section, we are confronted by the difficulty that the number of values of x in φx, and hence the number of terms in $\Sigma_x \varphi x$ and $\Pi_x \varphi x$ may not be finite.   And any use of mathematical induction, or of theorems dependent upon that principle for proof, will then be invalid in this connection.   Short of abandoning the proposed procedure, two alternatives are open to us: we can assume that the number of values of any variable in a propositional function is always finite; or we can assume that any law of the algebra which holds *whatever finite* number of elements be involved holds for any number of elements whatever.   The first of these assumptions would obviously be false.   But the second is true, and we shall make it.

This also resolves our difficulty concerning the possibility that the number of values of x in φx might not be even denumerable, and hence that the notation $\varphi x_1 + \varphi x_2 + \varphi x_3 + \dots$ and $\varphi x_1 \times \varphi x_2 \times \varphi x_3 \times \dots$ might be inadequate.   We can make the convention that if the number of values of x in any function, φx, be not finite, $\varphi x_1 + \varphi x_2 + \varphi x_3 + \dots$, or $\Sigma_x \varphi x$, and $\varphi x_1 \times \varphi x_2 \times \varphi x_3 \times \dots$, or $\Pi_x \varphi x$, shall be so dealt with that any theorem to be proved will be demonstrated to hold for *any finite* number of values of x in φx; and this being proved, our assumption allows us to extend the theorem to any case in which the values of the variable in the function are infinite in number.   This principle will be satisfactorily covered by the convention that $\varphi x_1 + \varphi x_2 + \varphi x_3 + \dots$ and $\varphi x_1 \times \varphi x_2 \times \varphi x_3 \times \dots$ shall always be supposed to have a *finite but undetermined* number of terms, and any theorem thus proved shall be presumed independent of the number of distinct values of any variable, x, which is involved.[7]

This postulate, and the convention which makes it operative, will be supposed to extend also to functions of any number of variables, and to sums, products, and negatives of functions.

No further postulates are required, but the following definitions are needed:

10·01 $\Sigma \varphi x = \Sigma_x \varphi x = \varphi x_1 + \varphi x_2 + \varphi x_3 + \dots$.   Def.

10·02 $\Pi \varphi x = \Pi_x \varphi x = \varphi x_1 \times \varphi x_2 \times \varphi x_3 \times \dots$.   Def.

10·03 $-\varphi x = -\{\varphi x\}$.   Def.

[7] This procedure, though not invalid, is far from ideal, as are many other details of this general method.   We shall gather the main criticisms together in the last section of this chapter.   But it is a fact that in spite of the many defects of the method, the results which it gives are without exception valid.

10·031 $-\varphi x_n = -\{\varphi x_n\}.$ Def.

10·04 $-\Pi_x \varphi x = -\{\Pi_x \varphi x\}.$ Def.

10·05 $-\Sigma_x \varphi x = -\{\Sigma_x \varphi x\}$ Def.

The last four merely serve to abbreviate the notation.

Elementary theorems concerning propositions which involve values of one variable are as follows:

10·1 $\Sigma \varphi x = -\Pi - \varphi x.$

[5·951] $\varphi x_1 + \varphi x_2 + \varphi x_3 + \ldots = -\{-\varphi x_1 \times -\varphi x_2 \times -\varphi x_3 \times \ldots\}.$

10·12 $\Pi \varphi x = -\Sigma - \varphi x.$

[5·95] $\varphi x_1 \times \varphi x_2 \times \varphi x_3 \times \ldots = -\{-\varphi x_1 + -\varphi x_2 + -\varphi x_3 + \ldots\}.$

10·1 states that "For some values of x, φx is true" is equivalent to the denial of "For all values of x, φx is false". 10·12 states that "For all values of x, φx is true" is equivalent to the denial of "For some values of x, φx is false". These two represent the extension of De Morgan's Theorem to propositions which involve values of variables. They might be otherwise stated: "It is true that *all* x is $\cdots$" is equivalent to "It is false that *some* x is *not* $\cdots$"; and "It is true that *some* x is $\cdots$" is equivalent to "It is false that *all* x is *not* $\cdots$".

10·2 $\Pi \varphi x \subset \varphi x_n.$

[5·99] $\varphi x_1 \times \varphi x_2 \times \varphi x_3 \times \ldots \subset \varphi x_1$
       and $\varphi x_1 \times \varphi x_2 \times \varphi x_3 \times \ldots \subset \varphi x_2$
       and $\varphi x_1 \times \varphi x_2 \times \varphi x_3 \times \ldots \subset \varphi x_3$, etc., etc.

10·21 $\varphi x_n \subset \Sigma \varphi x.$

[5·991] $\varphi x_1 \subset \varphi x_1 + \varphi x_2 + \varphi x_3 + \ldots$
       and $\varphi x_2 \subset \varphi x_1 + \varphi x_2 + \varphi x_3 + \ldots$
       and $\varphi x_3 \subset \varphi x_1 + \varphi x_2 + \varphi x_3 + \ldots$, etc., etc.

By 10·2, if φx is true for all values of x, then it is true for any given value of x, or "What is true of all is true of any given one". By 10·21, If φx is true for one given value of x, then it is true for *some* value of x, or "What is true of a certain one is true of some". It might be thought that the implication stated by 10·21 is reversible. But we do not have $\Sigma \varphi x \subset \varphi x_n$, because φx_n may be φx_2, and $\Sigma \varphi x \subset \varphi x_2$ would not hold generally. For example, let $\varphi x = $ "Today (x) is Monday". Then $\Sigma \varphi x$ will mean "Some day is Monday", but φx_n will mean "Today (Jan. 1) is Monday", or will mean "Today (Feb. 23) is Monday", etc. "Some day is Monday" does

not imply "Jan. 1 is Monday", and does not imply "Feb. 23 is Monday"—
does not imply that any one given day is Monday. x_n in φx_n means "a
certain value of x" in a sense which is not simply equivalent to "some
value of x". No translation of φx_n will give its exact significance in this
respect.

10·22 $\Pi \varphi x \subset \Sigma \varphi x.$

$\qquad$ [5·1, 10·2·21]

Whatever is true of all is true of some.

10·23 $\Pi \varphi x$ is equivalent to "Whatever value of x, in φx, x_n may be, φx_n".

$\qquad \Pi \varphi x = \varphi x_1 \times \varphi x_2 \times \varphi x_3 \times \ldots = (\varphi x_1 \times \varphi x_2 \times \varphi x_3 \times \ldots = 1)$ [9·01]

$\qquad$ And [5·971] $\varphi x_1 \times \varphi x_2 \times \varphi x_3 \times \ldots = 1$ is equivalent to the set
$\qquad \varphi x_1 = 1, \quad \varphi x_2 = 1, \quad \varphi x_3 = 1, \quad \ldots.$

$\qquad$ And [9·01] $\varphi x_n = 1$ is equivalent to φx_n.

$\qquad$ Hence $\Pi \varphi x$ is equivalent to the set $\varphi x_1, \varphi x_2, \varphi x_3, \ldots.$

This proposition is not tautological. It states the equivalence of the
product $\varphi x_1 \times \varphi x_2 \times \varphi x_3 \times \ldots$ with the system of separate propositions
$\varphi x_1, \varphi x_2, \varphi x_3$, etc. It is by virtue of the possibility of this proposition
that the translation of $\Pi \varphi x$ as "For all values of x, φx is true" is legitimate.
In this proof we make use of the principle, $p = (p = 1)$—the only case in
which it is directly required in the calculus of propositional functions.

By virtue of 10·23 we can pass directly from any theorem of the Two-
Valued Algebra to a corresponding theorem of the calculus of propositional
functions. If we have, for example, $p \subset p + q$, we have also "Whatever
value of x, in φx, x_n may be, $\varphi x_n \subset \varphi x_n + P$". And hence we have, by
10·23, $\Pi_x[\varphi x \subset \varphi x + P]$. We shall later see the importance of this: it
gives us, for every theorem concerning "material implication", a corresponding theorem concerning "formal implication".

Next, we give various forms of the principle by which any proposition
may be imported into, or exported out of, the scope of a Π or Σ operator.

10·3 $\Sigma \varphi x + P = \Sigma_x(\varphi x + P).$

$\qquad \Sigma \varphi x + P = (\varphi x_1 + \varphi x_2 + \varphi x_3 + \ldots) + P$

$\qquad \qquad = (\varphi x_1 + P) + (\varphi x_2 + P) + (\varphi x_3 + P) + \ldots$ [5·981]

$\qquad \qquad = \Sigma_x(\varphi x + P)$

10·31 $P + \Sigma \varphi x = \Sigma_x(P + \varphi x).$

$\qquad$ Similar proof.

10·3 may be read: "'Either for some x, φx is true, or P is true' is equivalent to 'For some x, either φx is true or P is true'''. And 10·31 may be read: "'Either P is true or, for some x, φx is true' is equivalent to 'For some x, either P is true or φx is true'''.

10·32 $\Pi \varphi x + P = \Pi_x(\varphi x + P).$

$$\begin{aligned}
\Pi \varphi x + P &= (\varphi x_1 \times \varphi x_2 \times \varphi x_3 \times \ldots) + P \\
&= (\varphi x_1 + P) \times (\varphi x_2 + P) \times (\varphi x_3 + P) \times \ldots \quad [5·941] \\
&= \Pi_x(\varphi x + P)
\end{aligned}$$

10·33 $P + \Pi \varphi x = \Pi_x(P + \varphi x).$

Similar proof.

"Either P is true or, for every x, φx is true" is equivalent to "For every x, either P is true or φx is true."

10·34 $\Sigma_x(\varphi x + P) = \Sigma_x(P + \varphi x).$

[4·3] $\Sigma \varphi x + P = P + \Sigma \varphi x.$ Hence [10·3·31] Q.E.D.

10·35 $\Pi_x(\varphi x + P) = \Pi_x(P + \varphi x).$

[10·32·33]

Exactly similar theorems hold where the relation of the two propositions is $\times$ instead of $+$. The proofs are so simple that only the first need be given.

10·36 $\Sigma \varphi x \times P = \Sigma_x(\varphi x \times P).$

$$\begin{aligned}
\Sigma \varphi x \times P &= (\varphi x_1 + \varphi x_2 + \varphi x_3 + \ldots) \times P \\
&= (\varphi x_1 \times P) + (\varphi x_2 \times P) + (\varphi x_3 \times P) + \ldots \quad [5·94] \\
&= \Sigma_x(\varphi x \times P)
\end{aligned}$$

"φx is true for some x, and P is true", is equivalent to "For some x, φx and P are both true".

10·361 $P \times \Sigma \varphi x = \Sigma_x(P \times \varphi x).$

10·37 $\Pi \varphi x \times P = \Pi_x(\varphi x \times P).$

10·371 $P \times \Pi \varphi x = \Pi_x(P \times \varphi x).$

10·38 $\Sigma_x(\varphi x \times P) = \Sigma_x(P \times \varphi x).$

10·381 $\Pi_x(\varphi x \times P) = \Pi_x(P \times \varphi x).$

We should perhaps expect that a proposition, P, might be imported into and exported out of the scope of an operator when the relation of P to the other member of the expression is $\subset$. But here the matter is not quite so simple.

10·4 $P \subset \Sigma \varphi x = \Sigma_x (P \subset \varphi x).$

$$[9·3] \quad P \subset \Sigma \varphi x = -P + \Sigma \varphi x = -P + (\varphi x_1 + \varphi x_2 + \varphi x_3 + \ldots)$$
$$= (-P + \varphi x_1) + (-P + \varphi x_2) + (-P + \varphi x_3) + \ldots$$
$$[5·981]$$
$$= (P \subset \varphi x_1) + (P \subset \varphi x_2) + (P \subset \varphi x_3) + \ldots \quad [9·3]$$
$$= \Sigma_x (P \subset \varphi x)$$

The relation $\subset$, in the above, is, of course, a material implication. But it is tedious to read continually "p materially implies q". We shall, then, translate $p \subset q$ simply by "p implies q", or by "If p, then q".

10·4 reads: "P implies that for some x, φx is true" is equivalent to "For some x, P implies that φx is true". This seems clear and obvious, but consider the next:

10·41 $\Sigma \varphi x \subset P = \Pi_x (\varphi x \subset P).$

$$[9·3] \quad \Sigma \varphi x \subset P = -\Sigma \varphi x + P = \Pi - \varphi x + P \quad [10·12]$$
$$= (-\varphi x_1 \times -\varphi x_2 \times -\varphi x_3 \times \ldots) + P$$
$$= (-\varphi x_1 + P) \times (-\varphi x_2 + P) \times (-\varphi x_3 + P) \ldots \quad [5·941]$$
$$= (\varphi x_1 \subset P) \times (\varphi x_2 \subset P) \times (\varphi x_3 \subset P) \ldots \quad [9·3]$$
$$= \Pi_x (\varphi x \subset P)$$

"'φx is true for some x' implies P" is equivalent to "For every x, φx implies P". It is easy to see that the second of these two expressions gives the first also: If φx *always implies* P, then if φx is *sometimes* true, P must be true. It is not so easy to see that $\Sigma \varphi x \subset P$ gives $\Pi_x (\varphi x \subset P)$. But we can put it thus: "If φx is ever true, then P is true" must mean "φx always implies P".

10·42 $P \subset \Pi \varphi x = \Pi_x (P \subset \varphi x).$

$$[9·3] \quad P \subset \Pi \varphi x = -P + \Pi \varphi x = -P + (\varphi x_1 \times \varphi x_2 \times \varphi x_3 \times \ldots)$$
$$= (-P + \varphi x_1) \times (-P + \varphi x_2) \times (-P + \varphi x_3) \times \ldots$$
$$[5·941]$$
$$= (P \subset \varphi x_1) \times (P \subset \varphi x_2) \times (P \subset \varphi x_3) \ldots \quad [9·3]$$
$$= \Pi_x (P \subset \varphi x)$$

"P implies that φx is true for every x" is equivalent to "For every x, P implies φx".

10·43 $\Pi \varphi x \subset P = \Sigma_x (\varphi x \subset P).$

$$[9·3] \quad \Pi \varphi x \subset P = -\Pi \varphi x + P = \Sigma - \varphi x + P \quad [10·1]$$
$$= (-\varphi x_1 + -\varphi x_2 + -\varphi x_3 + \ldots) + P$$

$$= (-\varphi x_1 + P) + (-\varphi x_2 + P) + (-\varphi x_3 + P) + \ldots$$
$$[5 \cdot 981]$$
$$= (\varphi x_1 \subset P) + (\varphi x_2 \subset P) + (\varphi x_3 \subset P) + \ldots \quad [9 \cdot 3]$$
$$= \Sigma_x (\varphi x \subset P)$$

"'φx is true for every x' implies that P is true" is equivalent to "For some x, φx implies P". At first sight this theorem seems to commit the "fallacy of division" going one way, and the "fallacy of composition" going the other. It suggests the ancient example about the separate hairs and baldness. Suppose φx be "If x is a hair of Mr. Blank's, x has fallen out". And let P be "Mr. Blank is bald". Then $\Pi \varphi x \subset P$ will represent "If all of Mr. Blank's hairs have fallen out, then Mr. Blank is bald". And $\Sigma_x (\varphi x \subset P)$ will represent "There is some hair of Mr. Blank's such that if this hair has fallen out, Mr. Blank is bald". In this example, $\Pi \varphi x \subset P$ is obviously true, but $\Sigma_x (\varphi x \subset P)$ is dubious, and their equivalence seems likewise doubtful. The explanation of the equivalence is this: we here deal with material implication, and $\varphi x_n \subset P$ means simply "It is false that (φx_n is true but P is false)". $\Pi \varphi x \subset P$ means, in this example, "It is false that all Mr. Blank's hairs have fallen out but Mr. Blank is not bald"; and $\Sigma_x (\varphi x \subset P)$ means "There is some one of Mr. Blank's hairs such that 'This hair has fallen out but Mr. Blank is not bald' is false". No necessary connection is predicated between the falling out of any single hair and baldness—material implication is not that type of relation.

If we compare the last four theorems, we observe that an operator in the *consequent* of an implication is not changed by being extended in scope to include the whole relation, but an operator in the *antecedent* is changed from Π to Σ, from Σ to Π. This is due to the fact that $p \subset q$ is equivalent to $-p + q$, where the sign of the antecedent changes but the consequent remains the same; and to the law $-\Pi() = \Sigma-()$, $-\Sigma() = \Pi-()$.

The above principles, connecting any proposition, P, with a propositional function and its operator, are much used in later proofs. In fact, *all* the proofs *can* be carried out simply by the various forms of this principle and theorems $10 \cdot 1$–$10 \cdot 23$. Since P, in the above, may be any proposition, ψx_n, $\Sigma \psi x$, $\Pi \psi x$, etc., can be substituted for P in these theorems.

$(\varphi x + \psi x)$ and $(\varphi x \times \psi x)$ are, of course, functions of x. In order that $(\varphi x + \psi x)$ be significant, φx must be significant and ψx must be significant, and it is further requisite that "Either φx or ψx" have meaning. Such considerations determine the range of significance of complex functions like $(\varphi x + \psi x)$ and $(\varphi x \times \psi x)$. A value of x in such a function must be at once a value of x in φx and a value of x in ψx: x_n in φx_n and in ψx_n, in $(\varphi x_n + \psi x_n)$, denotes identically the same individual.

10·5 $\Sigma \varphi x + \Sigma \psi x = \Sigma_x(\varphi x + \psi x)$.

Since addition is associative and commutative,

$$\begin{aligned}
\Sigma \varphi x + \Sigma \psi x &= (\varphi x_1 + \varphi x_2 + \varphi x_3 + \ldots) + (\psi x_1 + \psi x_2 + \psi x_3 + \ldots) \\
&= (\varphi x_1 + \psi x_1) + (\varphi x_2 + \psi x_2) + (\varphi x_3 + \psi x_3) + \ldots \\
&= \Sigma_x(\varphi x + \psi x)
\end{aligned}$$

"Either for some x, φx, or for some x, ψx" is equivalent to "For some x, either φx or ψx".

If it be supposed that the functions, φx and ψx, may have different ranges—i. e., that the use of the same letter for the variable is not indicative of the range—then $\Sigma \varphi x + \Sigma \psi x$ might have meaning when $\Sigma_x(\varphi x + \psi x)$ did not. But in such a case the proposition which states their equivalence will not have meaning. We shall make the convention that x_n in φx_n and x_n in ψx_n are identical, not only in $(\varphi x_n + \psi x_n)$ and $(\varphi x_n \times \psi x_n)$, but wherever φx and ψx are connected, as in $\Sigma \varphi x + \Sigma \psi x$. Where there is no such presumption, it is always possible to use different letters for the variable, as $\Sigma \varphi x + \Sigma \psi y$. But even without this convention, the above theorem will always be true when it is significant—i. e., it is never false— and a similar remark applies to the other theorems of this section.

10·51 $\Pi \varphi x \times \Pi \psi x = \Pi_x(\varphi x \times \psi x)$.

Since $\times$ is associative and commutative, similar proof.

We might expect $\Sigma \varphi x \times \Sigma \psi x = \Sigma_x(\varphi x \times \psi x)$ to hold, but it does not. "For some x, x is ugly, and for some x, x is beautiful", is not equivalent to, "For some x, x is ugly and x is beautiful". Instead of an equivalence, we have an implication:

10·52 $\Sigma_x(\varphi x \times \psi x) \subset \Sigma \varphi x \times \Sigma \psi x$.

$$\Sigma_x(\varphi x \times \psi x) = (\varphi x_1 \times \psi x_1) + (\varphi x_2 \times \psi x_2) + (\varphi x_3 \times \psi x_3) + \ldots$$

[5·2] $(\varphi x_n \times \psi x_n) \subset \varphi x_n$, and $(\varphi x_n \times \psi x_n) \subset \psi x_n$

Hence [5·31] $\Sigma_x(\varphi x \times \psi x) \subset \Sigma \varphi x$, and $\Sigma_x(\varphi x \times \psi x) \subset \Sigma \psi x$

Hence [5·34] $\Sigma_x(\varphi x \times \psi x) \subset \Sigma \varphi x \times \Sigma \psi x$

Similarly, $\Pi \varphi x + \Pi \psi x = \Pi_x(\varphi x + \psi x)$ fails to hold. "Either for every x, x is ugly, or for every x, x is beautiful", is not equivalent to, "For every x, either x is ugly or x is beautiful". Some x's may be ugly and others beautiful. But we have:

10·53 $\Pi\varphi x + \Pi\psi x \subset \Pi_x(\varphi x + \psi x).$

[5·21] $\varphi x_n \subset (\varphi x_n + \psi x_n),$ and $\psi x_n \subset (\varphi x_n + \psi x_n)$

Hence [5·3] $\Pi\varphi x \subset \Pi_x(\varphi x + \psi x),$ and $\Pi\psi x \subset \Pi_x(\varphi x + \psi x)$

Hence [5·33] $\Pi\varphi x + \Pi\psi x \subset \Pi_x(\varphi x + \psi x)$

In the proof of the last two theorems, we write a lemma for φx_n instead of writing it for φx_1, for φx_2, for φx_3, etc. For example, in 10·52 we write $(\varphi x_n \times \psi x_n) \subset \varphi x_n$, instead of writing

$$(\varphi x_1 \times \psi x_1) \subset \varphi x_1$$
$$(\varphi x_2 \times \psi x_2) \subset \varphi x_2$$
$$(\varphi x_3 \times \psi x_3) \subset \varphi x_3, \text{ etc., etc.}$$

The proofs are somewhat more obvious with this explanation. This method of writing such lemmas will be continued.

With two propositional functions, φx and ψx, we can form two implication relations, $\Sigma_x(\varphi x \subset \psi x)$ and $\Pi_x(\varphi x \subset \psi x)$. But $\Sigma_x(\varphi x \subset \psi x)$ states only that there is a value of x for which either φx is false or ψx is true: and this relation conveys so little information that it is hardly worth while to study its properties.

$\Pi_x(\varphi x \subset \psi x)$ is the relation of "formal implication"—"For every x, at least one of the two, 'φx is false' and 'ψx is true', is a true statement". The *negative* of $\Pi_x(\varphi x \subset \psi x)$ is $\Sigma_x(\varphi x \times -\psi x)$, so that $\Pi_x(\varphi x \subset \psi x)$ may also be read "It is false that there is any x such that φx is true and ψx false". The material implication, $p \subset q$, states only "At least one of the two, 'p is false' and 'q is true', is a true statement"; or, "It is false that p is true and q false". The material implication, $\varphi x_n \subset \psi x_n$, states only "At least one of the two, 'φ is false of x_n' and 'ψ is true of x_n', is a true statement"; or "It is false that φx_n is true and ψx_n is false". But the *formal* implication, $\Pi_x(\varphi x \subset \psi x)$, states that *however* x_n *be chosen*, it is false that φx_n is true and ψx_n is false—in the whole range of φx and ψx, there is not a case in which φx is true and ψx false. To put it another way, $\Pi_x(\varphi x \subset \psi x)$ means "Whatever has the predicate φ has also the predicate ψ".

This relation has more resemblance to the ordinary meaning of "implies" than material implication has. But formal implication, it should be remembered, is simply a class or aggregate of material implications; $\Pi_x(\varphi x \subset \psi x)$ is simply the joint assertion of $\varphi x_1 \subset \psi x_1$, $\varphi x_2 \subset \psi x_2$, $\varphi x_3 \subset \psi x_3$, etc., where each separate assertion is a material implication.

The properties of formal implication are especially important, because upon this relation are based certain derivatives in the calculus of classes and in the calculus of relations.

10·6 $\Pi_x(\varphi x \subset \psi x) = \Pi_x(-\varphi x + \psi x) = \Pi_x -(\varphi x \times -\psi x)$.

$\quad$ [9·3] $\varphi x_n \subset \psi x_n = -\varphi x_n + \psi x_n = -(\varphi x_n \times -\psi x_n)$

Hence [10·23] Q.E.D.

10·61 $\Pi_x(\varphi x \subset \psi x) \subset (\varphi x_n \subset \psi x_n)$.

$\quad$ [10·2]

If φx formally implies ψx, then φx_n materially implies ψx_n.

10·611 $[\Pi_x(\varphi x \subset \psi x) \times \varphi x_n] \subset \psi x_n$.

$\quad$ [9·4, 10·61]

If φx formally implies ψx and φ is true of x_n, then ψ is true of x_n. This is one form of the syllogism in *Barbara*: for example, "If for every x, 'x is a man' implies 'x is a mortal', and Socrates is a man, then Socrates is a mortal".

10·62 $\Pi_x(\varphi x \subset \psi x) \subset \Sigma_x(\varphi x \subset \psi x)$.

$\quad$ [10·22]

10·63 $\Pi_x(\varphi x \subset \psi x) \subset (\Pi \varphi x \subset \Pi \psi x)$.

$\quad$ [10·61] If $\Pi_x(\varphi x \subset \psi x)$, then $\varphi x_n \subset \psi x_n$

$\quad$ Hence [5·3] Q.E.D.

10·631 $[\Pi_x(\varphi x \subset \psi x) \times \Pi \varphi x] \subset \Pi \psi x$.

$\quad$ [9·4, 10·62]

If φx always implies ψx and φx is always true, then ψx is always true.

10·64 $\Pi_x(\varphi x \subset \psi x) \subset (\Sigma \varphi x \subset \Sigma \psi x)$.

$\quad$ [10·61, 5·31]

10·641 $[\Pi_x(\varphi x \subset \psi x) \times \Sigma \varphi x] \subset \Sigma \psi x$.

$\quad$ [9·4, 10·64]

If φx always implies ψx and φx is sometimes true, then ψx is sometimes true.

10·65 $[\Pi_x(\varphi x \subset \psi x) \times \Pi_x(\psi x \subset \zeta x)] \subset \Pi_x(\varphi x \subset \zeta x)$.

$\quad$ [10·61] If $\Pi_x(\varphi x \subset \psi x)$ and $\Pi_x(\psi x \subset \zeta x)$, then $\varphi x_r \subset \psi x_n$ and $\psi x_n \subset \zeta x_n$.

$\quad$ Hence [5·1] whatever value of x, x_n may be, $\varphi x_n \subset \zeta x_n$.

$\quad$ Hence [10·23] $\Pi_x(\varphi x \subset \zeta x)$

This theorem states that formal implication is a transitive relation. It is another form of the syllogism in *Barbara*. For example let $\varphi x = $ 'x is a Greek', $\psi x = $ 'x is a man', and $\zeta x = $ 'x is a mortal'; $10 \cdot 65$ will then read: "If for every x, 'x is a Greek' implies 'x is a man', and for every x, 'x is a man' implies 'x is a mortal', then for every x, 'x is a Greek' implies 'x is a mortal'".

$10 \cdot 65$ may also be given the form:

10·651 $\Pi_x(\varphi x \subset \psi x) \subset [\Pi_x(\psi x \subset \zeta x) \subset \Pi_x(\varphi x \subset \zeta x)]$.

   [9·4, 10·65]

10·652 $\Pi_x(\psi x \subset \zeta x) \subset [\Pi_x(\varphi x \subset \psi x) \subset \Pi_x(\varphi x \subset \zeta x)]$.

   [9·4, 10·65]

10·66 $\Pi_x(\varphi x \subset \psi x) = \Pi_x(-\psi x \subset -\varphi x)$.

   [3·1] $(\varphi x_n \subset \psi x_n) = (-\psi x_n \subset -\varphi x_n)$
   Hence [2·2, 5·3] Q.E.D.

Any further theorems concerning formal implication can be derived from the foregoing.

"Formal equivalence" is reciprocal formal implication, just as material equivalence is reciprocal material implication. The properties of formal equivalence follow immediately from those of formal implication.

10·67 $\Pi_x(\varphi x = \psi x) = [\Pi_x(\varphi x \subset \psi x) \times \Pi_x(\psi x \subset \varphi x)]$.

   Whatever value of x, x_n may be, [2·2] $\varphi x_n = \psi x_n$ is equivalent to the pair, $\varphi x_n \subset \psi x_n$ and $\psi x_n \subset \varphi x_n$.
   Hence [10·23] Q.E.D.

10·68 $[\Pi_x(\varphi x = \psi x) \times \Pi_x(\psi x = \zeta x)] \subset \Pi_x(\varphi x = \zeta x)$.

   Whatever value of x, x_n may be, if $\varphi x = \psi x$ and $\psi x = \zeta x$, then $\varphi x = \zeta x$.   Hence [10·23] Q.E.D.

10·681 $\Pi_x(\varphi x = \psi x) \subset [\Pi_x(\psi x = \zeta x) \subset \Pi_x(\varphi x = \zeta x)]$.

   [10·68, 9·4]

10·682 $\Pi_x(\psi x = \zeta x) \subset [\Pi_x(\varphi x = \psi x) \subset \Pi_x(\varphi x = \zeta x)]$.

   [10·68, 9·4]

Formal equivalence, as indicated by the last three theorems, is a transitive relation.

10·69 $\Pi_x(\varphi x = \psi x) \subset (\varphi x_n = \psi x_n)$; $\Pi_x(\varphi x = \psi x) \subset (\Pi \varphi x = \Pi \psi x)$;   and $\Pi_x(\varphi x = \psi x) \subset (\Sigma \varphi x = \Sigma \psi x)$.

   [2·2, 10·61·62·63]

10·691 $\Pi_x(\varphi x = \psi x) = \Pi_x(-\varphi x = -\psi x)$.

[3·2, 10·23]

If we wish to investigate the propositions which can be formed from functions of the type of $(\varphi x \times \psi y)$ and $(\varphi x + \psi y)$, where the range of significance of φx may differ from that of ψy, we find that these will involve two operators—$\Sigma_x\Pi_y(\varphi x; \psi y)$, $\Pi_y\Sigma_x(\varphi x; \psi y)$, etc. And these are special cases of a function of two variables. $(\varphi x \times \psi y)$ and $(\varphi x + \psi y)$ are special cases of $\zeta(x, y)$. Hence we must first investigate functions of two variables in general.

III. Propositional Functions of Two or More Variables

A propositional function of two variables, $\varphi(x, y)$, gives the derivative propositions $\varphi(x_m, y_n)$, $\Pi_x\varphi(x, y_n)$, $\Sigma_x\Sigma_y\varphi(x, y)$, $\Sigma_y\Pi_x\varphi(x, y)$, etc. The range of significance of $\varphi(x, y)$ will comprise all the pairs (x, y) such that $\varphi(x, y)$ is either true or false. We here conceive of a class of individuals, x_1, x_2, x_3, etc., and a class of individuals, y_1, y_2, y_3, etc., such that for any one of the x's and any one of the y's, $\varphi(x, y)$ is either true or false.

As has already been pointed out, the function may be such that the class of values of x is the same as the class of values of y, or the values of x may be distinct from the values of y. If, for example, $\varphi(x, y)$ be "x is brother of y", the class of x's for which $\varphi(x, y)$ is significant consists of identically the same members as the class of y's for which $\varphi(x, y)$ is significant.[9] In such a case, the range of significance of $\varphi(x, y)$ is the class of all the ordered couples which can be formed by combining any member of the class with itself or with any other. Thus if the members of such a class be a_1, a_2, a_3, etc., the class of couples in question will be[10]

$$(a_1, a_1), \ (a_1, a_2), \ (a_1, a_3), \ \ldots$$
$$(a_2, a_1), \ (a_2, a_2), \ (a_2,\,a_3), \ \ldots$$
$$(a_3, a_1), \ (a_3, a_2), \ (a_3, a_3), \ \ldots$$
$$\ldots \text{ Etc., etc.}$$

But if $\varphi(x, y)$ represent "x is a citizen of y", or "x is a proposition about y", or "x is a member of the class y", the class of x's and the class of y's for which $\varphi(x, y)$ is significant will be mutually exclusive.

---

[9] Presuming that "A is brother of A" is significant—i. e., false.

[10] Schröder treats all relatives as derived from such a class of ordered couples. (See *Alg. Log.*, iii, first three chapters.) But this is an unnecessary restriction of the logic of relatives.

Although $\varphi(x, y)$ represents some relation of x and y, it does not necessarily represent any relation of the algebra, such as $x \subset y$ or $x = y$; and it *cannot* represent relations which are not assertable.

$\varphi(x_1, y)$, $\varphi(x_2, y)$, etc., are propositional functions of one variable, y. Hence $\Pi_y\varphi(x_1, y)$, $\Pi_y\varphi(x_2, y)$, $\Sigma_y\varphi(x_1, y)$, etc., are *propositions*, the meaning and properties of which follow from preceding definitions and theorems. And $\Pi_y\varphi(x, y)$, $\Sigma_y\varphi(x, y)$, $\Pi_x\varphi(x, y)$, and $\Sigma_x\varphi(x, y)$ are propositional functions of one variable. We can, then, define propositions involving two variables and two operators, as follows:

11·01 $\Pi_x\Pi_y\varphi(x, y) = \Pi_x\{\Pi_y\varphi(x, y)\}$.   Def.

11·02 $\Sigma_x\Pi_y\varphi(x, y) = \Sigma_x\{\Pi_y\varphi(x, y)\}$.   Def.

11·03 $\Pi_x\Sigma_y\varphi(x, y) = \Pi_x\{\Sigma_y\varphi(x, y)\}$.   Def.

11·04 $\Sigma_x\Sigma_y\varphi(x, y) = \Sigma_x\{\Sigma_y\varphi(x, y)\}$.   Def.

It will be seen from these definitions that our explanation of the range of significance of functions of two variables was not strictly required; it follows from the explanation for functions of one variable. The same convention regarding the number of values of variables and interpretation of the propositions is also extended from the theory of functions of one variable to the theory of functions of two.

(Where the first variable has a subscript, the comma between the two will be omitted: $\varphi(x_2y)$ is $\varphi(x_2, y)$, etc.)

Since $\Pi_y\varphi(x, y)$ is a propositional function of one variable, x, the definition, 10·02, gives us

$$\Pi_x\Pi_y\varphi(x, y) = \Pi_x\{\Pi_y\varphi(x, y)\} = \Pi_y\varphi(x_1y) \times \Pi_y\varphi(x_2y) \times \Pi_y\varphi(x_3y) \times \ldots$$

And the expansion of this last expression, again by 10·02, is

$$\{\varphi(x_1y_1) \times \varphi(x_1y_2) \times \varphi(x_1y_3) \times \ldots\}$$
$$\times \{\varphi(x_2y_1) \times \varphi(x_2y_2) \times \varphi(x_2y_3) \times \ldots\}$$
$$\times \{\varphi(x_3y_1) \times \varphi(x_3y_2) \times \varphi(x_3y_3) \times \ldots\}$$
$$\times \ldots \text{ Etc., etc.}$$

And similarly, by 10·01,

$$\Sigma_x\Pi_y\varphi(x, y) = \Sigma_x\{\Pi_y\varphi(x, y)\} = \Pi_y\varphi(x_1y) + \Pi_y\varphi(x_2y) + \Pi_y\varphi(x_3y) + \ldots$$

And the expansion of the last expression, by 10·02, is

$$\{\varphi(x_1y_1) \times \varphi(x_1y_2) \times \varphi(x_1y_3) \times \ldots\}$$
$$+ \{\varphi(x_2y_1) \times \varphi(x_2y_2) \times \varphi(x_2y_3) \times \ldots\}$$
$$+ \{\varphi(x_3y_1) \times \varphi(x_3y_2) \times \varphi(x_3y_3) \times \ldots\}$$
$$+ \ldots \text{ Etc., etc.}$$

Or, in general, any propositional function with two operators is expanded into a two-dimensional array of propositions as follows:

(1) The operator nearest the function indicates the relation (+ or ×) between the constituents *in each line*.

(2) The subscript of the operator nearest the function indicates the letter which varies *within the lines*.

(3) The operator to the left indicates the relation (+ or ×) *between each two lines*.

(4) The subscript of the operator to the left indicates the letter which varies *from line to line*.

Some caution must be exercised in interpreting such propositions as $\Sigma_x\Pi_y\varphi(x, y)$, etc. It is usually sufficient to read $\Sigma_x\Pi_y$ "For some x and every y", but strictly it should be "For some x, every y is such that". Thus $\Sigma_x\Pi_y\varphi(x, y)$ should be "For some x, every y is such that $\varphi(x, y)$ is true". And $\Pi_y\Sigma_x\varphi(x, y)$ should be "For every y, some x is such that $\varphi(x, y)$ is true". The two here chosen illustrate the necessity of caution, which may be made clear as follows:

$$\Sigma_x\Pi_y\varphi(x, y) \; = \; \Pi_y\varphi(x_1y) + \Pi_y\varphi(x_2y) + \Pi_y\varphi(x_3y) + \ldots$$

That is, $\Sigma_x\Pi_y\varphi(x, y)$ means "Either for x_1 and every y, $\varphi(x, y)$ is true, or for x_2 and every y, $\varphi(x, y)$ is true, or for x_3 and every y, $\varphi(x, y)$ is true, . . . or for some other particular x and every y, $\varphi(x, y)$ is true". On the other hand,

$$\Pi_y\Sigma_x\varphi(x, y) \; = \; \Sigma_x\varphi(x, y_1) \times \Sigma_x\varphi(x, y_2) \times \Sigma_x\varphi(x, y_3) \times \ldots$$

That is, $\Pi_y\Sigma_x\varphi(x, y)$ means "For some x and y_1, $\varphi(x, y)$ is true, *and* for some x and y_2, $\varphi(x, y)$ is true, *and* for some x and y_3, $\varphi(x, y)$ is true, *and* . . ."; or "Given *any* y, there is one x (at least) such that $\varphi(x, y)$ is true". The following illustration of the difference of these two is given in *Principia Mathematica*: [11] Let $\varphi(x, y)$ be the propositional function "If y is a proper fraction, then x is a proper fraction greater than y". Then for all values of y, we have $\Sigma_x\varphi(x, y_n)$, so that $\Pi_y\Sigma_x\varphi(x, y)$ is satisfied. In fact, $\Pi\,\Sigma_x\varphi(x, y)$ expresses the proposition: "If y is a proper fraction, then there is always a proper fraction greater than y". But $\Sigma_x\Pi_y\varphi(x, y)$ expresses the proposition: "There is a proper fraction which is greater than any proper fraction", which is false.

In this example, if we should read $\Sigma_x\Pi_y$ "For some x and every y";

[11] See I, p. 161.

$\Pi_y\Sigma_x$ "For every y and some x", we should make equivalent these two very different propositions. But cases where this caution is required are infrequent, as we shall see.

Where both operators are Π or both Σ, the two-dimensional array of propositions can be turned into a one-dimensional array, since every relation throughout will be in the one case $\times$, in the other $+$, and both of these are associative and commutative. It follows from our discussion of the range of significance of a function of two variables that any such function, $\varphi(x, y)$, may be treated as a function of the *single* variable, the *ordered couple*, (x, y). Hence we can make the further conventions:

11·05 $\Sigma_x\Sigma_y\varphi(x, y) = \Sigma_{(x,\ y)}\varphi(x, y) = \Sigma_{x,\ y}\varphi(x, y).$

11·06 $\Pi_x\Pi_y\varphi(x, y) = \Pi_{(x,\ y)}\varphi(x, y) = \Pi_{x,\ y}\varphi(x, y).$

The second half of each of these serves merely to simplify notation.

11·07 If x_r and y_s be any values of x and y, respectively, in $\varphi(x, y)$, there is a value of (x, y)—say, $(x, y)_n$—such that $\varphi(x, y)_n = \varphi(x_r y_s)$.

11·05 and 11·06 could be derived from 11·07, but the process is tedious, and since our interest in such a derivation would be purely incidental, we prefer to set down all three as assumptions.

If we wish to identify a given constituent of $\Sigma_{x,\ y}\varphi(x, y)$ with a constituent of $\Sigma_x\Sigma_y\varphi(x, y)$, some convention of the order of terms in $\Sigma_{x,\ y}\varphi(x, y)$ is required, because if the order of constituents in $\Sigma_x\Sigma_y\varphi(x, y)$ be unaltered, this identification will be impossible unless the number of values of y is determined—which, by our convention, need not be the case. Hence we make, concerning the order of terms in $\Sigma_{x,\ y}\varphi(x, y)$, the following convention: $\varphi(x_m y_n)$ precedes $\varphi(x_r y_s)$ if $m + n < r + s$, and where $m + n = r + s$, if $n < s$. Thus the order of terms in $\Sigma_{x,\ y}\varphi(x, y)$ will be

$$\varphi(x_1 y_1) + \varphi(x_2 y_1) + \varphi(x_1 y_2) + \varphi(x_3 y_1) + \varphi(x_2 y_2) + \varphi(x_1 y_3) + \varphi(x_4 y_1) + \ldots$$

This arrangement determines an order independent of the number of values of x, or of y, so that the equivalent of $\varphi(x, y)_n$ in terms of $\varphi(x_r y_s)$ can always be specified.[12] An exactly similar convention is supposed to govern the arrangement of terms in $\Pi_{x,\ y}\varphi(x, y)$ and their identification with the terms of $\Pi_x\Pi_y\varphi(x, y)$. These conventions of order are never required in the proof of theorems: we note them here only to obviate any theoretical

[12] This arrangement turns the two-dimensional array into a one-dimensional by the familiar device for denumerating the rationals—i. e., by proceeding along successive diagonals, beginning with the upper left-hand corner.

objection. The identification of $\Sigma_x\Sigma_y\varphi(x, y)$ with $\Sigma_{x,\,y}\varphi(x, y)$, and of $\Pi_x\Pi_y\varphi(x, y)$ with $\Pi_{x,\,y}\varphi(x, y)$, is of little consequence for the theory of propositional functions itself, but it will be of some importance in the theory of relations which is to be derived from the theory of functions of two or more variables.

Having now somewhat tediously cleared the ground, we may proceed to the proof of theorems. Since $\Sigma_{x,\,y}\varphi(x, y)$ and $\Pi_{x,\,y}\varphi(x, y)$ *may be* regarded as involving only one variable, (x, y), many theorems here follow at once from those of the preceding section.

11·1 $\Sigma_{x,\,y}\varphi(x, y) = \Sigma_x\Sigma_y\varphi(x, y) = -\Pi_{x,\,y}-\varphi(x, y) = -\{\Pi_x\Pi_y-\varphi(x, y)\}.$

  [11·05·06, 10·05]

11·12 $\Pi_{x,\,y}\varphi(x, y) = \Pi_x\Pi_y\varphi(x, y) = -\Sigma_{x,\,y}-\varphi(x, y) = -\{\Sigma_x\Sigma_y-\varphi(x, y)\}.$

  [11·05·06, 10·04]

11·2 $\Pi_{x,\,y}\varphi(x, y) \subset \varphi(x, y)_n.$

  [10·2]

11·21 $\varphi(x, y)_n \subset \Sigma_{x,\,y}\varphi(x, y).$

  [10·21]

11·22 $\Pi_{x,\,y}\varphi(x, y) \subset \Sigma_{x,\,y}\varphi(x, y).$

  [10·22]

11·23 $\Pi_{x,\,y}\varphi(x, y)$ is equivalent to "Whatever value of (x, y), in $\varphi(x, y)$, $(x, y)_n$ may be, $\varphi(x, y)_n$".

  [10·23]

11·24 $\Pi_x\Pi_y\varphi(x, y)$ is equivalent to "Whatever values of x and y, in $\varphi(x, y)$, x_r and y_s may be, $\varphi(x_ry_s)$".

  [10·23] $\Pi_x\Pi_y\varphi(x, y)$ is equivalent to "Whatever value of x, in $\Pi_y\varphi(x, y)$, x_r may be, $\Pi_y\varphi(x_ry)$". And $\Pi_y\varphi(x_ry)$ is equivalent to "Whatever value of y, in $\varphi(x,y)$, y_s may be, $\varphi(x_ry_s)$". But [11·01] the values of x in $\Pi_y\varphi(x_ry)$ are the values of x in $\varphi(x, y)$. Hence Q.E.D.

11·25 "Whatever value of (x, y), in $\varphi(x, y)$, $(x, y)_n$ may be, $\varphi(x, y)_n$" is equivalent to "Whatever values of x and y, in $\varphi(x, y)$, x_r and y_s may be, $\varphi(x_ry_s)$".

  [11·06·23·24]

11·26 $\Pi_x\Pi_y\varphi(x, y) \subset \Pi_y\varphi(x_ny).$

  [11·01, 10·2]

11·27 $\Pi_x\Pi_y\varphi(x, y) = \Pi_y\Pi_x\varphi(x, y)$.

Since $\times$ is associative and commutative, Q.E.D.

11·28 $\Sigma_x\Sigma_y\varphi(x, y) = \Sigma_y\Sigma_x\varphi(x, y)$.

Since $+$ is associative and commutative, Q.E.D.

11·29 $\Pi_x\Pi_y\varphi(x, y) \subset \Pi_x\varphi(x, y_n)$.

[11·26·27]

11·291 $\Pi_x\Pi_y\varphi(x, y) \subset \varphi(x_r y_s)$.

[2·2, 11·24]

11·3 $\Pi_x\Pi_y\varphi(x, y) \subset \Sigma_x\Pi_y\varphi(x, y)$.

[11·01, 10·21]

11·31 $\Sigma_x\Pi_y\varphi(x, y) \subset \Pi_y\Sigma_x\varphi(x, y)$.

[11·03] $\Pi_y\Sigma_x\varphi(x, y) = \quad \{ \varphi(x_1 y_1) + \varphi(x_2 y_1) + \varphi(x_3 y_1) + \ldots \}$
$\times \{ \varphi(x_1 y_2) + \varphi(x_2 y_2) + \varphi(x_3 y_2) + \ldots \}$
$\times \{ \varphi(x_1 y_3) + \varphi(x_2 y_3) + \varphi(x_3 y_3) + \ldots \}$
$\times \ldots$ Etc., etc.

Since $\times$ is distributive with reference to $+$, this expression is equal to the sum of the products of each column separately, plus the sum of all the cross-products, that is, to

$A + \{ \varphi(x_1 y_1) \times \varphi(x_1 y_2) \times \varphi(x_1 y_3) \times \ldots \}$
$+ \{ \varphi(x_2 y_1) \times \varphi(x_2 y_2) \times \varphi(x_2 y_3) \times \ldots \}$
$+ \{ \varphi(x_3 y_1) \times \varphi(x_3 y_2) \times \varphi(x_3 y_3) \times \ldots \}$
$+ \ldots$ Etc., etc.

where A is the sum of all cross-products.

But [11·02] this is $\Sigma_x\Pi_y\varphi(x, y) + A$.

Hence $\Sigma_x\Pi_y\varphi(x, y) + A = \Pi_y\Sigma_x\varphi(x, y)$.

Hence [5·21] $\Sigma_x\Pi_y\varphi(x, y) \subset \Pi_y\Sigma_x\varphi(x, y)$.

We have already called attention to the fact that the implication of 11·31 is not reversible—that $\Sigma_x\Pi_y\varphi(x, y)$ and $\Pi_y\Sigma_x\varphi(x, y)$ are not equivalent.

11·32 $\Pi_x\Sigma_y\varphi(x, y) \subset \Sigma_x\Sigma_y\varphi(x, y)$.

[11·03] $\Pi_x\Sigma_y\varphi(x, y) = \Sigma_y\varphi(x_1 y) \times \Sigma_y\varphi(x_2 y) \times \Sigma_y\varphi(x_3 y) \times \ldots$

[11·04] $\Sigma_x\Sigma_y\varphi(x, y) = \Sigma_y\varphi(x_1 y) + \Sigma_y\varphi(x_2 y) + \Sigma_y\varphi(x_3 y) + \ldots$

And [5·992] $\Sigma_y\varphi(x_1 y) \times \Sigma_y\varphi(x_2 y) \times \Sigma_y\varphi(x_3 y) \times \ldots$

$\subset \Sigma_y\varphi(x_1 y) + \Sigma_y\varphi(x_2 y) + \Sigma_y\varphi(x_3 y) + \ldots$

We have also the propositions concerning formal implication where functions of two variables are concerned. The formal implication of $\psi(x, y)$ by $\varphi(x, y)$ may be written either $\Pi_{x,\ y}[\varphi(x, y) \subset \psi(x, y)]$ or $\Pi_x \Pi_y[\varphi(x, y) \subset \psi(x, y)]$. By 11·06, these two are equivalent. We shall give the theorems only in the first of these forms.

11·4 $\quad \Pi_{x,\ y}[\varphi(x, y) \subset \psi(x, y)] \ = \ \Pi_{x,\ y}[-\varphi(x, y) + \psi(x, y)]$
$$= \Pi_{x,\ y}-[\varphi(x, y) \times -\psi(x, y)].$$
[10·6]

11·41 $\quad \Pi_{x,\ y}[\varphi(x, y) \subset \psi(x, y)] \subset [\varphi(x, y)_n \subset \psi(x, y)_n].$
[10·61]

11·411 $\quad \{\Pi_{x,\ y}[\varphi(x, y) \subset \psi(x, y)] \times \varphi(x, y)_n\} \subset \psi(x, y)_n.$
[10·611]

11·42 $\quad \Pi_{x,\ y}[\varphi(x, y) \subset \psi(x, y)] \subset \Sigma_{x,\ y}[\varphi(x, y) \subset \psi(x, y)].$
[10·62]

11·43 $\quad \Pi_{x,\ y}[\varphi(x, y) \subset \psi(x, y)] \subset [\Pi_{x,\ y}\varphi(x, y) \subset \Pi_{x,\ y}\psi(x, y)].$
[10·63]

11·431 $\quad \{\Pi_{x,\ y}[\varphi(x, y) \subset \psi(x, y)] \times \Pi_{x,\ y}\varphi(x, y)\} \subset \Pi_{x,\ y}\psi(x, y).$
[10·631]

11·44 $\quad \Pi_{x,\ y}[\varphi(x, y) \subset \psi(x, y)] \subset [\Sigma_{x,\ y}\varphi(x, y) \subset \Sigma_{x,\ y}\psi(x, y)].$
[10·64]

11·441 $\quad \{\Pi_{x,\ y}[\varphi(x, y) \subset \psi(x, y)] \times \Sigma_{x,\ y}\varphi(x, y)\} \subset \Sigma_{x,\ y}\psi(x, y).$
[10·641]

11·45 $\quad \{\Pi_{x,\ y}[\varphi(x, y) \subset \psi(x, y)] \times \Pi_{x,\ y}[\psi(x, y) \subset \zeta(x, y)]\}$
$$\subset \Pi_{x,\ y}[\varphi(x, y) \subset \zeta(x, y)].$$
[10·65]

11·451 $\quad \Pi_{x,\ y}[\varphi(x, y) \subset \psi(x, y)]$
$$\subset \{\Pi_{x,\ y}[\psi(x, y) \subset \zeta(x, y)] \subset \Pi_{x,\ y}[\varphi(x, y) \subset \zeta(x, y)]\}.$$
[10·651]

11·452 $\quad \Pi_{x,\ y}[\psi(x, y) \subset \zeta(x, y)]$
$$\subset \{\Pi_{x,\ y}[\varphi(x, y) \subset \psi(x, y)] \subset \Pi_{x,\ y}[\varphi(x, y) \subset \zeta(x, y)]\}.$$
[10·652]

11·46 $\quad \Pi_{x,\ y}[\varphi(x, y) \subset \psi(x, y)] = \Pi_{x,\ y}[-\psi(x, y) \subset -\varphi(x, y)].$
[10·66]

Similarly, we have the theorems concerning the formal equivalence of functions of two variables.

11·47 $\Pi_{x,\,y}[\varphi(x,\,y) = \psi(x,\,y)] = \{\Pi_{x,\,y}[\varphi(x,\,y) \subset \psi(x,\,y)]$
$$\times \Pi_{x,\,y}[\psi(x,\,y) \subset \varphi(x,\,y)]\}.$$
[10·67]

11·48 $\{\Pi_{x,\,y}[\varphi(x,\,y) = \psi(x,\,y)] \times \Pi_{x,\,y}[\psi(x,\,y) = \zeta(x,\,y)]\}$
$$\subset \Pi_{x,\,y}[\varphi(x,\,y) = \zeta(x,\,y)].$$
[10·68]

11·481 $\Pi_{x,\,y}[\varphi(x,\,y) = \psi(x,\,y)] \subset \{\Pi_{x,\,y}[\psi(x,\,y) = \zeta(x,\,y)]$
$$\subset \Pi_{x,\,y}[\varphi(x,\,y) = \zeta(x,\,y)]\}.$$
[10·681]

11·482 $\Pi_{x,\,y}[\psi(x,\,y) = \zeta(x,\,y)] \subset \{\Pi_{x,\,y}[\varphi(x,\,y) = \psi(x,\,y)]$
$$\subset \Pi_{x,\,y}[\varphi(x,\,y) = \zeta(x,$$
[10·682]

11·49 $\Pi_{x,\,y}[\varphi(x,\,y) = \psi(x,\,y)] \subset [\varphi(x,\,y)_n = \psi(x,\,y)_n]$
$$\subset [\Pi_{x,\,y}\varphi(x,\,y) = \Pi_{x,\,y}\psi(x,\,y)]$$
$$\subset [\Sigma_{x,\,y}\varphi(x,\,y) = \Sigma_{x,\,y}\psi(x,\,y)].$$
[10·69]

11·491 $\Pi_{x,\,y}[\varphi(x,\,y) = \psi(x,\,y)] = \Pi_{x,\,y}[-\varphi(x,\,y) = -\psi(x,\,y)].$
[10·691]

Further propositions concerning functions of two variables are simple consequences of the above.

The method by which such functions are treated readily extends to those of three or more variables. $\varphi(x,\,y,\,z)$ may be treated as a function of three variables, or as a function of one variable, the ordered triad $(x,\,y,\,z)$; just as $\psi(x,\,y)$ can be treated as a function of x and y, or of the ordered pair $(x,\,y)$. Strictly, new definitions are required with each extension of our theory to a larger number of variables, but the method of such extension will be entirely obvious. For three variables, we should have

$$\Pi_x\Pi_y\Pi_z\varphi(x,\,y,\,z) = \Pi_x\{\Pi_y\Pi_z\varphi(x,\,y,\,z)\}$$
$$\Sigma_x\Pi_y\Pi_z\varphi(x,\,y,\,z) = \Sigma_x\{\Pi_y\Pi_z\varphi(x,\,y,\,z)\}$$
Etc., etc.

It is interesting to note that the most general form for the analogues of 11·05 and 11·06 will be

$$\Pi_{(x,\,y,\,z)}\varphi(x,\,y,\,z) = \Pi_x\Pi_{(y,\,z)}\varphi(x,\,y,\,z)$$
$$\text{and} \quad \Sigma_{(x,\,y,\,z)}\varphi(x,\,y,\,z) = \Sigma_x\Sigma_{(y,\,z)}\varphi(x,\,y,\,z)$$

Since $\Pi_x\Pi_{(y,\,z)}\varphi(x,\,y,\,z) = \Pi_{(y,\,z)}\varphi(x_1y,\,z) \times \Pi_{(y,\,z)}\varphi(x_2y,\,z) \times \Pi_{(y,\,z)}\varphi(x_3y,\,z)$

×..., and $\Pi_{(y,\ z)}\varphi(x_ny,\ z) = \Pi_y\Pi_z\varphi(x_ny,\ z)$, etc., we shall be able to *deduce*

$$\Pi_{(x,\ y,\ z)}\varphi(x,\ y,\ z) = \Pi_x\Pi_{(y,\ z)}\varphi(x,\ y,\ z) = \Pi_{(x,\ y)}\Pi_z\varphi(x,\ y,\ z)$$
$$= \Pi_y\Pi_{(x,\ z)}\varphi(x,\ y,\ z) = \Pi_x\Pi_y\Pi_z\varphi(x,\ y,\ z)$$

And similarly for $\Sigma_{(x,\ y,\ z)}$. This calls our attention to the fact that $\varphi(x, y, z)$ can be treated not only as a function of three variables or as a function of one, but also as a function of two, x and (y, z) or (x, y) and z or (x, z) and y.

In general, the conventions of notation being extended to functions of any number of variables, in the obvious way, the analogues of preceding theorems for functions of two will follow.

We failed to treat of such expressions as $\Pi\varphi x \times \Pi\psi y$, $\Sigma\varphi x + \Pi\psi y$, etc., under the head of functions of one variable. The reason for this omission was that such expressions find their significant equivalents in propositions of the type $\Pi_x\Pi_y(\varphi x \times \psi y)$, $\Sigma_x\Pi_y(\varphi x + \psi y)$, etc., and these are special cases of functions of two variables. We may also remind the reader of the difference between two such expressions as $\Pi\varphi x + \Pi\psi x$ and $\Pi\varphi x + \Pi\psi y$. The ranges of the two functions, φ and ψ, need not be identical; there may be values of x in φx which are not values of y in ψy. But in any expression of the form $\varphi x_n \times \psi x_n$, x_n as a value of x in φx must be identical with x_n as a value of x in ψx. For this reason, we have adopted the convention that where the same letter is used for the variable in two related functions, these functions have the same range. Hence the case where we have φx and ψy is the more general case, in which the functions are not restricted to the same range. Theorems involving functions of this type will not always be significant for every choice of φ and ψ. There may even be cases in which an implication is not significant though its hypothesis is significant. But for whatever functions such theorems are significant, they will be *true*; they will never be false for any functions, however chosen.

The meaning of an expression such as $\Sigma_x\Pi_y(\varphi x + \psi y)$ follows from the definition of $\Sigma_x\Pi_y\varphi(x, y)$.

$$\begin{aligned}
\Sigma_x\Pi_y(\varphi x + \psi y) &= \Pi_y(\varphi x_1 + \psi y) + \Pi_y(\varphi x_2 + \psi y) + \Pi_y(\varphi x_3 + \psi y) + \ldots\\
&= \quad\{(\varphi x_1 + \psi y_1) \times (\varphi x_1 + \psi y_2) \times (\varphi x_1 + \psi y_3) \times \ldots\}\\
&\quad + \{(\varphi x_2 + \psi y_1) \times (\varphi x_2 + \psi y_2) \times (\varphi x_2 + \psi y_3) \times \ldots\}\\
&\quad + \{(\varphi x_3 + \psi y_1) \times (\varphi x_3 + \psi y_2) \times (\varphi x_3 + \psi y_3) \times \ldots\}\\
&\quad + \ldots \text{ Etc., etc.}
\end{aligned}$$

And for any such expression with two operators we have the same type of two-dimensional array as for a function of two variables in general. The only difference is that here the function itself has a special form, $\varphi x + \psi y$ or $\varphi x \times \psi y$, etc.

12·1 $\Pi \varphi x \times \Pi \psi y = \Pi \psi y \times \Pi \varphi x = \Pi_x \Pi_y (\varphi x \times \psi y) = \Pi_x \Pi_y (\psi y \times \varphi x)$
$$= \Pi_y \Pi_x (\varphi x \times \psi y) = \Pi_y \Pi_x (\psi y \times \varphi x).$$

(1) [1·3] $\Pi \varphi x \times \Pi \psi y = \Pi \psi y \times \Pi \varphi x.$

(2) $\Pi \varphi x \times \Pi \psi y = (\varphi x_1 \times \varphi x_2 \times \varphi x_3 \times \ldots) \times \Pi \psi y$
$$= (\varphi x_1 \times \Pi \psi y) \times (\varphi x_2 \times \Pi \psi y) \times (\varphi x_3 \times \Pi \psi y) \times \ldots$$
$$[5 \cdot 98]$$
$$= \Pi_y (\varphi x_1 \times \psi y) \times \Pi_y (\varphi x_2 \times \psi y)$$
$$\times \Pi_y (\varphi x_3 \times \psi y) \times \ldots \quad [10 \cdot 371]$$
$$= \Pi_x \Pi_y (\varphi x \times \psi y). \quad [11 \cdot 01]$$

(3) By (2) and 1·3,
$$\Pi \varphi x \times \Pi \psi y = (\Pi \psi y \times \varphi x_1) \times (\Pi \psi y \times \varphi x_2)$$
$$\times (\Pi \psi y \times \varphi x_3) \times \ldots$$
$$= \Pi_y (\psi y \times \varphi x_1) \times \Pi_y (\psi y \times \varphi x_2)$$
$$\times \Pi_y (\psi y \times \varphi x_3) \times \ldots \quad [10 \cdot 37]$$
$$= \Pi_x \Pi_y (\psi y \times \varphi x). \quad [11 \cdot 01]$$

(4) Similarly, $\Pi \psi y \times \Pi \varphi x = \Pi_y \Pi_x (\psi y \times \varphi x) = \Pi_y \Pi_x (\varphi x \times \psi y).$

" φx is true for every x and ψy is true for every y" is equivalent to "For every x and every y, φx and ψy are both true", etc.

12·2 $\Sigma \varphi x + \Sigma \psi y = \Sigma \psi y + \Sigma \varphi x = \Sigma_x \Sigma_y (\varphi x + \psi y) = \Sigma_x \Sigma_y (\psi y + \varphi x)$
$$= \Sigma_y \Sigma_x (\varphi x + \psi y) = \Sigma_y \Sigma_x (\psi y + \varphi x).$$

(1) [4·3] $\Sigma \varphi x + \Sigma \psi y = \Sigma \psi y + \Sigma \varphi x.$

(2) $\Sigma \varphi x + \Sigma \psi y = (\varphi x_1 + \varphi x_2 + \varphi x_3 + \ldots) + \Sigma \psi y$
$$= (\varphi x_1 + \Sigma \psi y) + (\varphi x_2 + \Sigma \psi y) + (\varphi x_3 + \Sigma \psi y) + \ldots$$
$$[5 \cdot 981]$$
$$= \Sigma_y (\varphi x_1 + \psi y) + \Sigma_y (\varphi x_2 + \psi y)$$
$$+ \Sigma_y (\varphi x_3 + \psi y) + \ldots \quad [10 \cdot 31]$$
$$= \Sigma_x \Sigma_y (\varphi x + \psi y). \quad [11 \cdot 04]$$

(3) By (2) and 4·3,
$$\Sigma \varphi x + \Sigma \psi y = (\Sigma \psi y + \varphi x_1) + (\Sigma \psi y + \varphi x_2)$$
$$+ (\Sigma \psi y + \varphi x_2) + \ldots$$
$$= \Sigma_y (\psi y + \varphi x_1) + \Sigma_y (\psi y + \varphi x_2)$$
$$+ \Sigma_y (\psi y + \varphi x_3) + \ldots \quad [10 \cdot 3]$$
$$= \Sigma_x \Sigma_y (\psi y + \varphi x). \quad [11 \cdot 04]$$

(4) Similarly, $\Sigma \psi y + \Sigma \varphi x = \Sigma_y \Sigma_x (\psi y + \varphi x) = \Sigma_y \Sigma_x (\varphi x + \psi y).$

"Either for some x, φx, or for some y, ψy" is equivalent to "For some x and some y, either φx or ψy", etc.

12·3 $\quad \Sigma \varphi x \times \Sigma \psi y = \Sigma \psi y \times \Sigma \varphi x = \Sigma_x \Sigma_y (\varphi x \times \psi y) = \Sigma_x \Sigma_y (\psi y \times \varphi x)$
$$= \Sigma_y \Sigma_x (\varphi x \times \psi y) = \Sigma_y \Sigma_x (\psi y \times \varphi x).$$

(1) [1·3] $\Sigma \varphi x \times \Sigma \psi y = \Sigma \psi y \times \Sigma \varphi x$.

(2) $\Sigma \varphi x \times \Sigma \psi y = (\varphi x_1 + \varphi x_2 + \varphi x_3 + \ldots) \times \Sigma \psi y$
$$= (\varphi x_1 \times \Sigma \psi y) + (\varphi x_2 \times \Sigma \psi y) + (\varphi x_3 \times \Sigma \psi y) + \ldots$$
$$[5·94]$$
$$= \Sigma_y (\varphi x_1 \times \psi y) + \Sigma_y (\varphi x_2 \times \psi y) + \Sigma_y (\varphi x_3 \times \psi y)$$
$$+ \ldots \quad [10·361]$$
$$= \Sigma_x \Sigma_y (\varphi x \times \psi y). \quad [11·04]$$

(3) By (2) and 1·3,
$$\Sigma \varphi x \times \Sigma \psi y = (\Sigma \psi y \times \varphi x_1) + (\Sigma \psi y \times \varphi x_2) + (\Sigma \psi y \times \varphi x_3)$$
$$+ \ldots$$
$$= \Sigma_y (\psi y \times \varphi x_1) + \Sigma_y (\psi y \times \varphi x_2)$$
$$+ \Sigma_y (\psi y \times \varphi x_3) + \ldots \quad [10·36]$$
$$= \Sigma_x \Sigma_y (\psi y \times \varphi x). \quad [11·04]$$

(4) Similarly, $\Sigma \psi y \times \Sigma \varphi x = \Sigma_y \Sigma_x (\psi y \times \varphi x) = \Sigma_y \Sigma_x (\varphi x \times \psi y)$.

"For some x, φx, and for some y, ψy" is equivalent to "For some x and some y, φx and ψy", etc.

12·4 $\quad \Pi \varphi x + \Pi \psi y = \Pi \psi y + \Pi \varphi x = \Pi_x \Pi_y (\varphi x + \psi y) = \Pi_x \Pi_y (\psi y + \varphi x)$
$$= \Pi_y \Pi_x (\varphi x + \psi y) = \Pi_y \Pi_x (\psi y + \varphi x).$$

(1) [4·3] $\Pi \varphi x + \Pi \psi y = \Pi \psi y + \Pi \varphi x$.

(2) $\Pi \varphi x + \Pi \psi y = (\varphi x_1 \times \varphi x_2 \times \varphi x_3 \times \ldots) + \Pi \psi y$
$$= (\varphi x_1 + \Pi \psi y) \times (\varphi x_2 + \Pi \psi y) \times (\varphi x_3 + \Pi \psi y) \times \ldots$$
$$[5·941]$$
$$= \Pi_y (\varphi x_1 + \psi y) \times \Pi_y (\varphi x_2 + \psi y)$$
$$\times \Pi_y (\varphi x_3 + \psi y) \times \ldots \quad [10·371]$$
$$= \Pi_x \Pi_y (\varphi x + \psi y). \quad [11·01]$$

(3) By (2) and 4·3,
$$\Pi \varphi x + \Pi \psi y = (\Pi \psi y + \varphi x_1) \times (\Pi \psi y + \varphi x_2)$$
$$\times (\Pi \psi y + \varphi x_3) \times \ldots$$
$$= \Pi_y (\psi y + \varphi x_1) \times \Pi_y (\psi y + \varphi x_2)$$
$$\times \Pi_y (\psi y + \varphi x_3) \times \ldots \quad [10·37]$$
$$= \Pi_x \Pi_y (\psi y + \varphi x). \quad [11·01]$$

(4) Similarly, $\Pi \psi y + \Pi \varphi x = \Pi_y \Pi_x (\psi y + \varphi x) = \Pi_y \Pi_x (\varphi x + \psi y)$.

"Either for every x, φx, or for every y, ψy" is equivalent to "For every x

and every y, either φx or ψy ", etc.   At first glance this theorem may seem invalid.   One may say: "Suppose φx be 'If x is a number, it is odd', and ψy be 'If y is a number, it is even'.   Then $\Pi \varphi x + \Pi \psi y$ will be 'Either every number is odd or every number is even', but $\Pi_x \Pi_y (\varphi x + \psi y)$ will be 'Every number is either odd or even'".   The mistake of this supposed illustration lies in misreading $\Pi_x \Pi_y (\varphi x + \psi y)$.   It is legitimate to choose, as in this case, φx and ψy such that their range is identical: but it is not legitimate to read $\Pi_x \Pi_y (\varphi x + \psi y)$ as if each given value of x were connected with a *corresponding* value of y.   To put it another way: $\Pi_x \Pi_x (\varphi x + \psi x)$, as a special case of $\Pi_x \Pi_y (\varphi x + \psi y)$, would not be "For every value of x, either φx or ψx", but would be "For any two values of x, or for any value of x and itself, either φx or ψx".   Thus $\Pi_x \Pi_y (\varphi x + \psi y)$ in the supposed illustration would not be as above, but is in fact "For any pair of numbers, or for any number and itself, either one is odd or the other is even"—so that $\Pi \varphi x + \Pi \psi y$ and $\Pi_x \Pi_y (\varphi x + \psi y)$ would here both be false, and are equivalent.

A somewhat similar caution applies to the interpretation of the next two theorems.   The analogues of these, in $\varphi(x, y)$, do not hold.

12·5 $\Sigma \varphi x + \Pi \psi y = \Pi \psi y + \Sigma \varphi x = \Sigma_x \Pi_y (\varphi x + \psi y) = \Sigma_x \Pi_y (\psi y + \varphi x)$
$$= \Pi_y \Sigma_x (\varphi x + \psi y) = \Pi_y \Sigma_x (\psi y + \varphi x).$$

(1) [4·3] $\Sigma \varphi x + \Pi \psi y = \Pi \psi y + \Sigma \varphi x$.
(2) By proof similar to (2) in 12·2, $\Sigma \varphi x + \Pi \psi y = \Sigma_x \Pi_y (\varphi x + \psi y)$.
And by proof similar to (3) in 12·2, $\Sigma \varphi x + \Pi \psi y = \Sigma_x \Pi_y (\psi y + \varphi x)$.
(3) By proof similar to (2) in 12·4, $\Pi \psi y + \Sigma \varphi x = \Pi_y \Sigma_x (\psi y + \varphi x)$.
And by proof similar to (3) in 12·4, $\Pi \psi y + \Sigma \varphi x = \Pi_y \Sigma_x (\varphi x + \psi y)$.

"Either for some x, φx, or for every y, ψy " is equivalent to "For some x and every y, either φx or ψy ", etc.

12·6 $\Sigma \varphi x \times \Pi \psi y = \Pi \psi y \times \Sigma \varphi x = \Sigma_x \Pi_y (\varphi x \times \psi y) = \Sigma_x \Pi_y (\psi y \times \varphi x)$
$$= \Pi_y \Sigma_x (\varphi x \times \psi y) = \Pi_y \Sigma_x (\psi y \times \varphi x).$$

(1) [1·3] $\Sigma \varphi x \times \Pi \psi y = \Pi \psi y \times \Sigma \varphi x$.
(2) By proof similar to (2) in 12·3, $\Sigma \varphi x \times \Pi \psi y = \Sigma_x \Pi_y (\varphi x \times \psi y)$.
And by proof similar to (3) in 12·3, $\Sigma \varphi x \times \Pi \psi y = \Sigma_x \Pi_y (\psi y \times \varphi x)$.
(3) By proof similar to (2) in 12·1, $\Pi \psi y \times \Sigma \varphi x = \Pi_y \Sigma_x (\psi y \times \varphi x)$.
And by proof similar to (3) in 12·1, $\Pi \psi y \times \Sigma \varphi x = \Pi_y \Sigma_x (\varphi x \times \psi y)$.

"For some 'x, φx, and for every y, ψy " is equivalent to "For some x and every y, φx and ψy ", etc.

We may generalize theorems $12 \cdot 1$–$12 \cdot 6$ by saying that for functions of the type $(\varphi x + \psi y)$ and $(\varphi x \times \psi y)$ the order of operators and of members in the function is indifferent; and for propositions of the type

$$\left.\begin{matrix}\Pi \\ \Sigma\end{matrix}\right\} \varphi x \left\{\begin{matrix}+ \\ \times\end{matrix}\right\} \left\{\begin{matrix}\Pi \\ \Sigma\end{matrix}\right\} \psi y$$

the operators may be combined, and the functions combined in the relation between the propositions.

It will be unnecessary to give here the numerous theorems which follow from $10 \cdot 5$–$12 \cdot 6$ by the principles $p\,q \subset p$, $p \subset p + q$, and $\Pi \varphi x \subset \Sigma \varphi x$, etc. For example, $10 \cdot 51$,

$$\Pi \varphi x \times \Pi \psi x = \Pi_x(\varphi x \times \psi x)$$

gives at once

(1) $\Pi_x(\varphi x \times \psi x) \subset \Pi \varphi x$
(2)   " $\subset \Pi \psi x$
(3)   " $\subset \Sigma \varphi x$
(4)   " $\subset \Sigma \psi x$
(5)   " $\subset \Pi \varphi x \times \Sigma \psi x$
(6)   " $\subset \Sigma \varphi x + \Sigma \psi x$
Etc., etc.

And $12 \cdot 2$, $\Sigma \varphi x + \Sigma \psi y = \Sigma_x \Sigma_y(\varphi x + \psi y)$, etc., gives

(1) $\Sigma \varphi x \subset \Sigma_x \Sigma_y(\varphi x + \psi y)$
(2) $\Sigma \psi y \subset$ "
(3) $\Pi \varphi x \subset$ "
(4) $\Pi \psi y \subset$ "
(5) $\Sigma \varphi x + \Pi \psi y \subset \Sigma_x \Sigma_y(\varphi x + \psi y)$
(6) $\Sigma \varphi x \times \Sigma \psi y \subset$ "
Etc., etc.

Another large group of theorems, only a little less obvious, follow from the combination of $\Pi \varphi x \subset \Pi \varphi x$, or $\Sigma \varphi x \subset \Sigma \varphi x$, with $\Pi \psi y \subset \Sigma \psi y$, giving by $5 \cdot 3$,

(1) $\Pi \varphi x + \Pi \psi y \subset \Pi \varphi x + \Sigma \psi y$
(2) $\Pi \varphi x \times \Pi \psi y \subset \Pi \varphi x \times \Sigma \psi y$
(3) $\Sigma \varphi x + \Pi \psi y \subset \Sigma \varphi x + \Sigma \psi y$
(4) $\Sigma \varphi x \times \Pi \psi y \subset \Sigma \varphi x \times \Sigma \psi y$
Etc., etc.

Each of these has a whole set of derivatives in which $\Pi \varphi x + \Pi \psi y$ is replaced by $\Pi_x\Pi_y(\varphi x + \psi y)$, etc., $\Pi\varphi x \times \Sigma\psi y$ by $\Pi_x\Sigma_y(\varphi x \times \psi y)$, etc. We give, in summary form, the derivatives of (2), by way of illustration:

Any one of	$\subset$	any one of
$\Pi\varphi x \times \Pi\psi y$		$\Pi\varphi x \times \Sigma\psi y$
$\Pi_x\Pi_y(\varphi x \times \psi y)$		$\Pi_x\Sigma_y(\varphi x \times \psi y)$
$\Pi_x\Pi_y(\psi y \times \varphi x)$		$\Pi_x\Sigma_y(\psi y \times \varphi x)$
$\Pi_y\Pi_x(\psi y \times \varphi x)$		$\Sigma_y\Pi_x(\psi y \times \varphi x)$
$\Pi_y\Pi_x(\varphi x \times \psi y)$		$\Sigma_y\Pi_x(\varphi x \times \psi y)$
$\Pi\psi y \times \Pi\varphi x$		$\Sigma\psi y \times \Pi\varphi x$
		$\Pi\varphi x$
		$\Sigma\psi y$
		$\Pi\varphi x + \Pi\psi y$
		$\Pi_x\Pi_y(\varphi x + \psi y)$, etc., etc.
		$\Sigma\varphi x + \Sigma\psi y$
		$\Sigma_x\Sigma_y(\varphi x + \psi y)$, etc., etc.
		$\Pi\varphi x + \Sigma\psi y$
		$\Pi_x\Sigma_y(\varphi x + \psi y)$, etc., etc.

This table summarizes one hundred fifty-six theorems, and these are only a portion of those to be got by such procedures.

Functions of the type of $(\varphi x \times \psi y)$ and $(\varphi x + \psi y)$ give four different kinds of implication relation: (1) $\Pi_x\Pi_y(\varphi x \subset \psi y)$; (2) $\Pi_x\Sigma_y(\varphi x \subset \psi y)$; (3) $\Sigma_x\Pi_y(\varphi x \subset \psi y)$; and (4) $\Sigma_x\Sigma_y(\varphi x \subset \psi y)$. With the exception of the first, these relations are unfamiliar as "implications", though all of them could be illustrated from the field of mathematics. Nor are they particularly useful: the results to be obtained by their use can always be got by means of material implications or formal implications. Perhaps $\Pi_x\Pi_y(\varphi x \subset \psi y)$ is of sufficient interest for us to give its elementary properties.

12·7 $\Pi_x\Pi_y(\varphi x \subset \psi y) \subset (\varphi x_n \subset \Pi\psi y)$.

$\quad\quad$ [11·01] $\Pi_x\Pi_y(\varphi x \subset \psi y) = \Pi_y(\varphi x_1 \subset \psi y) \times \Pi_y(\varphi x_2 \subset \psi y)$
$$\times \Pi_y(\varphi x_3 \subset \psi y) \times \ldots$$
$$= (\varphi x_1 \subset \Pi\psi y) \times (\varphi x_2 \subset \Pi\psi y)$$
$$\times (\varphi x_3 \subset \Pi\psi y) \times \ldots \quad [10\cdot42]$$

And this last expression is equivalent to the set

$$\varphi x_1 \subset \Pi\psi y, \quad \varphi x_2 \subset \Pi\psi y, \quad \varphi x_3 \subset \Pi\psi y, \text{ etc.}$$

12·71 $\{\Pi_x\Pi_y(\varphi x \subset \psi y) \times \varphi x_n\} \subset \Pi\psi y$.

$\quad\quad$ [9·4, 12·7]

If for every x and every y, φx implies ψy, and for some given x, φx is true, then ψy is true for every y.

12·72 $\Pi_x\Pi_y(\varphi x \subset \psi y) = \Sigma \varphi x \subset \Pi \psi y = \Pi - \varphi x + \Pi \psi y.$

(1) If $\Pi_x\Pi_y(\varphi x \subset \psi y)$, then [12·7] $\varphi x_n \subset \Pi \psi y$.

Hence [5·981] $\Sigma \varphi x \subset \Pi \psi y$.

And if $\Sigma \varphi x \subset \Pi \psi y$, then [10·42] $\Pi_y(\Sigma \varphi x \subset \psi y)$, and hence [10·41] $\Pi_x\Pi_y(\varphi x \subset \psi y)$.

(2) [9·3] $\Sigma \varphi x \subset \Pi \psi y = -\Sigma \varphi x + \Pi \psi y = \Pi - \varphi x + \Pi \psi y.$

$\Pi_x\Pi_y(\varphi x \subset \psi y)$ is equivalent to "If there is *some* x for which φx is true, then ψy is true for *every* y".

12·73 $\{\Pi_x\Pi_y(\varphi x \subset \psi y) \times \Pi_y\Pi_z(\psi y \subset \zeta z)\} \subset \Pi_x\Pi_z(\varphi x \subset \zeta z).$

[12·72] If $\Pi_x\Pi_y(\varphi x \subset \psi y)$ and $\Pi_y\Pi_z(\psi y \subset \zeta z)$, then $\Sigma \varphi x \subset \Pi \psi y$ and $\Sigma \psi y \subset \Pi \zeta z$.

But [10·21] $\Pi \psi y \subset \Sigma \psi y$. Hence [5·1] $\Sigma \varphi x \subset \Pi \zeta z$, and [12·72] $\Pi_x\Pi_z(\varphi x \subset \zeta z)$.

This implication relation is here demonstrated to be transitive. In fact, it is, so to speak, more than transitive, as the next theorem shows.

12·74 $\{(\Sigma \varphi x \subset \Sigma \psi y) \times \Pi_y\Pi_z(\psi y \subset \zeta z)\} \subset \Pi_x\Pi_z(\varphi x \subset \zeta z).$

[12·72] $\Pi_y\Pi_z(\psi y \subset \zeta z) = \Sigma \psi y \subset \Pi \zeta z.$

And [5·1] if $\Sigma \varphi x \subset \Sigma \psi y$ and $\Sigma \psi y \subset \Pi \zeta z$, then $\Sigma \varphi x \subset \Pi \zeta z$, and [12·72] $\Pi_x\Pi_z(\varphi x \subset \zeta z).$

12·75 $\{\Pi_x\Pi_y(\varphi x \subset \psi y) \times (\Pi \psi y \subset \Pi \zeta z)\} \subset \Pi_x\Pi_z(\varphi x \subset \zeta z).$

[12·72] $\Pi_x\Pi_y(\varphi x \subset \psi y) = \Sigma \varphi x \subset \Pi \psi y.$

And [5·1] if $\Sigma \varphi x \subset \Pi \psi y$ and $\Pi \psi y \subset \Pi \zeta z$, then $\Sigma \varphi x \subset \Pi \zeta z$, and [12·72] $\Pi_x\Pi_z(\varphi x \subset \zeta z).$

IV. DERIVATION OF THE LOGIC OF CLASSES FROM THE CALCULUS OF PROPOSITIONAL FUNCTIONS

The logic of classes and the logic of relations can both be derived from the logic of propositional functions. In the present chapter, we have begun with a calculus of propositions, the Two-Valued Algebra, which includes all the theorems of the Boole-Schröder Algebra, giving these theorems the propositional interpretation. We have proved that, considered as belonging to the calculus of propositions, these theorems can validly be given the completely symbolic form: "If . . . , then . . ."

being replaced by "... ⊂ ...", "... is equivalent to ..." by "...
= ...", etc. The Two-Valued Algebra does not presuppose the Boole-Schröder Algebra; it simply includes it.

Suppose, then, we make the calculus of propositions—the Two-Valued Algebra—our fundamental branch of symbolic logic. We derive from it the calculus of propositional functions by the methods of the last two sections. We may then further derive the calculus of logical classes, and a calculus of relations, by methods which are to be outlined in this section and the next.

The present section will not develop the logic of classes, but will present the method of this development, and prove the possibility and adequacy of it. At the same time, certain differences will be pointed out between the calculus of classes as derived from that of propositional functions and the Boole-Schröder Algebra considered as a logic of classes. In order to distinguish class-symbols from the variables, x, y, z, in propositional functions, we shall here represent classes by α, β, γ, etc.

For the derivation of the logic of classes from that of propositional functions, a given class is conceived as the aggregate of individuals for which some propositional function is true. If φx_n represent "x is a man", then the aggregate of x's for which φx is true will constitute the class of men. If, then, $\hat{z}(\varphi z)$ represent the aggregate of individuals for which the propositional function φz is true, $\hat{z}(\varphi z)$ will be "the class determined by the function φz", or "the class determined by the possession of the character φ".[13] We can use α, β, γ, as an abbreviation for $\hat{z}(\varphi z)$, $\hat{z}(\psi z)$, $\hat{z}(\xi z)$, etc. $\alpha = \hat{z}(\varphi z)$ will mean "α is the class determined by the function φz". (In this connection, we should remember that φx and φz are the same function.)

The relation of an individual member of a class to the class itself will be symbolized by ϵ. $x_n \epsilon \alpha$ represents "x_n is a member of α"—or briefly "x_n is an α". This relation can be defined.

[13] We here borrow the notation of *Principia*. The corresponding notation of Peirce and Schröder involves the use of Σ, which is most confusing, because this Σ has a meaning entirely different from the Σ which is an operator of a propositional function. But in *Principia*, $\hat{z}(\varphi z)$ does not represent an aggregate of individuals; it represents "z such that φz". And $\hat{z}(\varphi z)$ is not a primitive idea but a notation supported by an elaborate theory. Our procedure above is inelegant and theoretically objectionable: we adopt it because our purpose here is expository only, and the working out of an elaborate technique would impede the exposition and very likely confuse the reader. As a fact, a more satisfactory theory on this point makes no important difference.

13·01 $x_n \, \epsilon \, \hat{z}(\varphi z) = \varphi x_n$ Def.

"x_n is a member of the class determined by φz" is equivalent to "φx_n is true".

(For convenience of reference, we continue to give each definition and theorem a number.)

The relation "α is contained in β" is the relation of the class α to the class β when every member of α is a member of β also. We shall symbolize "α is contained in β" by $\alpha \subset \beta$. The sign $\subset$ between α and β, or between $\hat{z}(\varphi z)$ and $\hat{z}(\psi z)$, will be "is contained in"; $\subset$ between propositions will be "implies", as before. $x_n \, \epsilon \, \alpha$ is, of course, a proposition; $x \, \epsilon \, \alpha$, a propositional function.

13·02 $\alpha \subset \beta = \Pi_x(x \, \epsilon \, \alpha \subset x \, \epsilon \, \beta)$ Def.

$\alpha \subset \beta$ is equivalent to "For every x, 'x is an α' implies 'x is a β'".

$\Pi_x(x \, \epsilon \, \alpha \subset x \, \epsilon \, \beta)$ is a formal implication. It will appear, as we proceed that the logic of classes is the logic of the formal implications and formal equivalences which obtain between the propositional functions which determine the classes.

13·03 $(\alpha = \beta) = \Pi_x(x \, \epsilon \, \alpha = x \, \epsilon \, \beta)$ Def.

$\alpha = \beta$ is equivalent to "For every x, 'x is a member of α' is equivalent to 'x is a member of β'". $\alpha = \beta$ thus represents the fact that α and β have the same *extension*—i. e., consist of identical members.

$x_n \, \epsilon \, \alpha$, $\alpha \subset \beta$, and $\alpha = \beta$ are *assertable* relations—propositions. But the logical product of two classes, and the logical sum, are not assertable relations. They are, consequently, defined not by means of propositions but by means of functions.

13·04 $\alpha \times \beta = \hat{x}\{(x \, \epsilon \, \alpha) \times (x \, \epsilon \, \beta)\}$ Def.

The product of two classes, α and β, is the class of x's determined by the propositional function "x is an α and x is a β". The class of the x's for which this is true constitute $\alpha \times \beta$, the class of those things which are both α's and β's.

The relation $\times$ between α and β is, of course, a different relation from $\times$ between propositions or between propositional functions. A similar remark applies to the use of $+$, which will represent the logical sum of two classes, as well as of two propositions or propositional functions. This double use of symbols will cause no confusion if it be remembered that α and β, $\hat{z}(\varphi z)$ and $\hat{z}(\psi z)$, etc., are classes, while $x \, \epsilon \, \alpha$ is a propositional function, and $x_n \, \epsilon \, \alpha$, $\alpha \subset \beta$, and $\alpha = \beta$ are propositions.

13·05 $\alpha + \beta = \hat{x}\{(x \in \alpha) + (x \in \beta)\}$ Def.

The sum of two classes, α and β, is the class of x's such that at least one of the two, 'x is an α' and 'x is a β', is true, or loosely, the class of x's such that either x is an α or x is a β.

The negative of a class can be similarly defined:

13·06 $-\alpha = \hat{x} - (x \in \alpha)$ Def.

The negative of α is the class of x's for which 'x is an α' is false.

The "universe of discourse", 1, may be defined by the device of selecting some propositional function which is true for all values of the variable. Such a function is $(\zeta x \subset \zeta x)$, whatever propositional function ζx may be.

13·07 $1 = \hat{x}(\zeta x \subset \zeta x)$ Def.

1 is the class of x's for which ζx implies ζx.[14] Since this is always true, 1 is the class of all x's. The "null-class", 0, will be the negative of 1.

13·08 $0 = -1$ Def.

That is, by 13·06, $0 = \hat{x} - (\zeta x \subset \zeta x)$, and since $-(\zeta x \subset \zeta x)$ is false for all values of x, the class of such x's will be a class with no members.

Suppose that $\alpha = \hat{z}(\varphi z)$ and $\beta = \hat{z}(\psi z)$. Then, by 13·01, $x_n \in \alpha = \varphi x_n$. Hence $\alpha \subset \beta$ will be $\Pi_x(\varphi x \subset \psi x)$, and $\alpha = \beta$ will be $\Pi_x(\varphi x = \psi x)$. This establishes at once the connection between the assertable relations of classes and formal implication and equivalence. To illustrate the way in which this connection enables us to derive the logic of classes from that of propositional functions, we shall prove a number of typical theorems.

It will be convenient to assume for the whole set of theorems:

$$\alpha = \hat{z}(\varphi z), \qquad \beta = \hat{z}(\psi z), \qquad \gamma = \hat{z}(\xi z)$$

13·1 $0 = \hat{x} - (\zeta x \subset \zeta x)$.

$\qquad$ $0 = -1$.   Hence [13·06] $0 = \hat{x} - (x \in 1)$.

$\qquad$ [13·01·07] $x \in 1 = \zeta x \subset \zeta x$.   Hence $0 = \hat{x} - (\zeta x \subset \zeta x)$.

13·2 $\Pi_x(x \in 1)$.

$\qquad$ [13·01·06] $x_n \in 1 = (\zeta x_n \subset \zeta x_n)$.

$\qquad$ Hence $\Pi_x(x \in 1) = \Pi_x(\zeta x \subset \zeta x)$.

$\qquad$ But [2·2] $\zeta x_n \subset \zeta x_n$.   Hence [10·23] $\Pi_x(\zeta x \subset \zeta x)$.

Every individual thing is a member of the "universe of discourse".

---

[14] This defines, not *the* universe of discourse, but "universe of discourse",—the range of significance of the chosen function, ζ. With 1 so defined, propositions which involve the classes $\hat{z}(\varphi z)$, $\hat{z}(\psi z)$, etc., and 1, will be significant whenever φ, ψ, etc., and ζ have the same range, and true if significant.

13·3 $\Pi_x -(x \,\epsilon\, 0)$.

$\qquad$ [13·01·06·07] $x_n \,\epsilon\, 0 = -(\zeta x_n \,\mathsf{C}\, \zeta x_n)$.

$\qquad$ Hence [3·2] $-(x_n \,\epsilon\, 0) = (\zeta x_n \,\mathsf{C}\, \zeta x_n)$.

$\qquad$ But $\zeta x_n \,\mathsf{C}\, \zeta x_n$. Hence [10·23] $\Pi_x(\zeta x \,\mathsf{C}\, \zeta x)$, and $\Pi_x -(x \,\epsilon\, 0)$.

For every x, it is false that $x \,\epsilon\, 0$—no individual is a member of the null-class.

13·4 $\alpha \,\mathsf{C}\, 1$.

$\qquad$ [13·01·06] $x_n \,\epsilon\, 1 = (\zeta x_n \,\mathsf{C}\, \zeta x_n)$.

$\qquad$ Since $\alpha = \hat{z}(\varphi z)$, [13·01] $x_n \,\epsilon\, \alpha = \varphi x_n$.

$\qquad$ [9·33] $(\zeta x_n \,\mathsf{C}\, \zeta x_n) \,\mathsf{C}\, [\varphi x_n \,\mathsf{C}\, (\zeta x_n \,\mathsf{C}\, \zeta x_n)]$.

$\qquad$ Hence since $\zeta x_n \,\mathsf{C}\, \zeta x_n$, $\varphi x_n \,\mathsf{C}\, (\zeta x_n \,\mathsf{C}\, \zeta x_n)$.

$\qquad$ Hence [10·23] $\Pi_x[\varphi x \,\mathsf{C}\, (\zeta x \,\mathsf{C}\, \zeta x)]$, and [13·2] $\alpha \,\mathsf{C}\, 1$.

Any class, α, is contained in the universe of discourse. It will be noted (13·2 and 13·4) that *individuals* are *members of* 1, *classes* are *contained in* 1. In the proof of 13·4, we make use of 9·33, "A true proposition is implied by any proposition". $\zeta x_n \,\mathsf{C}\, \zeta x_n$ is true. Hence it is implied by φx_n. And since this holds, whatever value of x, x_n may be, therefore,

$$\Pi_x[\varphi x \,\mathsf{C}\, (\zeta x \,\mathsf{C}\, \zeta x)]$$

But φx is the function which determines the class α; $\zeta x \,\mathsf{C}\, \zeta x$, the function which determines 1. Hence φx_n is $x_n \,\epsilon\, \alpha$, and $\zeta x_n \,\mathsf{C}\, \zeta x_n$ is $x_n \,\epsilon\, 1$. Consequently we have $\Pi_x (x \,\epsilon\, \alpha \,\mathsf{C}\, x \,\epsilon\, 1)$. And by the definition of the relation "is contained in", this is $\alpha \,\mathsf{C}\, 1$.

13·5 $0 \,\mathsf{C}\, \alpha$.

$\qquad$ [9·1] $-(x_n \,\epsilon\, 0)$ is equivalent to $(x_n \,\epsilon\, 0) = 0$.

$\qquad$ Hence [13·3] $(x_n \,\epsilon\, 0) = 0$, and [9·32] $(x_n \,\epsilon\, 0) \,\mathsf{C}\, \varphi x_n$.

$\qquad$ Hence [13·01] $x_n \,\epsilon\, 0 \,\mathsf{C}\, x_n \,\epsilon\, \alpha$, and [10·23] $\Pi_x(x \,\epsilon\, 0 \,\mathsf{C}\, x \,\epsilon\, \alpha)$.

$\qquad$ Hence [13·02] $0 \,\mathsf{C}\, \alpha$.

The null-class is contained in every class, α. In this proof, we use 9·32, "A false proposition implies any proposition". $-(\zeta x_n \,\mathsf{C}\, \zeta x_n)$ is false, and hence implies φx_n. But $-(\zeta x \,\mathsf{C}\, \zeta x)$ is the function which determines 0; and φx, the function which determines α. Hence $0 \,\mathsf{C}\, \alpha$.

$\qquad$ The proofs of the five theorems just given are fairly typical of those which involve 0 and 1. But the great body of propositions make more direct use of the connection between the relations of classes and formal implications or equivalences. This connection may be illustrated by the following:

13·6 $\hat{z}(\varphi z) \subset \hat{z}(\psi z) = \Pi_x(\varphi x \subset \psi x).$

$\qquad$ [13·02] $\hat{z}(\varphi z) \subset \hat{z}(\psi z) = \Pi_x[x \,\epsilon\, \hat{z}(\varphi z) \subset x \,\epsilon\, \hat{z}(\psi z)].$

$\qquad$ [13·01] $x_n \,\epsilon\, \hat{z}(\varphi z) = \varphi x_n,$ and $x_n \,\epsilon\, \hat{z}(\psi z) = \psi x_n.$

$\qquad$ Hence [2·1] $\Pi_x[x \,\epsilon\, \hat{z}(\varphi z) \subset x \,\epsilon\, \hat{z}(\psi z)] = \Pi_x(\varphi x \subset \psi x).$

"The class determined by φz is contained in the class determined by ψz" is equivalent to "For every x, φx implies ψx".

13·7 $[\hat{z}(\varphi z) = \hat{z}(\psi z)] = \Pi_x(\varphi x = \psi x).$

$\qquad$ [13·03] $[\hat{z}(\varphi z) = \hat{z}(\psi z)] = \Pi_x[x \,\epsilon\, \hat{z}(\varphi z) = x \,\epsilon\, \hat{z}(\psi z)].$

$\qquad$ [13·01] $x_n \,\epsilon\, \hat{z}(\varphi z) = \varphi x_n,$ and $x_n \,\epsilon\, \hat{z}(\psi z) = \psi x_n.$

$\qquad$ Hence $\Pi_x[x \,\epsilon\, \hat{z}(\varphi z) = x \,\epsilon\, \hat{z}(\psi z)] = \Pi_x(\varphi x = \psi x).$

"The class determined by φz is equivalent to the class determined by ψz" is equivalent to "For every x, φx is equivalent to ψx".

13·8 $(\alpha \subset \beta) = (-\beta \subset -\alpha).$

$\qquad$ [10·66] $\Pi_x[x \,\epsilon\, \hat{z}(\varphi z) \subset x \,\epsilon\, \hat{z}(\psi z)] = \Pi_x\{-[x \,\epsilon\, \hat{z}(\psi z)] \subset -[x \,\epsilon\, \hat{z}(\varphi z)]\}.$

$\qquad$ Hence $\Pi_x(x \,\epsilon\, \alpha \subset x \,\epsilon\, \beta) = \Pi_x[-(x \,\epsilon\, \beta) \subset -(x \,\epsilon\, \alpha)].$

$\qquad$ [13·01·06] $-(x \,\epsilon\, \alpha) = x \,\epsilon\, -\alpha,$ and $-(x \,\epsilon\, \beta) = x \,\epsilon\, -\beta.$

$\qquad$ Hence [13·02] $(\alpha \subset \beta) = (-\beta \subset -\alpha).$

13·9 $[(\alpha \subset \beta) \times (\beta \subset \gamma)] \subset (\alpha \subset \gamma).$

$\qquad$ [13·6] $(\alpha \subset \beta) = \Pi_x(\varphi x \subset \psi x),$ $(\beta \subset \gamma) = \Pi_x(\psi x \subset \xi x),$ and $(\alpha \subset \gamma)$

$\qquad = \Pi_x(\varphi x \subset \xi x).$

$\qquad$ And [10·65] $[\Pi_x(\varphi x \subset \psi x) \times \Pi_x(\psi x \subset \xi x)] \subset \Pi_x(\varphi x \subset \xi x).$

The relation "is contained in" is transitive. 13·9 is the first form of the syllogism in *Barbara*. The second form is:

13·91 $[(\alpha \subset \beta) \times (x_n \,\epsilon\, \alpha)] \subset (x_n \,\epsilon\, \beta).$

$\qquad$ [13·6] $(\alpha \subset \beta) = \Pi_x(\varphi x \subset \psi x).$

$\qquad$ [13·01] $(x_n \,\epsilon\, \alpha) = \varphi x_n,$ and $(x_n \,\epsilon\, \beta) = \psi x_n.$

$\qquad$ And [10·611] $[\Pi_x(\varphi x \subset \psi x) \times \varphi x_n] \subset \psi x_n.$

If the class α is contained in the class β, and x_n is a member of α, then x_n is a member of β.

13·92 $[(\alpha = \beta) \times (\beta = \gamma)] \subset (\alpha = \gamma).$

$\qquad$ [13·7] $(\alpha = \beta) = \Pi_x(\varphi x = \psi x),$ $(\beta = \gamma) = \Pi_x(\psi x = \xi x),$ and $(\alpha = \gamma) = \Pi_x(\varphi x = \xi x).$

$\qquad$ And [10·68] $[\Pi_x(\varphi x = \psi x) \times \Pi_x(\psi x = \xi x)] \subset \Pi_x(\varphi x = \xi x).$

The last three theorems illustrate particularly well the direct connection between formal implications and the relations of classes. 13·6 and 13·7 are alternative definitions of $\alpha \subset \beta$ and $\alpha = \beta$. Similar alternative definitions of the other relations would be: [15]

$$-[\hat{z}(\varphi z)] = \hat{z}(-\varphi z)$$
$$\hat{z}(\varphi z) \times \hat{z}(\psi z) = \hat{z}(\varphi z \times \psi z)$$
$$\hat{z}(\varphi z) + \hat{z}(\psi z) = \hat{z}(\varphi z + \psi z)$$

We may give one theorem especially to exemplify the way in which every proposition of the Two-Valued Algebra, since it gives, by 10·23, a formal implication or equivalence, gives a corresponding proposition concerning classes. We choose for this example the Law of Absorption.

13·92 $[\alpha + (\alpha \times \beta)] = \alpha$.

$[13\cdot04\cdot05]\ [\alpha + (\alpha \times \beta)] = \hat{x}\{(x \,\epsilon\, \alpha) + [(x \,\epsilon\, \alpha) \times (x \,\epsilon\, \beta)]\}$.

Hence $[13\cdot01]\ \{x_n \,\epsilon\, [\alpha + (\alpha \times \beta)]\}$
$$= \{(x_n \,\epsilon\, \alpha) + [(x_n \,\epsilon\, \alpha) \times (x_n \,\epsilon\, \beta)]\}. \quad (1)$$

But $[13\cdot03]\ \{[\alpha + (\alpha \times \beta)] = \alpha\}$
$$= \Pi_x[\{(x \,\epsilon\, \alpha) + [(x \,\epsilon\, \alpha) \times (x \,\epsilon\, \beta)]\} = (x \,\epsilon\, \alpha)]. \quad (2)$$

But $[13\cdot01]\ (x_n \,\epsilon\, \alpha) = \varphi x_n,\ (x_n \,\epsilon\, \beta) = \psi x_n$, and by (2),
$$\{[\alpha + (\alpha \times \beta)] = \alpha\} = \Pi_x\{[\varphi x + (\varphi x \times \psi x)] = \varphi x\}$$

But $[5\cdot4]\ [\varphi x_n + (\varphi x_n \times \psi x_n)] = \varphi x_n$.

Hence $[10\cdot23]\ \Pi_x\{[\varphi x + (\varphi x \times \psi x)] = \varphi x\}$.

All but the last two lines of this proof are concerned with establishing the connection between $[\alpha + (\alpha \times \beta)] = \alpha$ and the formal equivalence

$$\Pi_x\{[\varphi x + (\varphi x \times \psi x)] = \varphi x\}$$

Once this connection is made, we take that theorem of the Two-Valued Algebra which corresponds to $[\alpha + (\alpha \times \beta)] = \alpha$, namely 5·4, $(p + p\,q) = p$, substitute in it φx_n for p and ψx_n for q, and then generalize, by 10·23, to the formal equivalence which gives the proof. An exactly similar procedure will give, for most theorems of the Two-Valued Algebra, a corresponding theorem of the calculus of classes. The exceptions are such propositions as $p = (p = 1)$, which unite an element p with an implication or an equivalence. In other words, every theorem concerning classes can be derived from its analogue in the Two-Valued Algebra.

We may conclude our discussion of the derivation of the logic of classes

[15] As a fact, these definitions would be much more convenient for us, but we have chosen to give them in a form exactly analogous to the corresponding definitions of *Principia* (see I, p. 217).

from the logic of propositional functions by deriving the set of postulates for the Boole-Schröder Algebra given in Chapter II. This will prove that, beginning with the Two-Valued Algebra, as a calculus of propositions, the calculus of classes may be derived. This procedure may have the appearance of circularity, since in Section I of this chapter we presumed the propositions of the Boole-Schröder Algebra without repeating them. But the circularity is apparent only, since the Two-Valued Algebra is a distinct system.

The postulates of Chapter II, in a form consonant with our present notation, can be proved so far as these postulates express symbolic laws. The postulates of the *existence*, in the system, of $-\alpha$ when α exists, of $\alpha \times \beta$ when α and β exist, and of the class 0, must be supposed satisfied by the fact that we have exhibited, in their definitions, the logical functions which determine $\alpha \times \beta$, $-\alpha$, and 0.[16]

14·2 $(\alpha \times \alpha) = \alpha$.

$\quad$ [13·01] $x_n \,\epsilon\, \alpha \,=\, \varphi x_n$.

$\quad$ Hence [13·04] $x_n \,\epsilon\, (\alpha \times \alpha) = [(x_n \,\epsilon\, \alpha) \times (x_n \,\epsilon\, \alpha)] = (\varphi x_n \times \varphi x_n)$.

$\quad$ Hence [13·03] $[(\alpha \times \alpha) = \alpha] = \Pi_x\{[x \,\epsilon\, (\alpha \times \alpha)] = x \,\epsilon\, \alpha\}$

$\qquad\qquad\qquad\qquad\qquad\qquad = \Pi_x[(\varphi x \times \varphi x) = \varphi x]$.

$\quad$ But [1·2] $(\varphi x_n \times \varphi x_n) = \varphi x_n$.

$\quad$ Hence [10·23] $\Pi_x[(\varphi x \times \varphi x) = \varphi x]$.

14·3 $(\alpha \times \beta) = (\beta \times \alpha)$.

$\quad$ [13·03] $[(\alpha \times \beta) = (\beta \times \alpha)] = \Pi_x\{[x \,\epsilon\, (\alpha \times \beta)] = [x \,\epsilon\, (\beta \times \alpha)]\}$

$\qquad\qquad = \Pi_x\{[(x \,\epsilon\, \alpha) \times (x \,\epsilon\, \beta)] = [(x \,\epsilon\, \beta) \times (x \,\epsilon\, \alpha)]\}$.

$\qquad\qquad\qquad\qquad\qquad\qquad\qquad\qquad\qquad\qquad [13\cdot01\cdot04]$

$\quad$ Hence [13·01] $[(\alpha \times \beta) = (\beta \times \alpha)] = \Pi_x[(\varphi x \times \psi x) = (\psi x \times \varphi x)]$.

$\quad$ But [1·3] $(\varphi x_n \times \psi x_n) = (\psi x_n \times \varphi x_n)$.

$\quad$ Hence [10·23] $\Pi_x[(\varphi x \times \psi x) = (\psi x \times \varphi x)]$.

14·4 $(\alpha \times \beta) \times \gamma = \alpha \times (\beta \times \gamma)$.

$\quad$ [13·03] $[(\alpha \times \beta) \times \gamma = \alpha \times (\beta \times \gamma)] =$

$\quad = \Pi_x\big[\{x \,\epsilon\, [(\alpha \times \beta) \times \gamma]\} = \{x \,\epsilon\, [\alpha \times (\beta \times \gamma)]\}\big]$

$\quad = \Pi_x\big[\{[(x \,\epsilon\, \alpha) \times (x \,\epsilon\, \beta)] \times (x \,\epsilon\, \gamma)\} = \{(x \,\epsilon\, \alpha) \times [(x \,\epsilon\, \beta) \times (x \,\epsilon\, \gamma)]\}\big]$.

$\qquad\qquad\qquad\qquad\qquad\qquad\qquad\qquad\qquad\qquad [13\cdot01\cdot04]$

$\quad$ Hence [13·01] $[(\alpha \times \beta) \times \gamma = \alpha \times (\beta \times \gamma)]$

$\qquad\qquad\qquad = \Pi_x\{[(\varphi x \times \psi x) \times \xi x] = [\varphi x \times (\psi x \times \xi x)]\}$.

---

[16] A more satisfactory derivation of these existence postulates is possible when the theory of propositional functions is treated in greater detail. See *Principia*, I, pp. 217–18.

But [1·04] $(\varphi x_n \times \psi x_n) \times \xi x_n = \varphi x_n \times (\psi x_n \times \xi x_n)$.

Hence [10·23] $\Pi_x\{[(\varphi x \times \psi x) \times \xi x] = [\varphi x \times (\psi x \times \xi x)]\}$.

14·5 $\alpha \times 0 = 0$.

[13·1·01] $x_n \,\epsilon\, 0 = -(\zeta x_n \subset \zeta x_n)$.

[13·03·04] $[\alpha \times 0 = 0] = \Pi_x\{[(x_n \,\epsilon\, \alpha) \times (x_n \,\epsilon\, 0)] = (x_n \,\epsilon\, 0)\}$

$= \Pi_x\{[\varphi x \times -(\zeta x \subset \zeta x)] = -(\zeta x \subset \zeta x)\}$. [13·01]

But [2·2, 9·01] $(\zeta x_n \subset \zeta x_n) = 1$, and [3·2] $-(\zeta x_n \subset \zeta x_n) = 0$.

Hence [1·5] $[\varphi x_n \times -(\zeta x_n \subset \zeta x_n)] = 0 = -(\zeta x_n \subset \zeta x_n)$.

Hence [10·23] $\Pi_x\{[\varphi x \times -(\zeta x \subset \zeta x)] = -(\zeta x \subset \zeta x)\}$.

0, in the fourth and fifth lines of the above proof, is the 0 of the Two-Valued Algebra, not the 0 of the calculus of classes. Since the general method of these proofs will now be clear, the remaining demonstrations can be somewhat abbreviated.

14·61 $[(\alpha \times -\beta) = 0] \subset [(\alpha \times \beta) = \alpha]$.

[13·01·02·04·06] The theorem is equivalent to

$$\Pi_x\{[(\varphi x \times -\psi x) = (x \,\epsilon\, 0)] \subset [(\varphi x \times \psi x) = \varphi x]\}$$

But [13·3] $\Pi_x -(x \,\epsilon\, 0)$, and hence [9·1] $\Pi_x[(x \,\epsilon\, 0) = 0]$.

Hence the theorem is equivalent to

$$\Pi_x\{[(\varphi x \times -\psi x) = (x \,\epsilon\, 0)] \subset [(\varphi x \times \psi x) = \varphi x]\}$$

But [13·3] $\Pi_x -(x \,\epsilon\, 0)$, and hence [9·1] $\Pi_x[(x \,\epsilon\, 0) = 0]$.

Hence the theorem is equivalent to

$$\Pi_x\{[(\varphi x \times -\psi x) = 0] \subset [(\varphi x \times \psi x) = \varphi x]\}$$

But [1·61] $[(\varphi x_n \times -\psi x_n) = 0] \subset [(\varphi x_n \times \psi x_n) = \varphi x_n]$.

Hence [10·23] Q.E.D.

14·62 $\{[(\alpha \times \beta) = \alpha] \times [(\alpha \times -\beta) = \alpha]\} \subset (\alpha = 0)$.

The theorem is equivalent to

$$\Pi_x[\{[(\varphi x \times \psi x) = \varphi x] \times [(\varphi x \times -\psi x) = \varphi x]\} \subset [\varphi x = (x \,\epsilon\, 0)]]$$

But [13·3, 9·1] $\Pi_x[(x \,\epsilon\, 0) = 0]$.

Hence the theorem is equivalent to,

$$\Pi_x[\{[(\varphi x \times \psi x) = \varphi x] \times [(\varphi x \times -\psi x) = \varphi x]\} \subset (\varphi x = 0)]$$

But [1·62] $\{[(\varphi x_n \times \psi x_n) = \varphi x_n] \times [(\varphi x_n \times -\psi x_n) = \varphi x_n]\} \subset (\varphi x_n = 0)$.

Hence [10·23] Q.E.D.

The definition, $1 = -0$, follows readily from the definition given of 0 in this section. The other two definitions of Chapter II are derived as follows:

14·8 $(\alpha + \beta) = -(-\alpha \times -\beta)$.

The theorem is equivalent to $\Pi_x[(\varphi x + \psi x) = -(-\varphi x \times -\psi x)]$.

But [1·8] $(\varphi x_n + \psi x_n) = -(-\varphi x_n \times -\psi x_n)$.

Hence [10·23] Q.E.D.

14·9 $(\alpha \subset \beta) = [(\alpha \times \beta) = \alpha]$.

The theorem is equivalent to $\Pi_x(\varphi x \subset \psi x) = \Pi_x[(\varphi x \times \psi x) = \varphi x]$.

But [1·9] $(\varphi x_n \subset \psi x_n)$ is equivalent to $[(\varphi x_n \times \psi x_n) = \varphi x_n]$.

Hence [10·23·69] Q.E.D.

Since the postulates and definitions of the calculus of classes can be deduced from the theorems of the calculus of propositional functions, it follows that the whole system of the logic of classes can be so deduced. The important differences between the calculus of classes so derived and the Boole-Schröder Algebra, as a logic of classes, are two: (1) The Boole-Schröder Algebra lacks the ϵ-relation, and is thus defective in application, since it cannot distinguish the relation of an individual to the class of which it is a member from the relation of two classes one of which is contained in the other; (2) The theorems of the Boole-Schröder Algebra cannot validly be given the completely symbolic form, while those of the calculus of classes derived from the calculus of propositional functions can be given this form.[17]

V. The Logic of Relations

The logic of relations is derived from the theory of propositional functions of two or more variables, just as the logic of classes may be based upon the theory of propositional functions of one variable.

A relation, R, is determined in extension when we logically exhibit the class of all the couples (x, y) such that x has the relation R to y. If $\varphi(x, y)$ represent "x is parent of y", then $\hat{x}\,\hat{y}[\varphi(x, y)]$ is the relation "parent of". This defines the relation in extension: just as the extension of "red" is the class of all those things which have the property of being red, so the extension of the relation "parent of" is the class of all the parent-child couples in the universe. A relation is a *property* that is common to all the couples (or triads, etc.) of a certain class; the extension of the relation is, thus, the *class of couples* itself. The calculus of relations, like the calculus of propositions, and of classes, is a calculus of extensions.

---

[17] Oftentimes, as in Schröder, *Alg. Log.*, I, the relations of propositions in the algebra of classes have been represented in the symbols of the propositional calculus before that calculus has been treated *otherwise than as an interpretation of the Boole-Schröder Algebra*. But in such a case, if these symbols are regarded as *belonging to the system*, the procedure is invalid.

We assume, then, the idea of relation: the relation R meaning the class of couples (x, y) such that x has the relation R to y.

$$R = \hat{x}\,\hat{y}(x\,R\,y), \qquad S = \hat{w}\,\hat{z}(w\,S\,z), \qquad \text{etc.}$$

This notation is simpler and more suggestive than $R = \hat{x}\,\hat{y}[\varphi(x, y)]$, $S = \hat{w}\,\hat{z}[\psi(w, z)]$, but it means exactly the same thing. A triadic relation, T, will be such that

$$T = \hat{x}\,\hat{y}\,\hat{z}[T(x, y, z)]$$

or T is the class of triads (x, y, z) for which the propositional function $T(x, y, z)$ is true. But all relations can be defined as dyadic relations. A triadic relation can be interpreted as a relation of a dyad to an individual—that is to say, any function of three variables, $T(x, y, z)$, can be treated as a function of two variables, the couple (x, y) and z, or x and the couple (y, z). This follows from the considerations presented in concluding discussion of the theorems numbered $11\cdot$, in section III.[18] Similarly, a tetradic relation can be treated as a dyadic relation of dyads, and so on. Hence the theory of dyadic relations is a perfectly general theory.

Definitions exactly analogous to those for classes can be given.

15·01 $\quad (x, y)_n\ \epsilon\ \hat{z}\,\hat{w}[R(z, w)] = R(x, y)_n.$ Def.

It is exactly at this point that our theoretical considerations of the equivalence of $\varphi(x, y)_n$ and $\varphi(x_r\,y_s)$ becomes important. For this allows us to treat $R(x, y)$, or $(x\,R\,y)$, as a function of one or of two variables, at will; and by $11\cdot07$, we can give our definition the alternative form:

15·01 $\quad (x_m\,y_n)\ \epsilon\ \hat{z}\,\hat{w}\,(z\,R\,w) = x_m\,R\,y_n.$ Def.

"The couple $(x_m\,y_n)$ belongs to the field, or extension, of the relation determined by $(z\,R\,w)$" means that $x_m\,R\,y_n$ is true.

15·02 $\quad R \subset S = \Pi_{x,\,y}[(x\,R\,y) \subset (x\,S\,y)].$ Def.

This definition is strictly parallel to $13\cdot02$,

$$(\alpha \subset \beta) = \Pi_x\,(x\ \epsilon\ \alpha \subset x\ \epsilon\ \beta)$$

because, by $15\cdot01$, $(x\,R\,y)$ is $(x, y)\ \epsilon\ R$ and $(x\,S\,y)$ is $(x, y)\ \epsilon\ S$. A similar remark applies to the remaining definitions.

15·03 $\quad (R = S) = \Pi_{x,\,y}[(x\,R\,y) = (x\,S\,y)].$ Def.

R and S are equivalent in extension when, for every x and every y, $(x\,R\,y)$ and $(x\,S\,y)$ are equivalent assertions.

[18] See above, pp. 253 *ff.*

15·04 $R \times S = \hat{x}\,\hat{y}\,[(x\,R\,y) \times (x\,S\,y)].$ Def.

The logical product of two relations, R and S, is the class of couples $(x, y.$ such that x has the relation R to y and x has the relation S to y. If R is "friend of", and S is "colleague of", $R \times S$ will be "friend and colleague of")

15·05 $R + S = \hat{x}\,\hat{y}\,[(x\,R\,y) + (x\,S\,y)].$ Def.

The logical sum of two relations, R and S, is the class of couples (x, y) such that either x has the relation R to y or x has the relation S to y. $R + S$ will be "Either R of or S of".

15·06 $-R = \hat{x}\,\hat{y}\,-(x\,R\,y).$ Def.

$-R$ is the relation of x to y when x does not have the relation R to y.

It is important to note that $R \times S$, $R + S$, and $-R$ are relations: $x(R \times S)y$, $x(R + S)y$, and $x\,-R\,y$ are significant assertions.

The "universal-relation" and the "null-relation" are also definable after the analogy to classes.

15·07 $1 = \hat{x}\,\hat{y}\,[\zeta(x, y) \subset \zeta(x, y)].$ Def.

x has the universal-relation to y in case there is a function, ζ, such that $\zeta(x, y) \subset \zeta(x, y)$, i. e., in case x and y have *any* relation.

15·08 $0 = -1.$ Def.

Of course, 0, 1, + and × have different meanings for relations from their meanings for classes or for propositions. But these different meanings o 0, +, etc., are strictly analogous.

As was pointed out in Section III of this chapter, for every theorem involving functions of one variable, there is a similar theorem involving functions of two variables, due to the fact that a function $\varphi(x, y)$ may be regarded as a function of the single variable (x, y). Consequently, for each theorem of the calculus of classes, there is an exactly corresponding theorem in the calculus of relations. We may, then, cite as illustrations of this calculus the analogues of the theorems demonstrated to hold for classes; and no proofs will here be necessary. These proofs follow from the theorems of Section III, numbered 11·, exactly as the proofs for classes are given by the corresponding theorems in Section II, numbered 10 .

15·1 $0 = \hat{x}\,\hat{y}\,-[\zeta(x, y) \subset \zeta(x, y)].$

The null-relation is the relation of x to y when it is false that $\zeta(x, y)$ implies $\zeta(x, y)$, i. e., when x has no relation to y.[19] Of course, there is no such (x, y) couple which can significantly be *called* a couple.

[19] As in the case of the 1 and 0 of the class calculus, the 1 and 0 of relations, defined as

15·2 $\Pi_{x,\ y}[(x,\ y)\ \epsilon\ 1]$.

Every couple is a member of the universe of couples, or has the universal (dyadic) relation.

15·3 $\Pi_{x,\ y}\ -[(x,\ y)\ \epsilon\ 0]$.

No couple has the null-relation.

15·4 $R \subset 1$.

15·5 $0 \subset R$.

Every relation, R, is implied by the null-relation and implies the universal relation; or, whatever couple $(x,\ y)$ has the null-relation has also the relation R, and whatever couple has any relation, R, has also the universal-relation.

15·6 $(R \subset S) = \Pi_{x,\ y}[(x\ R\ y) \subset (x\ S\ y)]$.

For relations, $R \subset S$ is more naturally read "R implies S" than "R is contained in S". By 15·6, "R implies S" means "For every x and every y, if x has the relation R to y, then x has the relation S to y". Or "R implies S" means "Every $(x,\ y)$ couple related by R are also related by S".

15·7 $(R = S) = \Pi_{x,\ y}[(x\ R\ y) = (x\ S\ y)]$.

Two relations, R and S, are equivalent when the couples related by R are also related by S, and vice versa (remembering that $=$ is always a reciprocal relation $\subset$).

15·8 $(R \subset S) = (-S \subset -R)$.

If the relation R implies the relation S, then when S is absent R also will be absent.

15·9 $[(R \subset S) \times (S \subset T)] \subset (R \subset T)$.

The implication of one relation by another is a transitive relation.

15·91 $[(R \subset S) \times (x_m\ R\ y_n)] \subset (x_m\ S\ y_n)$.

If R implies S and a given couple are related by R, then this couple are related also by S.

15·92 $[(R = S) \times (S = T)] \subset (R = T)$.

The equivalence of relations is transitive.

If it be supposed that the postulates concerning the *existence* of relations are satisfied by exhibiting the functions which determine them, then, we have defined them, are such that propositions involving them are true whenever significant, and significant whenever the propositional functions determining the functions in question have the same range.

as in the case of classes, we can derive the postulates (or remaining postulates) for a calculus of relations from the theorems of the calculus of propositional functions. The demonstrations would be simply the analogues of those already given for classes, and may be omitted.

16·2 $(R \times R) = R.$

16·3 $(R \times S) = (S \times R).$

16·4 $(R \times S) \times T = R \times (S \times T).$

16·5 $R \times 0 = 0.$

16·61 $[(R \times -S) = 0] \subset [(R \times S) = R].$

16·62 $\{[(R \times S) = R] \times [(R \times -S) = R]\} \subset (R = 0).$

16·8 $(R + S) = -(-R \times -S).$

16·9 $(R \subset S) = [(R \times S) = R].$

These theorems may also be taken as confirmation of the fact that the Boole-Schröder Algebra holds for relations. In fact, "calculus of relations" most frequently means just that—the Boole-Schröder Algebra with the elements, *a*, *b*, *c*, etc., interpreted as relations taken in extension.

So far, the logic of relations is a simple analogue of the logic of classes. But there are many properties of relations for which classes present no analogies, and these peculiar properties are most important. In fact, the logistic development of mathematics, worked out by Peirce, Schröder, Frege, Peano and his collaborators, and Whitehead and Russell, has depended very largely upon a further study of the logic of relations. While we can do no more, within reasonable limits, than to suggest the manner of this development, it seems best that the most important of these properties of relations should be given in outline. But even this outline cannot be complete, because the theoretical basis provided by our previous discussion is not sufficient for completeness.

Every relation, R, has a converse, $\smile R$, which can be defined as follows:

17·01 $\smile R = \hat{y}\, \hat{x}\, (x\, R\, y).$ Def.

If x has the relation R to y, then y has the converse relation, $\smile R$, to x. It follows at once from the definition of $(x_m y_n) \,\epsilon\, R$ that

$$x_m\, R\, y_n = y_n \smile R\, x_m$$

because $(x_m\, R\, y_n) = (x_m y_n) \,\epsilon\, R = (y_n x_m) \,\epsilon\, \smile R = y_n \smile R\, x_m.$

The converse of the converse of R is R.

$$\smile(\smile R) = R$$

since $\smile(\smile R) = \hat{x}\,\hat{y}\,(y \smile R\,x) = \hat{x}\,\hat{y}\,(x\,R\,y) = R$. (This is not a proof: proof would require that we demonstrate

$$\Pi_{x,\,y}[(x,\,y) \,\epsilon\, \smile(\smile R) = (x,\,y) \,\epsilon\, R]$$

But it is obvious that such a demonstration may be given. In general, we shall not pause for proofs here, but merely indicate the method of proof.)

The properties of symmetrical relations follow from the theorems concerning converses. For any symmetrical relation T, $T = \smile T$. The universal relation, 1, and the null-relation, 0, are both symmetrical:

$$(x\,1\,y) = [\varsigma(x,\,y) \subset \varsigma(x,\,y)] = 1 = [\varsigma(y,\,x) \subset \varsigma(y,\,x)] = (y\,1\,x)$$

(The "1" in the middle of this 'proof' is obviously that of the calculus of propositions. Similarly for 0 in the next.)

$$(x\,0\,y) = -[\varsigma(x,\,y) \subset \varsigma(x,\,y)] = 0 = -[\varsigma(y,\,x) \subset \varsigma(y,\,x)] = (y\,0\,x)$$

It is obvious that if two relations are equivalent, their converses will be equivalent:

$$(R = S) = (\smile R = \smile S)$$

Not quite so obvious is the equivalent of $(R \subset S)$, in terms of $\smile R$ and $\smile S$. We might expect that $(R \subset S)$ would give $(\smile S \subset \smile R)$. Instead we have

$$(R \subset S) = (\smile R \subset \smile S)$$

for $(R \subset S) = \Pi_{x,\,y}[(x\,R\,y) \subset (x\,S\,y)] = \Pi_{x,\,y}[(y \smile R\,x) \subset (y \smile S\,x)]$
$$= (\smile R \subset \smile S)$$

"'Parent of' implies 'ancestor of'" is equivalent to "'Child of' implies 'descendent of'".

The converses of compound relations is as follows:

$$\smile(R \times S) = \smile R \times \smile S$$

for $x \smile(R \times S)y = y(R \times S)x = (y\,R\,x) \times (y\,S\,x) = (x \smile R\,y) \times (x \smile S\,y)$
$$= x(\smile R \times \smile S)y$$

If x is employer and exploiter of y, the relation of y to x is "employee of and exploited by". Similarly

$$\smile(R + S) = \smile R + \smile S$$

If x is either employer or benefactor of y, the relation of y to x is "either employee of or benefitted by".

Other important properties of relations concern "relative sums" and "relative products". These must be distinguished from the non-relative sum and product of relations, symbolized by + and ×. The non-relative product of "friend of" and "colleague of" is "friend and colleague of": their *relative* product is "friend of a colleague of". Their non-relative sum is "either friend of or colleague of": their *relative* sum is "friend of every non-colleague of". We shall denote the relative product of R and S by $R|S$, their relative sum by $R \dagger S$.

17·02 $R|S = \hat{x} \hat{z} \{\Sigma_y[(x \, R \, y) \times (y \, S \, z)]\}$.   Def.

$R|S$ is the relation of the couple (x, z) when for some y, x has the relation R to y and y has the relation S to z. x is friend of a colleague of z when, for some y, x is friend of y and y is colleague of z.

17·03 $R \dagger S = \hat{x} \hat{z} \{\Pi_y[(x \, R \, y) + (y \, S \, z)]\}$.   Def.

$R \dagger S$ is the relation of x to z when, for every y, either x has the relation R to y or y has the relation S to z. x is friend of all non-colleagues of z when, for every y, either x is friend of y or y is colleague of z.

It is noteworthy that neither relative products nor relative sums are commutative. "Friend of a colleague of" is not "colleague of a friend of". Nor is "friend of all non-colleagues of" the same as "colleague of all non-friends of". But both relations are associative.

$$R|(S|T) = (R|S)|T$$

for $\Sigma_x\{(w \, R \, x) \times [x(S \, T)z]\} = \Sigma_x\{(w \, R \, x) \times \Sigma_y[(x \, S \, y) \times (y \, T \, z)]\}$
$$= \Sigma_y \Sigma_x\{(w \, R \, x) \times [(x \, S \, y) \times (y \, T \, z)]\}$$
$$= \Sigma_y \Sigma_x\{[(w \, R \, x) \times (x \, S \, y)] \times (y \, T \, z)\}$$
$$= \Sigma_y\{\Sigma_x[(w \, R \, x) \times (x \, S \, z)] \times (y \, T \, z)\}$$
$$= \Sigma_y\{[w(R \, S)y] \times (y \, T \, z)\}$$

"Friend of a (colleague of a neighbor of)" is "(friend of a colleague) of a neighbor of".

Similarly, $R \dagger (S \dagger T) = (R \dagger S) \dagger T$

"Friend of all (non-colleagues of all non-neighbors of)" is "(friend of all non-colleagues) of all non-neighbors of".

De Morgan's Theorem holds for the negation of relative sums and products.

$$-(R|S) = -R \dagger -S$$

for $-\{\Sigma_y[(x \, R \, y) \times (y \, S \, z)]\} = \Pi_y -[(x \, R \, y) \times (y \, S \, z)]$
$$= \Pi_y[-(x \, R \, y) + -(y \, S \, z)]$$
$$= \Pi_y[(x -R \, y) + (y -S \, z)]$$

The negative of "friend of a colleague of" is "non-friend of all colleagues (non-non-colleagues) of ".

Similarly, $$-(R \dagger S) = -R \mid -S$$

The negative of "friend of all non-colleagues of" is "non-friend of a non-colleague of ".

Converses of relative sums and products are as follows:

$$\smile(R \mid S) = \smile S \mid \smile R$$

for

$$
\begin{aligned}
x \smile(R \mid S)z = z(R \mid S)x &= \Sigma_y[(z \ R \ y) \times (y \ S \ x)] \\
&= \Sigma_y[(y \ S \ x) \times (z \ R \ y)] \\
&= \Sigma_y[(x \smile S \ y) \times (y \smile R \ z)] \\
&= x(\smile S \mid \smile R)z
\end{aligned}
$$

If x is employer of a benefactor of z, then the relation of z to x is "benefitted by an employee of ".

Similarly, $$\smile(R \dagger S) = \smile S \dagger \smile R$$

If x is hater of all non-helpers of z, the relation of z to x is "helped by all who are not hated by ".

The relation of relative product is distributive with reference to non-relative addition.

$$R \mid (S + T) = (R \mid S) + (R \mid T)$$

for

$$
\begin{aligned}
x[R \mid (S + T)]z &= \Sigma_y\{(x \ R \ y) \times [y(S + T)z]\} \\
&= \Sigma_y\{(x \ R \ y) \times [(y \ S \ z) + (y \ T \ z)]\} \\
&= \Sigma_y\{[(x \ R \ y) \times (y \ S \ z)] + [(x \ R \ y) \times (y \ T \ z)]\} \\
&= [x(R \mid S)z] + [x(R \mid T)z]
\end{aligned}
$$

Similarly, $$(R + S) \mid T = (R \mid T) + (S \mid T)$$

"Either friend or colleague of a teacher of" is the same as "either friend of a teacher of or colleague of a teacher of ".

A somewhat curious formula is the following:

$$R \mid (S \times T) \subset (R \mid S) \times (R \mid T)$$

It holds since

$$
\begin{aligned}
x[R \mid (S \times T)]z &= \Sigma_y\{(x \ R \ y) \times [y(S \times T)z]\} \\
&= \Sigma_y\{(x \ R \ y) \times [(y \ S \ z) \times (y \ T \ z)]\}
\end{aligned}
$$

and since $a \times (b \times c) = (a \times b) \times (a \times c)$,

$$
\begin{aligned}
&= \Sigma_y\{[(x \ R \ y) \times (y \ S \ z)] \times [(x \ R \ y) \times (y \ T \ z)]\} \\
&\subset \Sigma_y[(x \ R \ y) \times (y \ S \ z)] \times \Sigma_y[(x \ R \ y) \times (y \ T \ z)]
\end{aligned}
$$

And this last expression is $[x(R \mid S)z] \times [x(R \mid T)z]$.

If x is student of a friend *and* colleague of z, then x is student of a friend and student of a colleague of z. The converse implication does not hold, because "student of a friend and colleague" requires that the friend and the colleague be identical, while "student of a friend and student of a colleague" does not. (Note the last step in the 'proof', where Σ_y is repeated, and observe that this step carries exactly that significance.)

Similarly, $$(R \times S) \mid T \subset (R \mid T) \times (S \mid T)$$

The corresponding formulae with $\dagger$ instead of $\mid$ are more complicated and seldom useful; they are omitted.

The relative sum is of no particular importance, but the relative product is a very useful concept. In terms of this idea, "powers" of a relation are definable:
$$R^2 = R \mid R, \qquad R^3 = R^2 \mid R, \qquad \text{etc.}$$

A transitive relation, S, is distinguished by the fact that $S^2 \subset S$, and hence $S^n \subset S$. The predecessors of predecessors of predecessors . . . of x are predecessors of x. This conception of the powers of a relation plays a prominent part in the analysis of serial order, and of the fundamental properties of the number series. By use of this and certain other concepts, the method of "mathematical induction" can be demonstrated to be completely deductive.[20]

In the work of De Morgan and Peirce, "relative terms" were not given separate treatment. The letters by which relations were symbolized were also interpreted as relative terms by a sort of systematic ambiguity. Any relation symbol also stood for the class of entities which have that relation to something. But in the logistic development of mathematics, since that time, notably in *Principia Mathematica*,[21] relative terms are given the separate treatment which they really require. The "domain" of a given relation, R—that is, the class of entities which have the relation R to something or other—may be symbolized by $D'R$, which can be defined as follows:

17·04 $D'R = \hat{x}[\Sigma_y(x \, R \, y)].$ Def.

The domain of R is the class of x's determined by the function "For some y, x has the relation R to y". If R be "employer of", $D'R$ will be the class of employers.

The "converse domain" of R—that is, the class of things to each of

[20] See *Principia*, I, Bk. II, Sect. E.
[21] See I, *33. The notation we use for domains and converse domains is that of *Principia*.

which something or other *has* the relation R—may be symbolized by $\mathrm{Cl}'R$ and similarly defined:

17·05 $\quad \mathrm{Cl}'R = \hat{y}[\Sigma_x(x \, R \, y)].\qquad$ Def.

The converse domain of R is the class of y's determined by the function "For some x, x has the relation R to y". If R be "employer of", $\mathrm{Cl}'R$ will be the class of employees.

The domain and converse domain of a relation, R, together constitute the "field" of R, $C'R$.

17·06 $\quad C'R = \hat{x}\{\Sigma_y[(x \, R \, y) + (y \, R \, x)]\}.$

The field of R will be the class of all terms which stand in either place in the relation. If R be "employer of", $C'R$ is the class of all those who are either employers or employees.

The elementary properties of such "relative terms" are all obvious:

$$x_n \, \epsilon \, \mathrm{D}'R = \Sigma_y(x_n \, R \, y)$$
$$y_n \, \epsilon \, \mathrm{Cl}'R = \Sigma_x(x \, R \, y_n)$$
$$x_n \, \epsilon \, C'R = \Sigma_y[(x_n \, R \, y) + (y \, R \, x_n)]$$
$$C'R = \mathrm{D}'R + \mathrm{Cl}'R$$

However, for the logistic development of mathematics, these properties are of the highest importance. We quote from *Principia Mathematica*: [22] "Let us . . . suppose that R is the sort of relation that generates a series, say the relation of less to greater among integers. Then $\mathrm{D}'R$ = all integers that are less than some other integer = all integers, $\mathrm{Cl}'R$ = all integers that are greater than some other integer = all integers except 0. In this case, $C'R$ = all integers that are either greater or less than some other integer = all integers . . . . Thus when R generates a series, $C'R$ becomes important. . . ."

We have now surveyed the most fundamental and important characters of the logic of relations, and we could not well proceed further without elaboration of a kind which is here inadmissible. But the reader is warned that we have no more than scratched the surface of this important topic. About 1890, Schröder could write "What a pity! To have a highly developed instrument and nothing to do with it". And he proceeded to make a beginning in the bettering of this situation by applying the logic of relatives to the logistic development of certain portions of Dedekind's theory of number. Since that time, the significance of symbolic logic has been completely demonstrated in the development of Peano's *Formulaire*

[22] I, p. 261.

and of *Principia Mathematica*. And the very head and front of this development is a theory of relations far more extended and complete than any previously given. We can here adapt the prophetic words which Leibniz puts into the mouth of Philalethes: "I begin to get a very different opinion of logic from that which I formerly had. I had regarded it as a scholar's diversion, but I now see that, in the way you understand it, it is a kind of universal mathematics."

VI. The Logic of *Principia Mathematica*

We have now presented the extensions of the Boole-Schröder Algebra— the Two-Valued Algebra, propositional functions and the propositions derived from them, and the application to these of the laws of the Two-Valued Algebra, giving the calculus of propositional functions. Beyond this, we have shown in outline how it is possible, beginning with the Two-Valued Algebra as a calculus of propositions, to derive the logic of classes in a form somewhat more satisfactory than the Boole-Schröder Algebra, and the logic of relations and relative terms. In so doing, we have presented as much of that development which begins with Boole and passes through the work of Peirce to Schröder as is likely to be permanently significant. But, our purpose here being expository rather than historical, we have not followed the exact forms which that development took. Instead, we have considerably modified it in the light of what symbolic logicians have learned since the publication of the work of Peirce and Schröder.

Those who are interested to note in detail our divergence from the historical development will be able to do so by reference to Sections VII and VIII of Chapter I. But it seems best here to point out briefly what these alterations are that we have made. In the first place, we have interpreted $\Sigma\varphi x$, $\Pi\varphi x$, $\Sigma\psi(x, y)$, etc., explicitly as sums or products of propositions of the form φx_n, $\psi(x_m y_n)$, etc. Peirce and Schröder avoided this, in consideration of the serious theoretical difficulties. But while they did not treat $\Pi\varphi x$ as an actual product, $\Sigma\varphi x$ as an actual sum, still the laws which they give for propositions of this type are those which result from such a treatment. There is no slightest doubt that the method by which Peirce discovered and formulated these laws is substantially the one which we have exhibited. And this explicit use of $\Pi\varphi x$ as the symbol for a product, $\Sigma\varphi x$ as the symbol of a sum, makes demonstration possible where otherwise a large number of assumptions must be made and, for further principles, a much more difficult and less obvious style of proof resorted to.

In this part of their work, Peirce and Schröder can hardly be said to have formulated the assumptions or given the proofs.

In the second place, the Boole-Schröder Algebra—the general outline of which is already present in Peirce's work—probably seemed to Peirce and Schröder an adequate calculus of classes (though there are indications in the paper of 1880 that Peirce felt its defects). With this system before them, they neglected the possibility ·of a better procedure, by beginning with the calculus of propositions and deriving the logic of classes from the laws which govern propositional functions. And although the principles which they formulate for propositional functions are as applicable to functions of one as of two variables, and are given for one as well as for two, their interest was almost entirely in functions of two and the calculus of relatives which may be derived from such functions. The logic of classes which we have outlined is, then, something which they laid the foundation for, but did not develop.

The main purposes of our exposition thus far in the chapter have been two: first, to make clear the relation of this earlier treatment of symbolic logic with the later and better treatment to be discussed in this section; and second, to present the logic of propositional functions and their derivatives in a form somewhat simpler and more easily intelligible than it might otherwise be. The theoretically sounder and more adequate logic of *Principia Mathematica* is given a form which—so far as propositional functions and their derivatives is concerned—seems to us to obscure, by its notation, the obvious and helpful mathematical analogies, and requires a style of proof which is much less obvious. With regard to this second purpose, we disclaim any idea that the development we have given is theoretically adequate; its chief value should be that of an introductory study, preparatory to the more complex and difficult treatment which obviates the theoretical shortcomings.

Incidentally, the exposition which has been given will serve to indicate how much we are indebted, for the recent development of our subject, to the earlier work of Peirce and Schröder.

The Peirce-Schröder symbolic logic is closely related to the logic of Peano's *Formulaire de Mathématiques* and of *Principia Mathematica*. This connection is easily overlooked by the student, with the result that the subject of his first studies—the Boole-Schröder Algebra and its applications—is likely to seem quite unrelated to the topic which later interests him—the logistic development of mathematics. Both the connections of these two and their differences are important. We shall attempt to point out both. And because, for one reason, clearness requires that we stick to a single illustration, our comparison will be between the content of preceding sections of this chapter and the mathematical logic of Book I, *Principia Mathematica.*[23]

The Two-Valued Algebra is a calculus produced by adding to and re-interpreting an algebra intended primarily to deal with the relations of classes. And it has several defects which reflect this origin. In the first place, the same logical relation is expressed, in this system, in two different ways. We have, for example, the proposition "If $p \subset q$ and $q \subset r$, then $p \subset r$", where p, q, and r are propositions. But "if . . . , then . . ." is supposed to be the same relation which is expressed by $\subset$ in $p \subset q$, $q \subset r$, and $p \subset r$. Also, "and" in "$p \subset q$ and $q \subset r$" is the relation which is other-wise expressed by $\times$—and so on, for the other logical relations. The system involves the use of "if . . . , then . . .", ". . . and . . .", "either . . . or . . .", ". . . is equivalent to . . .", and ". . . is not equivalent to . . .", just as any mathematical system may; yet these are exactly the relations $\subset$, $\times$, $+$, $=$, and $\neq$ whose properties are supposed to be investigated in the system. Thus *the system takes the laws of the logical relations of propositions for granted in order to prove them.* Nor is this paradox removed by the fact that we can demonstrate the interchange-ability of "if . . . , then . . ." and $\subset$, of ". . . and . . ." and $\times$, etc. For the very demonstration of this interchangeability takes for granted the logic of propositions; and furthermore, in the system as developed, it is impossible in most cases to give a law the completely symbolic form until it has *first* been proved in the form which involves the non-symbolic expression of relations. So that there is no way in which the circularity in the demonstration of the laws of propositions can be removed in this system.

Another defect of the Two-Valued Algebra is the redundance of forms. The proposition p or "p is true" is symbolized by p, by $p = 1$, by $p \neq 0$,

---

[23] Logically, as well as historically, the method of Peano's *Formulaire* is a sort of intermediary between the Peirce-Schröder mode of procedure and *Principia*. The general method of analysis and much of the notation follows that of the *Formulaire*. But the *Formulaire* is somewhat less concerned with the extreme of logical rigor, and somewhat more concerned with the detail of the various branches of mathematics. Perhaps for this reason, it lacks that detailed examination and analysis of fundamentals which is the dis-tinguishing characteristic of *Principia*. For example, the *Formulaire* retains the ambiguity of the relation $\supset$ (in our notation, $\subset$): $p \supset q$ may be either "the class p is contained in the class q", or "the proposition p implies the proposition q". In consequence, the *Formulaire* contains no specific theory of propositions.

etc., the negation of p or "p is false" by $-p$, $p = 0$, $-p = 1$, $p \neq 1$, etc. These various forms may, it is true, be reduced in number; p and $-p$ may be made to do service for all their various equivalents. But *these equivalents cannot be banished*, for *in the proofs* it is necessary to make use of the fact that $p = (p = 1) = (p \neq 0)$, $-p = (p = 0) = (-p = 1)$, etc., in order to demonstrate the theorems. Hence this redundance is not altogether avoidable.

Both these defects are removed by the procedure adopted for the calculus of propositions in *Principia Mathematica*.[24] Here $p = 1$, $p = 0$, etc., are not used; instead we have simply p and its negative, symbolized by $\sim p$. And, impossible as it may seem, the logic of propositions which every mathematical system has always taken for granted is not presumed. The primitive ideas are: (1) elementary propositions, (2) elementary propositional functions, (3) assertion, (4) assertion of a propositional function, (5) negation, (6) disjunction, or the logical sum; and finally, the idea of "equivalent by definition", which does not belong *in* the system but is merely a notation to indicate that one symbol or complex of symbols may be replaced by another. An elementary proposition is one which does not involve any variables, and an elementary propositional function is such as "not-p" where p is an undetermined elementary proposition. The idea of assertion is just what would be supposed—a proposition may be asserted or merely considered. The sign $\vdash$ prefaces all propositions which are asserted. An asserted propositional function is such as "A is A" where A is undetermined. The disjunction of p and q is symbolized by $p \vee q$, instead of $p + q$. $p \vee q$ means "At least one of the two propositions, p and q, is true".

The postulates and definitions are as follows:

$*1 \cdot 01 \quad p \supset q \, \boldsymbol{.} = \boldsymbol{.} \sim p \vee q. \qquad$ Df.

"p (materially) implies q" is the defined equivalent of "At least one of the two, 'p is false' and 'q is true', is a true proposition". (The explanation of propositions here is ours.) $p \supset q$ is the *same* relation which we have symbolized by $p \subset q$, not its converse.

(The propositions quoted will be given the number which they have in *Principia*. The asterisk which precedes the number will distinguish them from our propositions in earlier chapters or earlier sections of this chapter.)

The logical product of p and q is symbolized by $p \, q$, or $p \boldsymbol{.} q$.

---

[24] See Bk. I, Sect. A.

✳3·01 $p . q . = . \sim(\sim p \lor \sim q)$.   Df.

"p is true and q is true" is the defined equivalent of "It is false that at least one of the two, p and q, is false". This is, of course, a form of De Morgan's Theorem—in our notation, $(p\,q) = -(-p + -q)$.

The (material) equivalence of p and q is symbolized by $p \equiv q$ or $p . \equiv . q$.

✳4·01 $p \equiv q . = . p \supset q . q \supset p$.   Df.

"p is (materially) equivalent to q" is the defined equivalent of "p (materially) implies q and q (materially) implies p". In our notation, this would be $(p = q) = (p \subset q)(q \subset p)$. Note that ... $\equiv$ ... and ... $=$ ... Df are different relations in *Principia*.

The dots in these definitions serve as punctuation in place of parentheses and brackets. Two dots, :, takes precedence over one, as a bracket over a parenthesis, three over two, etc. In ✳4·01 we have only one dot after $=$, because the dot between $p \supset q$ and $q \supset p$ indicates a product: a dot, or two dots, indicating a product is always inferior to a stop indicated by the same number of dots but not indicating a product.

The postulates of the system in question are as follows:

✳1·1   Anything implied by a true elementary proposition is true.   Pp.
("Pp." stands for "Primitive proposition".)

✳1·11   When φx can be asserted, where x is a real variable, and $\varphi x \supset \psi x$ can be asserted, where x is a real variable, then ψx can be asserted, where x is a real variable.   Pp.

A "real variable" is such as p in $-p$.

✳1·2 $\vdash: p \lor p . \supset . p$.   Pp.

In our notation, $(p + p) \subset p$.

✳1·3 $\vdash: q . \supset . p \lor q$.   Pp.

In our notation, $q \subset (p + q)$.

✳1·4 $\vdash: p \lor q . \supset . q \lor p$.   Pp.

In our notation, $(p + q) \subset (q + p)$.

✳1·5 $\vdash: p \lor (q \lor r) . \supset . q \lor (p \lor r)$.   Pp.

In our notation, $[p + (q + r)] \subset [q + (p + r)]$.

✳1·6 $\vdash:. q \supset r . \supset: p \lor q . \supset . p \lor r$.   Pp.

In our notation, $(q \subset r) \subset [(p + q) \subset (p + r)]$.

Note that the sign of assertion in each of the above is followed by a sufficient number of dots to indicate that the whole of what follows is asserted.

∗1·7   If p is an elementary proposition, $\sim p$ is an elementary proposition. Pp.

∗1·71   If p and q are elementary propositions, $p \vee q$ is an elementary proposition. Pp.

∗1·72   If φp and ψp are elementary propositional functions which take elementary propositions as arguments, $\varphi p \vee \psi p$ is an elementary propositional function.   Pp.

This completes the list of assumptions. The last three have to do directly with the method by which the system is developed. By ∗1·7, any proposition which is assumed or proved for p may also be asserted to hold for $\sim p$, that is to say, $\sim p$ may be substituted for p or q or r, etc., in any proposition of the system.   By ∗1·71, $p \vee q$ may be substituted for p or q or r, etc.   And by ∗1·72, if any two complexes of the foregoing symbols which make sense as "statements" can be treated in a certain way in the system, their disjunction can be similarly treated.   By the use of all three of these, any combination such as $p \vee q$, $p \cdot q$, $p \supset q$, $p \equiv q$, $p \supset q \cdot q \supset p$, $\sim p \cdot \vee \cdot p \vee q$, $\sim p \vee \sim q$, etc., etc., may be substituted for p or q or r in any assumed proposition or any theorem. Such substitution, for which no postulates would ordinarily be stated, is one of the fundamental operations by which the system is developed.

Another kind of substitution which is fundamental is the substitution for any complex of symbols of its defined equivalent, where such exists. This operation is covered by the meaning assigned to "$\ldots = \ldots$ Df".

Only one other operation is used in the development of this calculus of elementary propositions—the operation for which ∗1·1 and ∗1·11 are assumed. If by such substitutions as have just been explained there results a complex of symbols in which the main, or asserted, relation is $\supset$, and if that part of the expression which precedes this sign is identical with a postulate or previous theorem, then that part of the expression which follows this sign may be asserted as a lemma or new theorem. In other words, a main, or asserted, sign $\supset$ has, by ∗1·1 and ∗1·11, the significant property of "If . . . , then . . .". This property is explicitly assumed in the postulates. The main thing to be noted about this operation of inference is that it is not so much a piece of reasoning as a mechanical, or strictly mathematical, operation for which a rule has been given. No "mental" operation is involved except that required to recognize a previous proposition followed by the main implication sign, and to set off what follows that sign as a new assertion. The use of this operation does not, then, mean that the processes and principles of ordinary logic are tacitly presupposed as warrant for the operations which give proof.

What is the significance of this assumption of the obvious in $*1\cdot1$, $*1\cdot11$, $*1\cdot7$, $*1\cdot71$, and $*1\cdot72$? Precisely this: these postulates explicitly assume so much of the logical operations as is necessary to develop the system, and beyond this the logic of propositions simply is not assumed. To illustrate this fact, it will be well to consider carefully an exemplary proof or two.

$*2\cdot01$ $\vdash: p \supset \sim p \,.\, \supset \,.\, \sim p$

     Dem. $\left[\text{Taut} \dfrac{\sim p}{p} \right] \vdash: \sim p \lor \sim p \,.\, \supset \,.\, \sim p$ (1)

         $[(1) \,.\, (*1\cdot01)] \vdash: p \supset \sim p \,.\, \supset \,.\, \sim p$

"Taut" is the abbreviation for the Principle of Tautology, $*1\cdot2$ above. $\sim p/p$ indicates that $\sim p$ is substituted in this postulate for p, giving (1). This operation is valid by $*1\cdot7$. Then by the definition $*1\cdot01$, above, $p \supset \sim p$ is substituted for its defined equivalent, $\sim p \lor \sim p$, and the proof is complete.

$*2\cdot05$ $\vdash: \,.\, q \supset r \,.\, \supset : p \supset q \,.\, \supset \,.\, p \supset r$

     Dem. $\left[\text{Sum} \dfrac{\sim p}{p} \right] \vdash: \,.\, q \supset r \,.\, \supset : \sim p \lor q \,.\, \supset \,.\, \sim p \lor r$ (1)

         $[(1) \,.\, (*1\cdot01)] \vdash: \,.\, q \supset r \,.\, \supset : p \supset q \,.\, \supset \,.\, p \supset r$

Here "Sum" refers to $*1\cdot6$, above. And (1) is what $*1\cdot6$ becomes when $\sim p$ is substituted for p. Then, by $*1\cdot01$, $p \supset q$ and $p \supset r$ are substituted for their defined equivalents, $\sim p \lor q$ and $\sim p \lor r$, in (1), and the resulting expression is the theorem to be proved.

The next proof illustrates the use of $*1\cdot1$ and $*1\cdot11$.

$*2\cdot06$ $\vdash: \,.\, p \supset q \,.\, \supset : q \supset r \,.\, \supset \,.\, p \supset r$

     Dem. $\left[\text{Comm} \dfrac{q \supset r, \; p \supset q, \; p \supset r}{p, \quad q, \quad r} \right]$

   $\vdash: : q \supset r \,.\, \supset : p \supset q \,.\, \supset \,.\, p \supset r : \,.\, \supset : \,.\, p \supset q \,.\, \supset : q \supset r \,.\, \supset \,.\, p \supset r$ (1)

     $[*2\cdot05] \vdash: \,.\, q \supset r \,.\, \supset : p \supset q \,.\, \supset \,.\, p \supset r$ (2)

     $[(1) \,.\, (2) \,.\, *1\cdot11] \vdash: \,.\, p \supset q \,.\, \supset : q \supset r \,.\, \supset \,.\, p \supset r$

"Comm" is $*2\cdot04$, previously proved, which is $p \boldsymbol{.} \supset \boldsymbol{.} q \supset r \boldsymbol{:} \supset \boldsymbol{:} q \supset \boldsymbol{.} p \supset r$. When, in this theorem, $q \supset r$ is substituted for p, $p \supset q$ for q, and $p \supset r$ for r, it becomes the long expression (1). Such substitutions are valid by $*1\cdot7$, $*1\cdot71$, and the definition $*1\cdot01$: if p is a proposition, $\sim p$ is a proposition; if $\sim p$ and q are propositions, $\sim p \vee q$ is a proposition; and $p \supset q$ is the defined equivalent of $\sim p \vee q$. Thus $p \supset q$ can be substituted for p. If we replace the dots by parentheses, etc., (1) becomes

$$\vdash \{(q \supset r) \supset [(p \supset q) \supset (p \supset r)]\} \supset \{(p \supset q) \supset [(q \supset r) \supset (p \supset r)]\}$$

But, as (2) states, what here precedes the main implication sign is identical with a previous theorem, $*2\cdot05$. Hence, by $*1\cdot11$, what follows this main implication sign—the theorem to be proved—can be asserted.

Further proofs would, naturally, be more complicated, but they involve no principle not exemplified in the above. These three operations—substitutions according to $*1\cdot7$, $*1\cdot71$, and $*1\cdot72$; substitution of defined equivalents; and "inference" according to $*1\cdot1$ and $*1\cdot11$—are the only processes which ever enter into any demonstration in the logic of *Principia*. The result is that this development avoids the paradox of taking the logic of propositions for granted in order to prove it. Nothing of the sort is assumed except these explicitly stated postulates whose use we have observed. And it results from this mode of development that the system is completely symbolic, except for a few postulates, $*1\cdot1$, $*1\cdot7$, etc., involving no further use of "if . . . , then . . .", "either . . . or . . .", ". . . and . . .", etc.

We have now seen that the calculus of propositions in *Principia Mathematica* avoids both the defects of the Two-Valued Algebra. The further comparison of the two systems can be made in a sentence: Except for the absence, in the logic of *Principia*, of the redundance of forms, p, $p = 1$, $p \neq 0$, etc., etc., and the absence of the entities 0 and 1, the two systems are identical. Any theorem of this part of *Principia* can be translated into a valid theorem of the Two-Valued Algebra, and any theorem of the Two-Valued Algebra not involving 0 and 1 otherwise than as $\{= 0\}$ or $\{= 1\}$ can be translated into a valid theorem of *Principia*. In fact, the qualification is not particularly significant, because *any* use of 0 and 1 in the Two-Valued Algebra reduces to their use as $\{= 0\}$ and $\{= 1\}$. For 0 as a term of a sum, and 1 as a factor, immediately disappear, while the presence of 0 as a factor and the presence of 1 in a sum can always be otherwise expressed. But $p = 0$ is $-p$, and $p = 1$ is p. Hence the two systems are simply identical so far as the logical significance of the propositions they contain is concerned.[25]

The comparison of our treatment of propositional functions with the same topic in *Principia* is not quite so simple.[26]

In the first place, there is, in *Principia*, the "theory of types," which concerns the range of significance of functions. But we shall omit consideration of this. Then, there are the differences of notation. Where we write $\Pi \varphi x$, or $\Pi_x \varphi x$, *Principia* has $(x) \cdot \varphi x$; and where we write $\Sigma \varphi x$, or $\Sigma_x \varphi x$, *Principia* has $(\exists x) \cdot \varphi x$. A further and more important difference may be made clear by citing the assumptions of *Principia*.

$*9 \cdot 01 \quad \sim\{(x) \cdot \varphi x\} \cdot = \cdot (\exists x) \cdot \sim \varphi x. \qquad$ Df.

$*9 \cdot 02 \quad \sim\{(\exists x) \cdot \varphi x\} \cdot = \cdot (x) \cdot \sim \varphi x. \qquad$ Df.

$*9 \cdot 03 \quad (x) \cdot \varphi x \cdot \vee p \mathbin{:} = \cdot (x) \cdot \varphi x \vee p. \qquad$ Df.

[25] This may be proved by noting that, properly translated, the postulates of each system are contained amongst the propositions of the other. Of the postulates in *Principia*, rendered in our notation:

$*1 \cdot 01$ is $(p \subset q) = (-p + q)$, which is contained in our theorem $9 \cdot 3$.

$*1 \cdot 2$ is $(p + p) \subset p$, which is a consequence of our theorems $2 \cdot 2$ and $5 \cdot 33$.

$*1 \cdot 3$ is, $p \subset (p + q)$, which is our theorem $5 \cdot 21$.

$*1 \cdot 4$ is $(p + q) \subset (q + p)$, which follows from our theorem $4 \cdot 3$, by $2 \cdot 2$.

$*1 \cdot 5$ is, $p + (q + r) \subset q + (p + r)$, which is a consequence of our theorems $4 \cdot 3$ and $4 \cdot 4$, by $2 \cdot 2$.

$*1 \cdot 6$ is $(q \subset r) \subset [(p + q) \subset (p + r)]$, which is a consequence of our theorem $5 \cdot 31$, by $2 \cdot 2$. The remaining (non-symbolic) postulates are tacitly assumed in our system.

Of our postulates, $1 \cdot 1$–$1 \cdot 9$ in Chap. II and $9 \cdot 01$ in Chap. IV:

$1 \cdot 1$ is a consequence of $*1 \cdot 7$ and $*1 \cdot 71$ in *Principia*.

$1 \cdot 2$ is $*4 \cdot 24$ in *Principia*.

$1 \cdot 3$ is $*4 \cdot 3$ in *Principia*.

$1 \cdot 4$ is $*2 \cdot 3$ in *Principia*.

$1 \cdot 5$ is equivalent to "If $x = 0$, then $a\, x = 0$", hence to $-x \subset -(a\, x)$, which is a consequence of $*3 \cdot 27$ in *Principia*, by $*2 \cdot 16$.

$1 \cdot 61$, in the form $-(x - a) \subset (x\, a = x)$, is a consequence of $*4 \cdot 71$ and $*4 \cdot 61$ in *Principia*, by $*4 \cdot 01$ and $*3 \cdot 26$.

$1 \cdot 62$, in the form $[(y\, a = y)(y - a = y)] \subset -y$, is a consequence of $*4 \cdot 71$, $*5 \cdot 16$, and $*2 \cdot 21$ in *Principia*.

$1 \cdot 7$ is equivalent to $[(x = 1)(y = 0)] \subset (x = -y)$, hence to $(x - y) \subset (x = -y)$, which is an immediate consequence of $*5 \cdot 1$ in *Principia*.

$1 \cdot 8$ is $*4 \cdot 57$ in *Principia*.

$1 \cdot 9$ is $*4 \cdot 71$ in *Principia*.

$9 \cdot 01$ is equivalent to $(q = 1) \subset [p = (p = q)]$, hence to $q \subset [p = (p = q)]$, which is an immediate consequence of $*5 \cdot 501$ in *Principia*.

[26] See *Principia*, I, 15–21.

In this last, note the difference in the scope of the "quantifier" (x) on the two sides. If the dots be replaced by parentheses, $*9\cdot03$ will be

$$\{[(x) \, \raisebox{0.3ex}{.} \, \varphi x] \vee p\} = \{(x) \, \raisebox{0.3ex}{.} \, [\varphi x \vee p]\}$$

A similar difference in the scope of (x) or $(\exists x)$ on the two sides characterizes each of the further definitions.[27]

$*9\cdot04$ $\quad p \, \raisebox{0.3ex}{.} \, \vee \, \raisebox{0.3ex}{.} \, (x) \, \raisebox{0.3ex}{.} \, \varphi x \, \raisebox{0.3ex}{:} = \, \raisebox{0.3ex}{.} \, (x) \, \raisebox{0.3ex}{.} \, p \vee \varphi x.$ Df.

$*9\cdot05$ $\quad (\exists x) \, \raisebox{0.3ex}{.} \, \varphi x \, \raisebox{0.3ex}{.} \, \vee \, \raisebox{0.3ex}{.} \, p \, \raisebox{0.3ex}{:} = \, \raisebox{0.3ex}{.} \, (\exists x) \, \raisebox{0.3ex}{.} \, \varphi x \vee p.$ Df.

$*9\cdot06$ $\quad p \, \raisebox{0.3ex}{.} \, \vee \, \raisebox{0.3ex}{.} \, (\exists x) \, \raisebox{0.3ex}{.} \, \varphi x \, \raisebox{0.3ex}{:} = \, \raisebox{0.3ex}{.} \, (\exists x) \, \raisebox{0.3ex}{.} \, p \vee \varphi x.$ Df.

$*9\cdot07$ $\quad (x) \, \raisebox{0.3ex}{.} \, \varphi x \, \raisebox{0.3ex}{.} \, \vee \, \raisebox{0.3ex}{.} \, (\exists y) \, \raisebox{0.3ex}{.} \, \psi y \, \raisebox{0.3ex}{:} = \, \raisebox{0.3ex}{:} \, (x) \, \raisebox{0.3ex}{:} \, (\exists y) \, \raisebox{0.3ex}{.} \, \varphi x \vee \psi y.$ Df.

$*9\cdot08$ $\quad (\exists y) \, \raisebox{0.3ex}{.} \, \psi y \, \raisebox{0.3ex}{.} \, \vee \, \raisebox{0.3ex}{.} \, (x) \, \raisebox{0.3ex}{.} \, \varphi x \, \raisebox{0.3ex}{:} = \, \raisebox{0.3ex}{:} \, (x) \, \raisebox{0.3ex}{:} \, (\exists y) \, \raisebox{0.3ex}{.} \, \psi y \vee \varphi x.$ Df.

Besides these definitions, there are four postulates (in addition to those which underlie the calculus of elementary propositions).

$*9\cdot1$ $\quad \vdash \raisebox{0.3ex}{:} \, \varphi x \, \raisebox{0.3ex}{.} \, \supset \, \raisebox{0.3ex}{.} \, (\exists z) \, \raisebox{0.3ex}{.} \, \varphi z.$ Pp.

$*9\cdot11$ $\quad \vdash \raisebox{0.3ex}{:} \, \varphi x \vee \varphi y \, \raisebox{0.3ex}{.} \, \supset \, \raisebox{0.3ex}{.} \, (\exists z) \, \raisebox{0.3ex}{.} \, \varphi z.$ Pp.

$*9\cdot12$ What is implied by a true premiss is true. Pp.

$*9\cdot13$ In any assertion containing a real variable, this real variable may be turned into an apparent variable for which all possible values are asserted to satisfy the function in question. Pp.

By our method, every one of these assumptions, except $*9\cdot12$, is a proved proposition. In our notation,

$*9\cdot01$ is $-\Pi\varphi x = \Sigma - \varphi x$, which is our theorem $10\cdot1$, with $-\varphi x$ substituted for φx.

$*9\cdot02$ is $-\Sigma\varphi x = \Pi - \varphi x$, which is our theorem $10\cdot12$, with $-\varphi x$ substituted for φx.

$*9\cdot03$ is $\Pi\varphi x + P = \Pi_x(\varphi x + P)$, which is our theorem $10\cdot32$.

$*9\cdot04$ is $P + \Pi\varphi x = \Pi_x(P + \varphi x)$, which is $10\cdot33$.

$*9\cdot05$ is $\Sigma\varphi x + P = \Sigma_x(\varphi x + P)$, which is $10\cdot3$.

$*9\cdot06$ is $P + \Sigma\varphi x = \Sigma_x(P + \varphi x)$, which is $10\cdot31$.

$*9\cdot07$ is $\Pi\varphi x + \Sigma\psi y = \Pi_x\Sigma_y(\varphi x + \psi y)$, which is contained in $12\cdot5$.

$*9\cdot08$ is $\Sigma\psi y + \Pi\varphi x = \Pi_x\Sigma_y(\psi y + \varphi x)$, which is also contained in $12\cdot5$.

The postulates require explanation. The authors of *Principia* use φy, φz, etc., to represent values of the function φx. In other words, where we have written φx_n they simply change the letter. This is a valid con-

[27] *Ibid.*, I, 135–38.

vention (though it often renders proofs confusing) because the range of φx is determined by φ, not by x, and x is—conventions aside—indifferent. z in φz, where we should write φx_n, is called a "real variable", x in $(x) \cdot \varphi x$ and $(\exists x) \cdot \varphi x$, an "apparent variable". With this explanation, it is clear that:

$*9 \cdot 1$ is $\varphi x_n \subset \Sigma \varphi x$, which is $10 \cdot 21$.

$*9 \cdot 11$ is $\varphi x_m + \varphi x_n \subset \Sigma \varphi x$, which is an immediate consequence of $10 \cdot 21$, by $5 \cdot 33$.

$*9 \cdot 13$ is "If whatever value of x, in φx, x_n may be, φx_n, then $\Pi \varphi x$," and this implication is contained in the equivalence stated by $10 \cdot 23$.

These principles which are assumed in *Principia Mathematica* are sufficient to give all further propositions concerning functions of one variable, without assuming $(x) \cdot \varphi x$ to be the product of φx_1, φx_2, etc. (or φy, φz, etc.), $(\exists x) \cdot \varphi x$ to be the sum of φx_1, φx_2, etc. These are simply assumed as new primitive ideas, $(x) \cdot \varphi x$ meaning "φx for all values of x", $(\exists x) \cdot \varphi x$ meaning "φx for some values of x". This procedure obviates all questions about the number of values of x in φx—which troubled us—and secures the universality of theorems involving propositional functions without any discussion or convention covering the cases in which the values of the variable are infinite in number. The *proofs* in *Principia* reflect this difference of method. They are, in general, what ours might have been if we had based all further proofs directly upon $10 \cdot 23$ and the propositions connecting $\Sigma \varphi x + P$ with $\Sigma_x(\varphi x + P)$, etc., not making any use, after $10 \cdot 23$, of the properties of $\Pi \varphi x$ as a product, or of $\Sigma \varphi x$ as a sum.

The theory of functions of two variables, in *Principia Mathematica*, requires two further assumptions:

$*11 \cdot 01$ $(x, y) \cdot \varphi(x, y) \cdot = \, : (x) : (y) \cdot \varphi(x, y)$.   Df.

$*11 \cdot 03$ $(\exists x, y) \cdot \varphi(x, y) \cdot = \, : (\exists x) : (\exists y) \cdot \varphi(x, y)$.   Df.

These are identically our assumptions:

$11 \cdot 06$ $\Pi_{x, \, y} \varphi(x, y) = \Pi_x \Pi_y \varphi(x, y)$, and

$11 \cdot 05$ $\Sigma_{x, \, y} \varphi(x, y) = \Sigma_x \Sigma_y \varphi(x, y)$.

The difference between the treatment of propositional functions which we have given and the treatment in *Principia* is not necessarily correlated with the difference between our treatment of *propositions* and theirs. The method by which we have developed the theory of propositional functions might exactly as well have been based upon the calculus of elementary propositions in *Principia* as upon the Two-Valued Algebra. A few minor alterations would be sufficient for this change. The different procedure for propositional functions, in the two cases, is a difference to be adjudged independently, without necessary reference to the defects of the Two-Valued Algebra which have been pointed out.

Beyond the important differences which have been mentioned, there are minor and trivial divergences between the two systems, due to the different use of notation. Neglecting these, we may say that the two methods give the same results, with the following exceptions:

1. There are certain complexities in *Principia* due to the theory of types.

2. In *Principia* the conditions of significance are explicitly investigated.

3. *Principia* contains a theory of "descriptions", account of which is here omitted.

But none of these exceptions is a *necessary* difference. They are due to the more elementary character of our presentation of the subject. We may, then, say loosely that the two methods give identical results.

The calculus of classes and of relations which we have outlined in the preceding sections bear a similar relation to the logic of classes and of relations in *Principia;* that is to say, there is much more detail and complexity of theory in *Principia*, but so far as our exposition goes, the two are roughly the same. And here there is no important difference of method.

It should now be clear how the logic of *Principia* is related to the logic we have presented, following in the main the methods of Peirce and Schröder. There is much difference of method, and, especially in the case of the calculus of propositions, this difference is in favor of *Principia*. And in *Principia* there is much more of theoretical rigor and consequent complexity: also there are important extensions, especially in the theory of "descriptions" and the logic of relatives. But so far as the logic which we have expounded goes, the two methods give roughly identical results. When we remember the date of the work of Peirce and Schröder, it becomes clear what is our debt to them for the better developments which have since been made.

APPENDIX

TWO FRAGMENTS FROM LEIBNIZ

(Translated from the Latin of Gehrhardt's text, *Die Philosophischen Schriften von G. W. Leibniz, Band VII, "Scientia Generalis. Characteristica,"* XIX and XX.)

These two fragments represent the final form of Leibniz's "universal calculus": their date is not definitely known, but almost certainly they were written after 1685. Of the two, XX is in all respects superior, as the reader will see, but XIX also is included because it contains the operation of "subtraction" which is dropped in XX. Leibniz's comprehension of the fact that + and − (or, in the more usual notation, "multiplication" and "division") are not simple inverses in this calculus, and his appreciation of the complexity thus introduced, is the chief point of interest in XIX. The distinction of "subtraction" (in intension) and negation, is also worthy of note. It will be observed that, in both these fragments, $A + B$ (or $A \oplus B$) may be interpreted in two ways: (1) As "both A and B" in intension; (2) as "either A or B", the class made up of the two classes A and B, in extension. The "logical" illustrations mostly follow the first interpretation, but in XX (see esp. *scholium to defs.* 3, 4, 5, *and* 6) there are examples of the application to logical classes in extension. The illustration of the propositions by the relations of line-segments also exhibits the application to relations of extension. Attention is specifically called to the parallelism between relations of intension and relations of extension in the remark appended to prop. 15, in XX. The *scholium to axioms* 1 *and* 2, in XX, is of particular interest as an illustration of the way in which Leibniz anticipates later logistic developments.

The Latin of the text is rather careless, and constructions are sometimes obscure. Gehrhardt notes (p. 232) that the manuscript contains numerous interlineations and is difficult to read in many places.

XIX

Non inelegans specimen demonstrandi in abstractis[1]

Def. 1. Two terms are the *same* (*eadem*) if one can be substituted for the other without altering the truth of any statement (*salva veritate*). If we have A and B, and A enters into some true proposition, and the substitution of B for A wherever it appears, results in a new proposition which is likewise true, and if this can be done for every such proposition, then A and B are said to be the *same;* and conversely, if A and B are the same, they can be substituted for one another as I have said. Terms which are the same are also called *coincident* (*coincidentia*); A and A are, of course, said to be the same, but if A and B are the same, they are called *coincident.*

Def. 2. Terms which are not the same, that is, terms which cannot always be substituted for one another, are *different* (*diversa*). *Corollary.* Whence also, whatever terms are not different are the same.

Charact. 1.[2] $A = B$ signifies that A and B are the *same*, or *coincident.*

Charact. 2.[3] $A \neq B$, or $B \neq A$, signifies that A and B are *different.*

Def. 3. If a plurality of terms taken together coincide with one, then any one of the plurality is said to *be in* (*inesse*) or to *be contained in* (*contineri*) that one with which they

---

[1] This title appears in the manuscript, but Leibniz has afterward crossed it out. Although pretentious, it expresses admirably the intention of the fragment, as well as of the next.

[2] We write $A = B$ where the text has $A \infty B$.

[3] We write $A \neq B$ where the text has A non ∞B.

coincide, and that one is called the *container*. And conversely, if any term be contained in another, then it will be one of a plurality which taken together coincide with that other. For example, if A and B taken together coincide with L, then A, or B, will be called the *inexistent (inexistens)* or the *contained;* and L will be called the *container*. However, it can happen that the container and the contained coincide, as for example, if (A and B) = L, and A and L coincide, for in that case B will contain nothing which is different from A. . . .[4]

Scholium. Not every inexistent thing is a part, nor is every container a whole—e. g., an inscribed square and a diameter are both in a circle, and the square, to be sure, is a certain part of the circle, but the diameter is not a part of it. We must, then, add something for the accurate explanation of the concept of whole and part, but this is not the place for it. And not only can those things which are not parts be contained in, but also they can be subtracted (or "abstracted", *detrahi*); e. g., the center can be subtracted from a circle so that all points except the center shall be in the remainder; for this remainder is the locus of all points within the circle whose distance from the circumference is less than the radius, and the difference of this locus from the circle is a point, namely the center. Similarly the locus of all points which are moved, in a sphere in which two distinct points on a diameter remain unmoved, is as if you should subtract from the sphere the axis or diameter passing through the two unmoved points.

On the same supposition [that A and B together coincide with L], A and B taken together are called *constituents (constituentia)*, and L is called *that which is constituted (constitutum)*.

Charact. 3. $A + B = L$ signifies that A *is in* or *is contained in L*.

Scholium.   Although A and B may have something in common, so that the two taken together are greater than L itself, nevertheless what we have here stated, or now state, will still hold. It will be well to make this clear by an example: Let L denote the straight line RX, and A denote a part of it, say the line RS, and B denote another part, say the line XY. Let either of these parts, RS or XY, be greater than half the whole line, RX; then certainly it cannot be said that $A + B$ equals L, or $RS + XY$ equals RX. For inasmuch as YS is a common part of RS and XY, $RS + XY$ will be equal to $RX + SY$. And yet it can truly be said that the lines RS and XY together *coincide* with the line RS.[5]

$$R \quad\quad Y \quad\quad S \quad\quad X$$

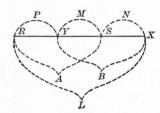

Def. 4.   If some term M is in A and also in B, it is said to be common to them, and they are said to be *communicating (communicantia)*.[6] But if they have nothing in common, as A and N (the lines RS and XS, for example), they are said to be *non-communicating (incommunicantia)*.

Def. 5.   If A is in L in such wise that there is another term, N, in which belongs everything in L except what is in A, and of this last nothing belongs in N, then A is said to be *subtracted (detrahi)* or taken away *(removeri)*, and N is called the *remainder (residuum)*.

Charact. 4. $L - A = N$ signifies that L is the container from which if A be *subtracted* the *remainder* is N.

Def. 6.   If some one term is supposed to coincide with a plurality of terms which are added *(positis)* or subtracted *(remotis)*, then the plurality of terms are called the *constituents*, and the one term is called the thing constituted.[7]

---

[4] Lacuna in the text, followed by "significet A, significabit Nihil".
[5] Italics ours.
[6] The text here has "communicatia", clearly a misprint.
[7] Leibniz's idea seems to be that if $A + N = L$ then L is "constituted" by A and N, and also if $L - A = N$ then L and A "constitute" N. But it may mean that if $L - A = N$, then A and N "constitute" L.

Scholium. Thus all terms which are in anything are constituents, but the reverse does not hold; for example, $L - A = N$, in which case L is not in A.

Def. 7. Constitution (that is, addition or subtraction) is either tacit or expressed,— N or $- M$ the tacit constitution of M itself, as A or $- A$ in which N is. The expressed constitution of N is obvious.[8]

Def. 8. *Compensation* is the operation of adding and subtracting the same thing in the same expression, both the addition and the subtraction being expressed [as $A + M - M$]. *Destruction* is the operation of dropping something on account of compensation, so that it is no longer expressed, and for $M - M$ putting Nothing.

Axiom 1. If a term be added to itself, nothing new is constituted or $A + A = A$.

Scholium. With numbers, to be sure, $2 + 2$ makes 4, or two coins added to two coins make four coins, but in that case the two added are not identical with the former two; if they were, nothing new would arise, and it would be as if we should attempt in jest to make six eggs out of three by first counting 3 eggs, then taking away one and counting the remaining 2, and then taking away one more and counting the remaining 1.

Axiom 2. If the same thing be added and subtracted, then however it enter into the constitution of another term, the result coincides with Nothing. Or A (however many times it is added in constituting any expression) $- A$ (however many times it is subtracted from that same expression) = Nothing.

Scholium. Hence $A - A$ or $(A + A \text{ ✦}) - A$ or $A_{\wedge}(A + A)$, etc. = Nothing. For by axiom 1, the expression in each case reduces to $A - A$.

Postulate 1. Any plurality of terms whatever can be added to constitute a single term; as for example, if we have A and B, we can write $A + B$, and call this L.

Post. 2. Any term, A, can be subtracted from that in which it is, namely $A + B$ or L, if the remainder be given as B, which added to A constitutes the container L—that is, on this supposition [that $A + B = L$] the remainder $L - A$ can be found.

Scholium. In accordance with this postulate, we shall give, later on, a method for finding the difference between two terms, one of which, A, is contained in the other, L, even though the remainder, which together with A constitutes L, should not be given— that is, a method for finding $L - A$, or $A + B - A$, although A and L only are given, and B is not.

Theorem 1

Terms which are the same with a third, are the same with each other.

If $A = B$ and $B = C$, then $A = C$. For if in the proposition $A = B$ (true by hyp.) C be substituted for B (which can be done by def. 1, since, by hyp., $B = C$), the result is $A = C$. Q.E.D.

Theorem 2

If one of two terms which are the same be different from a third term, then the other of the two will be different from it also.

If $A = B$ and $B \neq C$, then $A \neq C$. For if in the proposition $B \neq C$ (true by hyp.) A be substituted for B (which can be done by def. 1, since, by hyp., $A = B$), the result is $A \neq C$. Q.E.D.

[Theorem in the margin of the manuscript.]

Here might be inserted the following theorem: *Whatever is in one of two coincident terms, is in the other also.*

If A is in B and $B = C$, then also A is in C. For in the proposition A is in B (true by hyp.) let C be substituted for B.

Theorem 3

If terms which coincide be added to the same term, the results will coincide.

If $A = B$, then $A + C = B + C$. For if in the proposition $A + C = A + C$ (true

[8] This translation is literal: the meaning is obscure, but see the diagram above.

per se) you substitute B for A in one place (which can be done by def. 1, since $A = B$), it gives $A + C = B + C$. Q.E.D.

Corollary. *If terms which coincide be added to terms which coincide, the results will coincide.* If $A = B$ and $L = M$, then $A + L = B + M$. For (by the present theorem) since $L = M$, $A + L = A + M$, and in this assertion putting B for A in one place (since by hyp. $A = B$) gives $A + L = B + M$. Q.E.D.

Theorem 4

A container of the container is a container of the contained; or if that in which something is, be itself in a third thing, then that which is in it will be in that same third thing—that is, if A is in B and B is in C, then also A is in C.

For A is in B (by hyp.), hence (by def. 3 or charact. 3) there is some term, which we may call L, such that $A + L = B$. Similarly, since B is in C (by hyp.), $B + M = C$, and in this assertion putting $A + L$ for B (since we show that these coincide) we have $A + L + M = C$. But putting N for $L + M$ (by post. 1) we have $A + N = C$. Hence (by def. 3) A is in C. Q.E.D.

Theorem 5

Whatever contains terms individually contains also that which is constituted of them.

If A is in C and B is in C, then $A + B$ (constituted of A and B, def. 4) is in C. For since A is in C, there will be some term M such that $A + M = C$ (by def. 3). Similarly, since B is in C, $B + N = C$. Putting these together (by the corollary to th. 3), we have $A + M + B + N = C + C$. But $C + C = C$ (by ax. 1), hence $A + M + B + N = C$. And therefore (by def. 3) $A + B$ is in C. Q.E.D.[9]

Theorem 6

Whatever is constituted of terms which are contained, is in that which is constituted of the containers.

If A is in M and B is in N, then $A + B$ is in $M + N$. For A is in M (by hyp.) and M is in $M + N$ (by def. 3), hence A is in $M + N$ (by th. 4). Similarly, B is in N (by hyp.) and N is in $M + N$ (by def. 3), hence B is in $M + N$ (by th. 4). But if A is in $M + N$ and B is in $M + N$, then also (by th. 5) $A + B$ is in $M + N$. Q.E.D.

Theorem 7

If any term be added to that in which it is, then nothing new is constituted; or if B is in A, then $A + B = A$.

For if B is in A, then [for some C] $B + C = A$ (def. 3). Hence (by th. 3) $A + B = B + C + B = B + C$ (by ax. 1) $= A$ (by the above). Q.E.D.

Converse of the Preceding Theorem

If by the addition of any term to another nothing new is constituted, then the term added is in the other.

If $A + B = A$, then B is in A; for B is in $A + B$ (def. 3), and $A + B = A$ (by hyp.). Hence B is in A (by the principle which is inserted between ths. 2 and 3). Q.E.D.

Theorem 8

If terms which coincide be subtracted from terms which coincide, the remainders will coincide.

If $A = L$ and $B = M$, then $A - B = L - M$. For $A - B = A - B$ (true *per se*),

[9] In the margin of the manuscript at this point Leibniz has an untranslatable note, the sense of which is to remind him that he must insert illustrations of these propositions in common language.

and the substitution, on one or the other side, of L for A and M for B, gives $A - B = L - M$. Q.E.D.

[Note in the margin of the manuscript.] In dealing with concepts, *subtraction (detractio)* is one thing, negation another. For example, "non-rational man" is absurd or impossible. But we may say; An ape is a man except that it is not rational. [They are] men except in those respects in which man differs from the beasts, as in the case of Grotius's Jumbo[10] (*Homines nisi qua bestiis differt homo, ut in Jambo Grotii*). "Man" − "rational" is something different from "non-rational man". For "man" − "rational" = "brute". But "non-rational man" is impossible. "Man" − "animal" − "rational" is Nothing. Thus subtractions can give Nothing or simple non-existence—even less than nothing—but negations can give the impossible.[11]

THEOREM 9

(1) From an expressed compensation, the destruction of the term compensated follows, provided nothing be destroyed in the compensation which, being tacitly repeated, enters into a constitution outside the compensation [that is, $+ N - N$ appearing in an expression may be dropped, unless N be tacitly involved in some other term of the expression];

(2) The same holds true if whatever is thus repeated occur both in what is added and in what is subtracted outside the compensation;

(3) If neither of these two obtain, then the substitution of destruction for compensation [that is, the dropping of the expression of the form $+ N - N$] is impossible.

Case 1. If $A + N - M - N = A - M$, and A, N, and M be non-communicating. For here there is nothing in the compensation to be destroyed, $+ N - N$, which is also outside it in A or M—that is, whatever is added in $+ N$, however many times it is added, is in $+ N$, and whatever is subtracted in $- N$, however many times it is subtracted, is in $- N$. Therefore (by ax. 2) for $+ N - N$ we can put Nothing.

Case 2. If $A + B - B - G = F$, and whatever is common both to $A + B$ [i. e., to A and B] and to G and B, is M, then $F = A - G$. In the first place, let us suppose that whatever A and G have in common, if they have anything in common, is E, so that if they have nothing in common, then $E =$ Nothing. Thus [to exhibit the hypothesis of the case more fully] $A = E + Q + M$, $B = N + M$, and $G = E + H + M$, so that $F = E + Q + M + N - N - M - H - M$, where all the terms E, Q, M, N, and H are non-communicating. Hence (by the preceding case) $F = Q - H = E + Q + M - E - H - M = A - G$.

Case 3. If $A + B - B - D = C$, and that which is common to A and B does not coincide with that which is common to $B + D$ [i. e., to B and D], then we shall not have $C = A - D$. For let $B = E + F + G$, and $A = H + E$, and $D = K + F$, so that these constituents are no longer communicating and there is no need for further resolution. Then $C = H + E + F + G - E - F - G - K - F$, that is (by case 1) $C = H - K$, which is not $= A - D$ (since $A - D = H + E - K - F$), unless we suppose, contrary to hypothesis, that $E = F$—that is that B and A have something in common which is also common to B and D. This same demonstration would hold even if A and D had something in common.

[10] Apparently an allusion to some description of an ape by Grotius.
[11] This is not an unnecessary and hair-splitting distinction, but on the contrary, perhaps the best evidence of Leibniz's accurate comprehension of the logical calculus which appears in the manuscripts. It has been generally misjudged by the commentators, because the commentators have not understood the logic of intension. The distinction of the merely non-existent and the impossible (self-contradictory or absurd) is absolutely essential to any calculus of relations in intension. And this distinction of subtraction (or in the more usual notation, division) from negation, is equally necessary. It is by the confusion of these two that the calculuses of Lambert and Castillon break down.

Theorem 10

A subtracted term and the remainder are non-communicating.

If $L - A = N$, I affirm that A and N have nothing in common. For by the definition of "subtraction" and of "remainder", everything in L remains in N except that which is in A, and of this last nothing remains in N.

Theorem 11

Of that which is in two communicating terms, whatever part is common to both and the two exclusive parts are three non-communicating terms.

If A and B be communicating terms, and $A = P + M$ and $B = N + M$, so that whatever is in A and B both is in M, and nothing of that is in P or N, then P, M, and N are non-communicating. For P, as well as N, is non-communicating with M, since whatever is in M is in A and B both, and nothing of this description is in P or N. Then P and N are non-communicating, otherwise what is common to them would penetrate into A and B both.

Problem

To add non-coincident terms to given coincident terms so that the resulting terms shall coincide.

If $A = A$, I affirm that it is possible to find two terms, B and N, such that $B \neq N$ and yet $A + B = A + N$.

Solution. Choose some term M which shall be contained in A and such that, N being chosen arbitrarily, M is not contained in N nor N in M, and let $B = M + N$. And this will satisfy the requirements. Because $B = M + N$ (by hyp.) and M and N are neither of them contained in the other (by hyp.), and yet $A + B = A + N$, since $A + B = A + M + N$ and (by th. 7, since, by hyp., M is in A) this is $= A + N$.

Theorem 12

Where non-communicating terms only are involved, whatever terms added to coincident terms give coincident terms will be themselves coincident.

That is, if $A + B = C + D$ and $A = C$, then $B = D$, provided that A and B, as well as C and D, are non-communicating. For $A + B - C = C + D - C$ (by th. 8); but $A + B - C = A + B - A$ (by hyp. that $A = C$), and $A + B - A = B$ (by th. 9, case 1, since A and B are non-communicating), and (for the same reason) $C + D - C = D$. Hence $B = D$. Q.E.D.

Theorem 13

In general; *if other terms added to coincident terms give coincident terms, then the terms added are communicating.*

If A and A coincide or are the same, and $A + B = A + N$, I affirm that B and N are communicating. For if A and B are non-communicating, and A and N also, then $B = N$ (by the preceding theorem). Hence B and N are communicating. But if A and B are communicating, let $A = P + M$ and $B = Q + M$, putting M for that which is common to A and B and nothing of this description in P or Q. Then (by ax. 1) $A + B = P + Q + M = P + M + N$. But P, Q, and M are non-communicating (by th. 11). Therefore, if N is non-communicating with A—that is, with $P + M$—then (by the preceding theorem) it results from $P + Q + M = P + M + N$ that $Q = N$. Hence N is in B; hence N and B are communicating. But if, on the same assumption (namely, that $P + Q + M = P + M + N$, or A is communicating with B) N also be communicating with $P + M$ or A, then either N will be communicating with M, from which it follows that it will be communicating with B (which contains M) and the theorem will hold, or, N will be communicating with P, and in that case we shall in similar fashion let $P = G + H$ and $N = F + H$, so that G, F, and H are non-communicating (according to th. 11), and from $P + Q$

$+ M = P + M + N$ we get $G + H + Q + M = G + H + M + F + H$. Hence (by the preceding theorem) $Q = F$. Hence N ($= F + H$) and B ($= Q + M$) have something in common. Q.E.D.

Corollary. From this demonstration we learn the following: If any terms be added to the same or coincident terms, and the results coincide, and if the terms added are each non-communicating with that to which it is added,· then the terms added [to the same or coincidents] coincide with each other (as appears also from th. 12). But if one of the terms added be communicating with that to which it is added, and the other not, then [of these two added terms] the non-communicating one will be contained in the communicating one. Finally, if each of the terms is communicating with that to which it is added, then at least they will be communicating with each other (although in another connection it would not follow that terms which communicate with a third communicate with each other). To put it in symbols: $A + B = A + N$. If A and B are non-communicating, and A and N likewise, then $B = N$. If A and B are communicating but A and N are non-communicating, then N is in B. And finally, if B communicates with A, and likewise N communicates with A, then B and N at least communicate with each other.

XX

Def. 1. Terms which can be substituted for one another wherever we please without altering the truth of any statement (*salva veritate*), are the *same* (*eadem*) or *coincident* (*coincidentia*). For example, "triangle" and "trilateral", for in every proposition demonstrated by Euclid concerning "triangle", "trilateral" can be substituted without loss of truth.

$A = B$[12] *signifies* that A and B are the same, or as we say of the straight line XY and the straight line YX, $XY = YX$, or the shortest path of a [point] moving from X to Y coincides with that from Y to X.

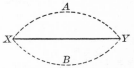

Def. 2. Terms which are not the same, that is, terms which cannot always be substituted for one another, are *different* (*diversa*). Such are "circle" and "triangle", or "square" (supposed perfect, as it always is in Geometry) and "equilateral quadrangle", for we can predicate this last of a rhombus, of which "square" cannot be predicated.

$A \neq B$[13] *signifies* that A and B are different, as for example, $R \_\_\_ Y \_\_\_ S \_\_\_ X$ the straight lines XY and RS.

Prop. 1. If $A = B$, *then also* $B = A$. *If anything be the same with another, then that other will be the same with it.* For since $A = B$ (by hyp.), it follows (by def. 1) that in the statement $A = B$ (true by hyp.) B can be substituted for A and A for B; hence we have $B = A$.

Prop. 2. If $A \neq B$, *then also* $B \neq A$. *If any term be different from another, then that other will be different from it.* Otherwise we should have $B = A$, and in consequence (by the preceding prop.) $A = B$, which is contrary to hypothesis.

Prop. 3. If $A = B$ *and* $B = C$, *then* $A = C$. *Terms which coincide with a third term coincide with each other.* For if in the statement $A = B$ (true by hyp.) C be substituted for B (by def. 1, since $A = B$), the resulting proposition will be true.

Coroll. If $A = B$ and $B = C$ and $C = D$, then $A = D$; and so on. For $A = B = C$, hence $A = C$ (by the above prop.). Again, $A = C = D$; hence (by the above prop.) $A = D$.

Thus since equal things are the same in magnitude, the consequence is that things equal to a third are equal to each other. The Euclidean construction of an equilateral triangle makes each side equal to the base, whence it results that they are equal to each

[12] $A = B$ for $A \propto B$, as before.
[13] $A \neq B$ for A non $\propto B$, as before.

other. If anything be moved in a circle, it is sufficient to show that the paths of any two successive periods, or returns to the same point, coincide, from which it is concluded that the paths of any two periods whatever coincide.

Prop. 4. *If $A = B$ and $B \neq C$, then $A \neq C$.* *If of two things which are the same with each other, one differ from a third, then the other also will differ from that third.* For if in the proposition $B \neq C$ (true by hyp.) A be substituted for B, we have (by def. 1, since $A = B$) the true proposition $A \neq C$.

Def. 3. *A is in L,* or *L contains A,* is the same as to say that L can be made to coincide with a plurality of terms, taken together, of which A is one.

Def. 4. Moreover, all those terms such that whatever is in them is in L, are together called *components* (*componentia*) with respect to the L thus *composed* or constituted.

$B \oplus N = L$ *signifies* that B is in L; and that B and N together compose or constitute L.[14] The same thing holds for a larger number of terms.

Def. 5. I call terms one of which is in the other *subalternates* (*subalternantia*), as A and B if either A is in B or B is in A.

Def. 6. Terms neither of which is in the other [I call] *disparate* (*disparata*).

Axiom 1. $B \oplus N = N \oplus B$, or transposition here alters nothing.

Post. 2. Any plurality of terms, as A and B, can be added to compose a single term, $A \oplus B$ or L.

Axiom 2. $A \oplus A = A$. If nothing new be added, then nothing new results, or repetition here alters nothing. (For 4 coins and 4 other coins are 8 coins, but not 4 coins and the same 4 coins already counted.)

Prop. 5. *If A is in B and $A = C$, then C is in B.* *That which coincides with the inexistent, is inexistent.* For in the proposition, A is in B (true by hyp.), the substitution of C for A (by def. 1 of coincident terms, since, by hyp., $A = C$) gives, C is in B.

Prop. 6. *If C is in B and $A = B$, then C is in A.* *Whatever is in one of two coincident terms, is in the other also.* For in the proposition, C is in B, the substitution of A for C (since $A = C$) gives, A is in B. (This is the converse of the preceding.)

Prop. 7. *A is in A.* *Any term whatever is contained in itself.* For A is in $A \oplus A$ (by def. of "inexistent", that is, by def. 3) and $A \oplus A = A$ (by ax. 2). Therefore (by prop. 6), A is in A.

Prop. 8. *If $A = B$, then A is in B.* *Of terms which coincide, the one is in the other.* This is obvious from the preceding. For (by the preceding) A is in A—that is (by hyp.), in B.

Prop. 9. *If $A = B$, then $A \oplus C = B \oplus C$.* *If terms which coincide be added to the same term, the results will coincide.* For if in the proposition, $A \oplus C = A \oplus C$ (true *per se*), for A in one place be substituted B which coincides with it (by def. 1), we have $A \oplus C = B \oplus C$.

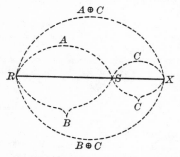

A "triangle"
B "trilateral" $\Big\}$ coincide

$A \oplus C$ "equilateral triangle"
$B \oplus C$ "equilateral trilateral" $\Big\}$ coincide

---

[14] In this fragment, as distinguished from XIX, the logical or "real" sum is represented by $\oplus$. Leibniz has carelessly omitted the circle in many places, but we write $\oplus$ wherever this relation is intended.

Scholium. This proposition cannot be converted—much less, the two which follow. A method for finding an illustration of this fact will be exhibited below, in the problem which is prop. 23.

Prop. 10. *If $A = L$ and $B = M$, then $A \oplus B = L \oplus M$. If terms which coincide be added to terms which coincide, the results will coincide.* For since $B = M, A \oplus B = A \oplus M$ (by the preceding), and putting L for the second A (since, by hyp., $A = L$) we have $A \oplus B = L \oplus M$.

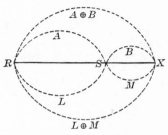

A "triangle", and L "trilateral" coincide. B "regular" coincides with M "most capacious of equally-many-sided figures with equal perimeters". "Regular triangle" coincides with "most capacious of trilaterals making equal peripheries out of three sides".

Scholium. This proposition cannot be converted, for if $A \oplus B = L \oplus M$ and $A = L$, still it does not follow that $B = M$,—and much less can the following be converted.

Prop. 11. *If $A = L$ and $B = M$ and $C = N$, then $A \oplus B \oplus C = L \oplus M \oplus N$.* And so on. *If there be any number of terms under consideration, and an equal number of them coincide with an equal number of others, term for term, then that which is composed of the former coincides with that which is composed of the latter.* For (by the preceding, since $A = L$ and $B = M$) we have $A \oplus B = L \oplus M$. Hence, since $C = N$, we have (again by the preceding) $A \oplus B \oplus C = L \oplus M \oplus N$.

Prop. 12. *If B is in L, then $A \oplus B$ will be in $A \oplus L$. If the same term be added to what is contained and to what contains it, the former result is contained in the latter.* For $L = B \oplus N$ (by def. of "inexistent"), and $A \oplus B$ is in $B \oplus N \oplus A$ (by the same), that is, $A \oplus B$ is in $L \oplus A$.

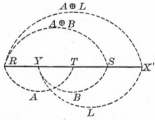

B "equilateral", L "regular", A "quadrilateral". "Equilateral" is in or is attribute of "regular". Hence "equilateral quadrilateral" is in "regular quadrilateral" or "perfect square". YS is in RX. Hence $RT \oplus YS$, or RS, is in $RT \oplus RX$, or in $\overset{?}{R}X$.

Scholium. This proposition cannot be converted; for if $A \oplus B$ is in $A \oplus L$, it does not follow that B is in L.

Prop. 13. *If $L \oplus B = L$, then B is in L. If the addition of any term to another does not alter that other, then the term added is in the other.* For B is in $L \oplus B$ (by def. of "inexistent") and $L \oplus B = L$ (by hyp.), hence (by prop. 6) B is in L.

$RY \oplus RX = RX$. Hence RY is in RX.
RY is in RX. Hence $RY \oplus RX = RX$.

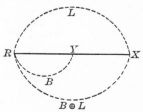

Let L be "parallelogram" (every side of which is parallel to some side),[15] B be "quadrilateral".

"Quadrilateral parallelogram" is in the same as "parallelogram".

Therefore to be quadrilateral is in [the intension of] "parallelogram".

Reversing the reasoning, to be quadrilateral is in "parallelogram".

Therefore, "quadrilateral parallelogram" is the same as "parallelogram".

Prop. 14. If B is in L, then $L \oplus B = L$. Subalternates compose nothing new; or if any term which is in another be added to it, it will produce nothing different from that other. (Converse of the preceding.) If B is in L, then (by def. of "inexistent") $L = B \oplus P$. Hence (by prop. 9) $L \oplus B = B \oplus P \oplus B$, which (by ax. 2) is $= B \oplus P$, which (by hyp.) is $= L$.

Prop. 15. If A is in B and B is in C, then also A is in C. What is contained in the contained, is contained in the container. For A is in B (by hyp.), hence $A \oplus L = B$ (by def. of "inexistent"). Similarly, since B is in C, $B \oplus M = C$, and putting $A \oplus L$ for B in this statement (since we have shown that these coincide), we have $A \oplus L \oplus M = C$. Therefore (by def. of "inexistent") A is in C.

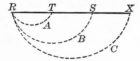

RT is in RS, and RS in RX.
Hence RT is in RX.
A "quadrilateral", B "parallelogram", C "rectangle".

To be quadrilateral is in [the intension of] "parallelogram", and to be parallelogram is in "rectangle" (that is, a figure every angle of which is a right angle). If instead of concepts *per se*, we consider individual things comprehended by the concept, and put A for "rectangle", B for "parallelogram", C for "quadrilateral", the relations of these can be inverted. For all rectangles are comprehended in the number of the parallelograms, and all parallelograms in the number of the quadrilaterals. Hence also, all rectangles are contained amongst (*in*) the quadrilaterals. In the same way, all men are contained amongst (*in*) all the animals, and all animals amongst all the material substances, hence all men are contained amongst the material substances. And conversely, the concept of material substance is in the concept of animal, and the concept of animal is in the concept of man. For to be man contains [or implies] being animal.

Scholium. This proposition cannot be converted, and much less can the following.

Coroll. If $A \oplus N$ is in B, N also is in B. For N is in $A \oplus N$ (by def. of "inexistent").

Prop. 16. If A is in B and B is in C and C is in D, then also A is in D. And so on. That which is contained in what is contained by the contained, is in the container. For if A is in B and B is in C, A also is in C (by the preceding). Whence if C is in D, then also (again by the preceding) A is in D.

Prop. 17. If A is in B and B is in A, then $A = B$. Terms which contain each other coincide. For if A is in B, then $A \oplus N = B$ (by def. of "inexistent"). But B is in A (by hyp.), hence $A \oplus N$ is in A (by prop. 5). Hence (by coroll. prop. 15) N also is in A. Hence (by prop. 14) $A = A \oplus N$, that is, $A = B$.

$RT, N; RS, A; SR \oplus RT, B.$

To be trilateral is in [the intension of] "triangle", and to be triangle is in "trilateral". Hence "triangle" and "trilateral" coincide. Similarly, to be omniscient is to be omnipotent.

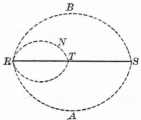

Prop. 18. *If A is in L and B is in L, then also $A \oplus B$ is in L. What is composed of two, each contained in a third, is itself contained in that third.* For since A is in L (by hyp.), it can be seen that $A \oplus M = L$ (by def. of "inexistent"). Similarly, since B is in L, it can be seen that $B \oplus N = L$. Putting these together, we have (by prop. 10) $A \oplus M \oplus B \oplus N = L \oplus L$. Hence (by ax. 2)[16] $A \oplus M \oplus B \oplus N = L$. Hence (by def. of

[16] The number of the axiom is given in the text as 5, a misprint.

"inexistent") $A \oplus B$ is in L.

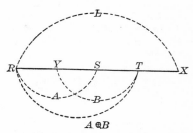

RYS is in *RX*.
YST is in *RX*.
Hence *RT* is in *RX*.

A "equiangular", B "equilateral", $A \oplus B$ "equiangular equilateral" or "regular", L "square". "Equiangular" is in [the intension of] "square", and "equilateral" is in "square". Hence "regular" is in "square".

Prop. 19. *If A is in L and B is in L and C is in L, then $A \oplus B \oplus C$ is in L.* And so on. *Or in general, whatever contains terms individually, contains also what is composed of them.* For $A \oplus B$ is in L (by the preceding). But also C is in L (by hyp.), hence (once more by the preceding) $A \oplus B \oplus C$ is in L.

Scholium. It is obvious that these two propositions and similar ones can be converted. For if $A \oplus B = L$, it is clear from the definition of "inexistent" that A is in L, and B is in L. Likewise, if $A \oplus B \oplus C = L$, it is clear that A is in L, and B is in L, and C is in L.[17] Also that $A \oplus B$ is in L, and $A \oplus C$ is in L, and $B \oplus C$ is in L. And so on.

Prop. 20. *If A is in M and B is in N, then $A \oplus B$ is in $M \oplus N$. If the former of one pair be in the latter and the former of another pair be in the latter, then what is composed of the former in the two cases is in what is composed of the latter in the two cases.* For A is in M (by hyp.) and M is in $M \oplus N$ (by def. of "inexistent"). Hence (by prop. 15) A is in $M \oplus N$. Similarly, since B is in N and N is in $M \oplus N$, then also (by prop. 18) $A \oplus B$ is in $M \oplus N$.

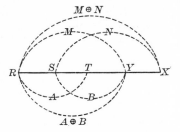

RT is in *RY* and *ST* is in *SX*, hence *RT* $\oplus$ *ST*, or *RY*, is in *RY* $\oplus$ *SX*, or in *RX*.[18]

If A be "quadrilateral" and B "equiangular", $A \oplus B$ will be "rectangle". If M be "parallelogram" and N "regular", $M \oplus N$ will be "square". Now "quadrilateral" is in [the intension of] "parallelogram", and "equiangular" is in "regular", hence "rectangle" (or "equiangular quadrilateral") is in "regular parallelogram or square".

Scholium. This proposition cannot be converted. Suppose that A is in M and $A \oplus B$ is in $M \oplus N$, still it does not follow that B is in N; for it might happen that B as well as A is in M, and whatever is in B is in M, and something different in N. Much less, therefore, can the following similar proposition be converted.

Prop. 21. *If A is in M and B is in N and C is in P, then $A \oplus B \oplus C$ is in $M \oplus N \oplus P$.*

[17] To be consistent, Leibniz should have written "$A \oplus B$ is in L" instead of "$A \oplus B = L$", and "$A \oplus B \oplus C$ is in L" instead of "$A \oplus B \oplus C = L$"—but note the method of the proof.

[18] The text has *RY* here instead of *RX*: the correction is obvious.

And so on. *Whatever is composed of terms which are contained, is in what is composed of the containers.* For since A is in M and B is in N, (by the preceding), $A \oplus B$ is in $M \oplus N$. But C is in P, hence (again by the preceding) $A \oplus B \oplus C$ is in $M \oplus N \oplus P$.

Prop. 22. *Two disparate terms, A and B, being given, to find a third term, C, different from them and such that with them it composes subalternates $A \oplus C$ and $B \oplus C$*—that is, such that although A and B are neither of them contained in the other, still $A \oplus C$ and $B \oplus C$ shall one of them be contained in the other.

Solution. If we wish that $A \oplus C$ be contained in $B \oplus C$, but A be not contained in B, this can be accomplished in the following manner: Assume (by post. 1) some term, D, such that it is not contained in A, and (by post. 2) let $A \oplus D = C$, and the requirements are satisfied.

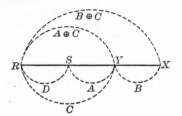

For $A \oplus C = A \oplus A \oplus D$ (by construction) $= A \oplus D$ (by ax. 2). Similarly, $B \oplus C = B \oplus A \oplus D$ (by construction). But $A \oplus D$ is in $B \oplus A \oplus D$ (by def. 3). Hence $A \oplus C$ is in $B \oplus C$. Which was to be done.[19]

SY and YX are disparate. If $RS \oplus SY = YR$, then $SY \oplus YR$ will be in $XY \oplus YR$.

Let A be "equilateral", B "parallelogram", D "equiangular", and C "equiangular equilateral" or "regular", where it is obvious that although "equilateral" and "parallelogram" are disparate, so that neither is in the other, yet "regular equilateral" is in "regular parallelogram" or "square". But, you ask, will this construction prescribed in the problem succeed in all cases? For example, let A be "trilateral", and B "quadrilateral"; is it not then impossible to find a concept which shall contain A and B both, and hence to find $B \oplus C$ such that it shall contain $A \oplus C$, since A and B are incompatible? I reply that our general construction depends upon the second postulate, in which is contained the assumption that any term and any other term can be put together as components. Thus God, soul, body, point, and heat compose an aggregate of these five things. And in this fashion also quadrilateral and trilateral can be put together as components. For assume D to be anything you please which is not contained in "trilateral", as "circle". Then $A \oplus D$ is "trilateral and circle",[20] which may be called C. But $C \oplus A$ is nothing but "trilateral and circle" again. Consequently, whatever is in $C \oplus B$ is also in "trilateral", in "circle", and in "quadrilateral". But if anyone wish to apply this general calculus of compositions of whatever sort to a special mode of composition; for example if one wish to unite "trilateral" and "circle" and "quadrilateral" not only to compose an aggregate but so that each of these concepts shall belong to the same subject, then it is necessary to observe whether they are compatible. Thus immovable straight lines at a distance from one another can be added to compose an aggregate but not to compose a continuum.

Prop. 23. *Two disparate terms, A and B, being given, to find a third, C, different from them* [*and such that $A \oplus B = A \oplus C$*].[21]

Solution. Assume (by post. 2) $C = A \oplus B$, and this satisfies the requirements. For since A and B are disparate (by hyp.)—that is (by def. 6), neither is in the other—

---

[19] Leibniz has carelessly substituted L in the proof where he has D in the proposition and in the figure. We read D throughout.

[20] Leibniz is still sticking to intensions in this example, however much the language may suggest extension.

[21] The proof, as well as the reference in the scholium to prop. 9, indicate that the statement of the theorem in the text is incomplete. We have chosen the most conservative emendation.

therefore (by prop. 13) it is impossible that $C = A$ or $C = B$. Hence these three are different, as the problem requires. Thus $A \oplus C = A \oplus A \oplus B$ (by construction), which (by ax. 2) is $= A \oplus B$. Therefore $A \oplus C = A \oplus B$. Which was to be done.

Prop. 24. To find a set of terms, of any desired number, which differ each from each and are so related that from them nothing can be composed which is new, or different from every one of them [i. e., such that they form a group with respect to the operation $\oplus$].

Solution. Assume (by post. 1) any terms, of any desired number, which shall be different from each other, A, B, C, and D, and from these let $A \oplus B = M$, $M \oplus C = N$, and $N \oplus D = P$. Then A, B, M, N, and P are the terms required. For (by construction) M is made from A and B, and hence A, or B, is in M, and M in N, and N in P. Hence (by prop. 16) any term which here precedes is in any which follows. But if two such are united as components, nothing new arises; for if a term be united with itself, nothing new arises; $L \oplus L = L$ (by ax. 2).[22] If one term be united with another as components, a term which precedes will be united with one which follows; hence a term which is contained with one which contains it, as $L \oplus N$, but $L \oplus N = N$ (by prop. 14).[23] And if three are united, as $L \oplus N \oplus P$, then a couple, $L \oplus N$, will be joined with one, P. But the couple, $L \oplus N$, by themselves will not compose anything new, but one of themselves, namely the latter, N, as we have shown; hence to unite a couple, $L \oplus N$, with one, P, is the same as to unite one, N, with one, P, which we have just demonstrated to compose nothing new. And so on, for any larger number of terms. Q.E.D.

Scholium. It would have been sufficient to add each term to the next, which contains it, as M, N, P, etc., and indeed this will be the situation, if in our construction we put $A =$ Nothing and let $B = M$. But it is clear that the solution which has been given is of somewhat wider application, and of course these problems can be solved in more than one way; but to exhibit all their possible solutions would be to demonstrate that no other ways are possible, and for this a large number of propositions would need to be proved first. But to give an example: five things, A, B, C, D, and E, can be so related that they will not compose anything new only in some one of the following ways: first, if A is in B and B in C and C in D and D in E; second, if $A \oplus B = C$ and C is in D and D in E; third, if $A \oplus B = C$ and A is in D and $B \oplus D = E$. The five concepts which follow are related in the last, or third, way; A "equiangular", B "equilateral", C "regular", D "rectangle", E "square", from which nothing can be composed which does not coincide with them, since "equiangular equilateral" coincides with "regular", and "equiangular" is in [the intension of] "rectangle", and "equilateral rectangle" coincides with "square". Thus "regular equiangular" figure is the same as that which is at once "regular" and "regular equilateral", and "equiangular rectangle" is "rectangle", and "regular rectangle" is "square".

Scholium to defs. 3, 4, 5, *and* 6. We say that the concept of the genus *is in* the concept of the species; the individuals of the species amongst (*in*) the individuals of the genus; a part in the whole; and indeed the ultimate and indivisible in the continuous, as a point is in a line, although a point is not a part of the line. Likewise the concept of the attribute or predicate is in the concept of the subject. And in general this conception is of the widest application. We also speak of that which is in something as contained in that in which it is. We are not here concerned with the notion of "contained" in general—with the manner in which those things which are "in" are related to one another and to that which contains them. Thus our demonstrations cover also those things which compose something in the distributive sense, as all the species together compose the genus. Hence all the inexistent things which suffice to constitute a container, or in which are all things which are in the container, are said to compose that container; as for example, $A \oplus B$ are said to *compose L*, if A, B, and L denote the straight lines RS, YX, and RX, for $RS \oplus YX = RX$. And such parts which complete the whole, I am accustomed to call "cointegrants", especially if they have no common part; if they have a common part, they are

[22] The number of the axiom is omitted in the text.
[23] The number of the prop. is omitted in the text.

called "co-members", as RS and RX. Whence it is clear that the same thing can be composed in many different ways if the things of which it is composed are themselves composite. Indeed if the resolution could finally be carried to infinity, the variations of composition would be infinite. Thus all synthesis and analysis depends upon the principles here laid down. And if those things which are contained are homogeneous with that in which they are contained, they are called parts and the container is called the whole. If two parts, however chosen, are such that a third can be found having a part of one and a part of the other in common, then that which is composed of them is continuous. Which illustrates by what small and simple additions one concept arises from another. And I call by the name "subalternates" those things one of which is in the other, as the species in the genus, the straight line RS in the straight line RX; "disparates" where the opposite is the case, as the straight lines RS and YX, two species of the same genus, perfect metal and imperfect metal—and particularly, members of the different divisions of the same whole, which (members) have something in common, as for example, if you divide "metal" into "perfect" and "imperfect", and again into "soluble in *aqua fortis*" and "insoluble", it is clear that "metal which is insoluble in *aqua fortis*" and "perfect metal" are two disparate things, and there is metal which is perfect, or is always capable of being fulminated in a cupel,[24] and yet is soluble in *aqua fortis*, as silver, and on the other hand, there is imperfect metal which is insoluble in *aqua fortis*, as tin.

Scholium to axioms 1 and 2. Since the ideal form of the general [or ideal form in general, *speciosa generalis*] is nothing but the representation of combinations by means of symbols, and their manipulation, and the discoverable laws of combination are various,[25] it results from this that various modes of computation arise. In this place, however, we have nothing to do with the theory of the variations which consist simply in changes of order [i. e., the theory of permutations], and AB [more consistently, $A \oplus B$] is for us the same as BA [or $B \oplus A$]. And also we here take no account of repetition—that is AA [more consistently, $A \oplus A$] is for us the same as A. Thus wherever these laws just mentioned can be used, the present calculus can be applied. It is obvious that it can also be used in the composition of absolute concepts, where neither laws of order nor of repetition obtain; thus to say "warm and light" is the same as to say "light and warm", and to say "warm fire" or "white milk", after the fashion of the poets, is pleonasm; white milk is nothing different from milk, and rational man—that is, rational animal which is rational—is nothing different from rational animal. The same thing is true when certain given things are said to be contained in (*inexistere*) certain things. For the real addition of the same is a useless repetition. When two and two are said to make four, the latter two must be different from the former. If they were the same, nothing new would arise, and it would be as if one should in jest attempt to make six eggs out of three by first counting 3 eggs, then taking away one and counting the remaining 2, and then taking away one more and counting the remaining 1. But in the calculus of numbers and magnitudes, A or B or any other symbol does not signify a certain object but anything you please with that number of congruent parts, for any two feet whatever are denoted by 2; if foot is the unit or measure, then $2 + 2$ makes the new thing 4, and 3 times 3 the new thing 9, for it is presupposed that the things added are always different (although of the same magnitude); but the opposite is the case with certain things, as with lines. Suppose we describe by a moving [point] the straight line, $RY \oplus YX = RYX$ or $P \oplus B = L$, going from R to X. If we suppose this same [point] then to return from X to Y and stop there, although it does indeed describe YX or B a second time, it produces nothing different than if it had described YX once. Thus $L \oplus B$ is the same as L—that is, $P \oplus B \oplus B$ or $RY \oplus YX \oplus XY$ is the same as $RY \oplus YX$. This caution is of much importance in making judgments, by means of the magnitude and motion of those things which generate[26] or describe, concerning the

[24] The text here has ". . . fulminabile persistens in capella": the correction is obvious.
[25] ". . . variaeque sint combinandi leges excogitabiles, . . ." "Excogitabiles", "discoverable by imagination or invention", is here significant of Leibniz's theory of the relation between the "universal calculus" and the progress of science.
[26] Reading "generant" for "generantur"—a correction which is not absolutely neces-

magnitude of those things which are generated or described. For care must be taken either that one [step in the process] shall not choose the track of another as its own—that is, one part of the describing operation follow in the path of another—or else [if this should happen] this [reduplication] must be subtracted so that the same thing shall not be taken too many times. It is clear also from this that "components", according to the concept which we here use, can compose by their magnitudes a *magnitude* greater than the magnitude of the *thing* which they compose.[27] Whence the composition of things differs widely from the composition of magnitudes. For example, if there are two parts, A or RS and B or RX, of the whole line L or RX, and each of these is greater than half of RX itself—if, for example, RX is 5 feet and RS 4 feet and YX 3 feet—obviously the magnitudes of the parts compose a magnitude of 7 feet, which is greater than that of the whole; and yet the lines RS and YX themselves compose nothing different from RX,—that is, $RS \oplus YX = RX$. Accordingly I here denote this real addition by $\oplus$, as the addition of magnitudes is denoted by $+$. And finally, although it is of much importance, when it is a question of the actual generation of things, what their order is (for the foundations are laid before the house is built), still in the mental construction of things the result is the same whichever ingredient we consider first (although one order may be more convenient than another), hence the order does not here alter the thing developed. This matter is to be considered in its own time and proper place. For the present, however, $RY \oplus YS \oplus SX$ is the same as $YS \oplus RY \oplus SX$.

Scholium to prop. 24. If RS and YX are different, indeed disparate, so that neither is in the other, then let $RS \oplus YX = RX$, and $RS \oplus RX$ will be the same as $YX \oplus RX$ For the straight line RX is always composed by a process of conception (*in notionibus*).

If A is "parallelogram" and B "equiangular" —which are disparate terms—let C be $A \oplus B$, that is, "rectangle". Then "rectangular parallelogram" is the same as "equiangular rectangle", for either of these is nothing different from "rectangle". In general, if Maevius is A and Titius B, the pair composed of the two men C, then Maevius together with this pair is the same as Titius together with this pair, for in either case we have nothing more than the pair itself. Another *solution* of this problem, one *more elegant but less general*, can be given if A and B have something in common, and this common term is given and

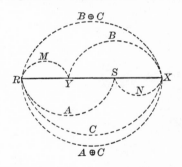

that which is peculiar to each of the terms A and B is also given. For let that which is exclusively A be M, and that which is exclusively B be N, and let $M \oplus N = D$ and let what is common to A and B be P. Then I affirm that $A \oplus D = B \oplus D$, for since $A = P \oplus M$ and $B = P \oplus N$, we have $A \oplus D = P \oplus M \oplus N$ and also $B \oplus D = P \oplus M \oplus N$.

sary, since a motion which generates a line is also itself generated; but, as the context shows, "generare" and "describere" are here synonymous.

   [27] Italics ours.

BIBLIOGRAPHY

The following bibliography contains titles of all the positive contributions to symbolic logic and logistic in the strict sense with which I am acquainted, as well as some, taken from the bibliographies of Venn and Peano, of works which I have not been able to get. But it is not complete. A few of the numerous general discussions of symbolic logic and logistic have also been listed, and certain mathematical books and papers which, though not strictly logistic, are of special interest to the student of that subject.

What are considered the most important contributions to symbolic logic, are indicated by an asterisk (*) preceding the title, while certain studies which should be especially helpful to students of this book are indicated by a "dagger" (†). Volume numbers of periodicals are given in bold-faced type.

ADAMSON, E. The logical copula and quantification of the predicate. London, Nutt, 1897.

ALSTED, J. H. Logicae systema harmonicum. Herbornae Nassoviorum, 1614.

AMATO, V. La teoria dei numeri reali fondata sui concetti del Russell. *Boll. Matem.* (Rome), **9** (1910), pp. 198–205.

ANDREOLI, C. Su un nuovo simbolo nell' algebra della logica. *Atti Soc. progr. Sci.* (Rome), **4**. *Riunione Napoli, dicembre* 1910, pp. 741 ff.

BAIN, A. Logic: Part I, Deduction. London, Longmans, 1870.

BARDILI, C. G. Grundriss der ersten Logik. Stuttgart, Löffland, 1800.

BAYNES, T. S. An essay on the new analytic of logical forms. (Hamilton Prize Essay, 1846.) Edinburgh, Sutherland, 1850.

———— Who discovered the principle of the quantification of the predicate? *Contemp. Rev.*, **22** (1873), pp. 318–23.

BENEKE, E. C. On the logical meaning of proper names. *Proc. Aristot. Soc.*, **3** (1905), pp. 12–29.

BENTHAM, G. Outline of a new system of logic. London, Hunt, 1827.

BERNOUILLI, J. Parallelismus ratiocinii logici et algebraici (1685): Opera (Geneve, Cramer, 1744), **1**, p. 214.

BERNSTEIN, B. A complete set of postulates for the logic of classes expressed in terms of the operation "exception", and a proof of the independence of a set of postulates due to del Ré. *Univ. Calif. Publ. Math.*, **1** (1914), pp. 87–96.

*———— A set of four independent postulates for Boolian algebras. *Trans., Amer. Math. Soc.*, **17** (1916), pp. 50–52.

———— A simplification of the Whitehead-Huntington set of postulates for Boolian algebras. *Amer. Math. Soc. Bull.*, **22** (1916), pp. 458–59.

BÔCHER, M. The fundamental conceptions and methods of mathematics. *Amer. Math. Soc. Bull.*, **11** (1904), pp. 115–35.

BOLZANO, B. Wissenschaftslehre: Versuch einer ausführlichen Darstellung der Logik. 4 vols. Sulzbach, Seidelschen Buchh., 1837. Neu herausgegeben von Alois Häfler, Leipzig, Felix Meiner, 1914.

*BOOLE, G. The mathematical analysis of logic. Cambridge, Macmillan, 1847.

*———— The calculus of logic. *Camb. and Dublin Math. Jour.*, **3** (1848), pp. 183–98.

———— On the theory of probabilities, and in particular on Mitchell's problem of the distribution of the fixed stars. *Phil. Mag.*, ser. 4, **1** (1851), pp. 521–30.

———— Further observations on the theory of probabilities. *Ibid.*, ser. 4, **2** (1851), pp. 96–101.

*———— An investigation of the laws of thought. London, Walton, 1854. Also reprinted as vol. 2 of Boole's Collected logical works; ed. by Jourdain, Chicago, Open Court Publ. Co., 1916.

———— Solution of a question in the theory of probabilities. *Phil. Mag.*, ser. 4, **7** (1854), pp. 29–32.

———— Reply to some observations published by Mr. Wilbraham . . . *Ibid.*, ser. 4, **8** (1854), pp. 87–91.

———— On the conditions by which the solutions of questions in the theory of probabilities are limited. *Ibid.*, pp. 91–98.

———— Further observations relating to the theories of probabilities . . . *Ibid.*, pp. 175–76.

*———— On a general method in the theory of probabilities. *Ibid.*, pp. 431–44.

———— On certain propositions in algebra connected with the theory of probabilities. *Ibid.*, ser. 4, **9** (1855), pp. 165–79.

*———— On the application of the theory of probabilities to the question of the combination of testimonies or judgments. (Keith Prize Essay.) *Trans. Roy. Soc. Edinburgh*, **21** (1857), pp. 597–653.

*———— On the theory of probabilities. *Phil. Trans. Roy. Soc.* (London), **152** (1862), pp. 225–52.

———— On the theory of probabilities. *Phil. Mag.*, ser. 4, **25** (1863), pp. 313–17.

———— Of propositions numerically definite. *Trans. Camb. Phil. Soc.*, **11** (1868), pp. 396–411.

BOOLE, MARY. Symbolical methods of study. London, Kegan, 1884.

BOURDILLAT, F. La réforme logique de Hamilton. Paris, Hachette, 1891.

BROWN, H. C. The logic of Mr. Russell. *Jour. of Phil., Psych. and Sci. Methods*, **8** (1911), pp. 85–91.

BRUNSCHWIEG, L. Les étapes de la philosophie mathématique. Paris, Alcan, 1912.

BRYANT, MRS. S. On the nature and functions of a complete symbolic language. *Mind*, **13** (1888), pp. 188–207.

———— The relation of mathematics to general formal logic. *Proc. Aristot. Soc.*, **2** (1901), pp. 105–34.

BUFFA, P. Alcune formule di logica. *Rev. de Mathém.* (Turin), **7** (1900), pp. 56–58.

———— Principî di logica. *Period. Matem.* (Livorno), **16** (1909), pp. 295–303, and **17** (1901), pp. 292–300.

BURALI-FORTI, C. Teoria delle grandezze: Parte IV del Formulario. *Riv. di Matem.* (Turin), **3** (1893).

———— Sulle classi derivate a destra e a sinistra. *Atti Accad. Torino*, **29** (1894).

———— I numeri negativi. *Riv. di Matem.*, **3** (1893), pp. 138 ff.

*———— Logica matematica. Milano, Hoepli, 1894.

———— Exercise de traduction en symboles de logique mathématique. *Bull. de Mathém. élémentaire* (Turin), 1897.

———— Sur les différentes méthodes logique pour la définition du nombre réel. *Bibl. du Cong. Int. de Phil.* (Paris), 1900, **3**, pp. 289–307.

———— Sui simboli di logica matematica. *Il Pitagora*, 1900, pp. 65 ff., 129 ff.

———— Sur l'égalité et sur l'introduction des éléments dérivés dans la science. *Enseign. mathém.*, 1901, pp. 246–61.

———— Gli enti astratti definiti come enti relativi ad un campo di nozioni. *Rend. Accad. Lincei* (Rome), ser. 5, **21: 2** (1912), pp. 677–82.

———— Sulla teoria génerale delle grandezze e dei numeri. *Atti Accad. Torino*, **39** (1903), pp. 256–82.

BUSCH, M. Anfangsgründe der logikalischen Algebra. Tübingen, Cotta, 1768.

CANTOR, G. Beiträge zur Begründung der transfiniten Mengenlehre. *Math. Annalen*, **46** (1895), pp. 481–512, and **49** (1897), pp. 207–46.

———— ———— Theory of transfinite numbers: translation by P. E. B. Jourdain. Chicago, Open Court Publ. Co., 1915.

CARROLL, LEWIS [pseud.] *see* S. H. HODGSON.

CASTELLANO, F. Alcune identità. *Rev. de Mathém.* (Turin), **7** (1900), pp. 58 ff.

CASTILLON, G. F. Réflexions sur la logique. *Berlin Acad. Mem.*, 1802.

*———— Sur un nouvel algorithme logique. *Ibid.*, 1803.

CAYLEY, A. On a question in the theory of probabilities (with discussion by Boole). *Phil. Mag.*, ser. 4, **23** (1862), pp. 352–65.

———— Note on the calculus of logic. *Quar. J. of Pure and Appl. Math.*, **11** (1871), pp. 282–83.

———— On compound combinations. *Mem. Manchester Lit. and Phil. Soc.*, **26** (1877), pp. 99–100.

CIPOLLA, M. Theoria de congruentias intra numeros integros. *Rev. de Mathém.* (Turin), **8** (1905).

———— Specimen de calculo arithmetico integrale. *Ibid.*

*CLIFFORD, W. K. Types of compound statement involving four classes. *Mem. Manchester Lit. and Phil. Soc.*, **26** (1879), pp. 81–96.

COHEN, M. R. The present situation in the philosophy of mathematics. *J. of Phil., Psych. &c.*, **8** (1911), pp. 533–46.

COUTURAT, L. La logique mathématique de M. Peano. *Rev. de Métaphysique et de Morale*, **7** (1899), pp. 616–46.

———— Sur une définition logique du nombre. *Ibid.*, **8** (1900), pp. 23–36.

———— Sur la définition du continuum. *Ibid.*, pp. 157–68.

———— L'algèbre universelle de M. Whitehead. *Ibid.*, pp. 323–62.

†———— La logique de Leibniz, d'après des documents inédits, Paris, Alcan, 1901.

———— Histoire de la langue universelle (en collaboration avec M. Leau.) Paris, Hachette, 1903.

———— Sur l'utilité de la logique algorithmique. *C.-R., II Cong. int. de Phil., Geneve 1904.*

———— Les principes des mathématiques. *Rev. de Mét. et de Mor.*, **12** (1904), pp. 19–50, 211–40, 664–98, 810–44, **13** (1905), pp. 224–56.

———— Définitions et démonstrations mathématiques. *Enseign. Mathém.*, 1905.

———— Les définitions mathématiques. *Ibid.*, pp. 27 ff.

*———— Les principes des mathématiques, avec un appendice sur la philosophie des mathématiques de Kant. Paris, Alcan, 1905.

†———— L'algèbre de la logique. Paris, Gauthier-Villars, 1905.

†———— ———— The algebra of logic; translated by L. G. Robinson. Chicago, Open Court Publ. Co., 1914.

———— Pour la logistique: réponse à M. Poincaré. *Rev. de Mét. et de Mor.*, **14** (1906), pp. 208–50.

———— La logique et la philosophie contemporaine. *Ibid.*, pp. 318–41.

†———— Die Prinzipien der Logik. *Encyc. d. phil. Wiss.*, hrsg. v. A. Ruge, **1**, *Logik*, pp. 137–201.

†———— ———— The principles of logic; translated by B. E. Meyer. *Encyc. of Phil. Sci.*, **1**, *Logic*, pp. 136–239.

———— For logistics. *Mind*, **22** (1912), pp. 481–523.

———— Des propositions particulières et de la portée existentielle. *Rev. de Mét. et de Mor.*, **21** (1913), pp. 256–59.

———— Sur les rapports logique des concepts et des propositions. *Ibid.*, **24** (1917), pp. 15–58.

———— La logique algorithmique et le calcul de probabilités. *Ibid.*, pp. 291–313.

DALGARNO, G. Ars signorum, vulgo character universalis et lingua philosophica. Ed. 4. Glasgow, Maitland Club, 1834.

DARJES, J. G.   Introductio in artem inveniendi seu logicam theoretico-practicam. Ed. 2.   Jenae, 1747.
——— Weg zur Wahrheit.   1776.
DAVIS, E. W.   Some groups in logic.   *Amer. Math. Soc. Bull.*, **9** (1903), pp. 346–48.
DEDEKIND, R.   Was sind und was sollen die Zahlen.   Braunschweig, Vierwig, 1888.
——— Stetigkeit und irrationalen Zahlen.   Ed. 3.   Braunschweig, Vierwig, 1905.
——— Essays on the theory of numbers.   (The two preceding translated by W. W. Beman.)   Chicago, Open Court Publ. Co., 1909.
DE LAGUNA, T.   On certain logical paradoxes.   *Phil. Rev.*, **25** (1916), pp. 16–27.
——— Opposition and the syllogism.   *J. of Phil., Psych., &c.*, **9** (1912), pp. 393–400.
DELBOEUF, J.   Essai de logique scientifique.   Liége, Desoer, 1865.
——— Logique algorithmique.   *Rev. Phil.*, **2** (1876), pp. 225–52, 335–55, 545–95. Also published separately, Liége et Bruxelles, 1877.
†*DEL RÉ, A.   Lezioni di algebra della logica.   Naples, 1907.
——— Sulla indipendenza dei postulati della logica.   *Rend. Accad. Sci.* (Naples), ser. 3, **17** (1911), pp. 450–58.
*DE MORGAN, A.   Formal logic; or, The calculus of inference, necessary and probable.   London, Taylor, 1847.
*——— Series of five papers, "On the syllogism, etc."   *Trans. Camb. Phil. Soc.*
    1) **8** (1846), pp. 379–408.
    2) **9** (1850), pp. 79–127.
    3) **10** (1858), pp. 173–230.
    4) *Ibid.* (1860), 331–*358.
    5) *Ibid.* (1863), pp. 428–87.
*——— Syllabus of a proposed system of logic.   London, Walton, 1860.
——— On indirect demonstration.   *Phil. Mag.*, ser. 4, **4** (1852), pp. 435–38.
*DINES, L. L.   Complete existential theory of Sheffer's postulates for Boolean algebras. *Amer. Math. Soc. Bull.*, **21** (1915), pp. 183–88.
DROBISCH, M. W.   Neue Darstellung der Logik nach ihren einfachsten Verhältnissen. Leipzig, Voss, 1836.
DUFUMIER, H.   Les théories logico-métaphysiques de MM. B. Russell et G. E. Moore. *Rev. de Mét. et de Mor.*, **17** (1909), pp. 620–53.
——— Les tendances de la logique contemporaine.   *Rev. Phil.*, **74** (1912), pp. 359–78.
——— La généralization mathématique.   *Rev. de Mét. et de Mor.*, **19** (1911), pp. 723–58.
——— La philosophie des mathématiques de MM. Russell et Whitehead.   *Ibid.*, **20** (1912), pp. 538–66.
——— La logique des classes et la théorie des ensembles.   *Ibid.*, **23** (1916), pp. 623–31.
ELLIS, A. J.   On the algebraical analogues of logical relations.   *Proc. Roy. Soc.* (London), **21** (1873), pp. 497–98.
ELLIS, R. L.   Boole's laws of thought.   Report of British Assoc. for Advancement of Science, **40** (1870), (Sect.) pp. 12–14.
EULER, L.   Letters on different subjects in natural philosophy addressed to a German princess.   New York, Harper, 1872.
FAGGI, A.   Sulla natura delle propozioni logiche.   Palermo, Reber, 1898.
FRANKL, W. M.   Gegenstandstheoretische Beiträge zur Lehre vom sogenannten logische Quadrat.   *Arch. f. sys. Phil.*, **13** (1907), pp. 346–66.
——— Ein Kalkul für kategorische (Gewissheits-) Schlüsse.   *Ibid.*, **19** (1913), pp. 1–8.
FRANKLIN, F.   A point of logical notation (proposing a numerical notation).   *Johns Hopkins Univ. Circ.*, **1** (1879–82), p. 131, Apr. 1881.
FRANKLIN, MRS. LADD-.   *See* LADD-FRANKLIN, C.
FRÉCHET, M.   Sur quelque points du calcul fonctionnel.   *Rend. Circ. Matem. di Palermo*, **22** (1906), pp. 1–74.
——— Les ensembles abstraits et le calcul fonctionnel.   *Ibid.*, **30** (1910), pp. 1–26.

Bibliography311

*Frege, G. Begriffsschrift, eine der arithmetischen nachgebildete Formelsprache des reinen Denkens. Halle, Nebert, 1879.

—— Anwendung der Begriffsschrift: Vortrag. *Sitz. d. Jena. Gesell. f. Med. u. Naturwiss.*, 1879.

—— Ueber den Zweck der Begriffsschrift. *Ibid.*, Jan. 1882.

*—— Die Grundlagen der Arithmetik, eine logisch-mathematische Untersuchung über den Begriff der Zahl. Breslau, Koebner, 1884.

*—— Ueber formale Theorien der Arithmetik. *Sitz. d. Jena. Gesell. f. Med. u. Naturwiss.*, 1885, pp. 94–104.

—— Function und Begriff. *Vortrag gehalten in der Sitzung vom 9. Januar. 1891, der Jena. Gesell. f. Med. u. Naturwiss.*, Jena, 1891.

—— Ueber Sinn und Bedeutung. *Zeitsch. f. Phil.*, **100** (1892), pp. 25–50.

—— Ueber Begriff und Gegenstand. *Viertelj. f. wiss. Phil.*, **16** (1892), pp. 192–205.

*—— Grundgesetze der Arithmetik, begriffsschriftlich abgeleitet. 2 vols. Jena, Pohle, 1893–1903.

—— Translated portions. *Monist*, **25** (1915), pp. 481–94, **26** (1916), pp. 182–99, **27** (1917), pp. 114–27.

—— Kritische Beleuchtung einiger Punkte in E. Schröders Vorlesungen über die Algebra der Logik. *Arch. f. sys. Phil.*, **1** (1895), pp. 433–56.

—— Ueber die Begriffsschrift des Herrn Peano und mein eigene. *Ber. d. math. Klasse d. Gesell. d. Wiss. zu Leipzig*, 6. Juli, 1896.

Geissler, K. Ueber Notwendigkeit, Wirklichkeit, Möglichkeit und die Grundlagen der Mathematik. *Arch. f. sys. Phil.*, **11** (1905), pp. 1–26.

—— Identität und Gleichheit mit Beiträgen zur Lehre von den Mannigfältigkeiten. *Zeitsch. f. Phil.*, **126** (1905), pp. 168–88.

Gergonne, J. D. Essai de dialectique rationelle. *Ann. de Mathém. pure et appl.*, **7**, pp. 189 ff.

Geyser, J. Logistik und Relationslogik. *Phil. Jahrb.*, **22**, 2. Heft.

—— Grundlagen der Logik und Erkenntnisslehre. Münster, Schoningh, 1909.

Gilman, B. I. On propositions and the syllogism, with remarks by C. S. Peirce; and on propositions called spurious. *Johns Hopkins Univ. Circ.*, **1** (1879–82), pp. 240–41, Aug. 1882.

—— Operations in relative number, with applications to the theory of probabilities. In *Studies in Logic* by members of Johns Hopkins Univ., pp. 107–25.

Grassmann, H. Die lineale Ausdehnungslehre (1844). Leipzig, Wigand, 1878.

*Grassmann, R. Die Wissenschaftslehre oder Philosophie. Stettin, Grassmann, 1872–90. Issued in parts.

Gregory, D. F. On the real nature of symbolic algebra. *Trans. Roy. Soc. Edinburgh*, **14** (1838), pp. 208–16.

Hadamard, J. La logistique et la notion de nombre entier. *Rev. gén. des sci.*, **16** (1906), pp. 906–14.

Hagemann, G. Logik und Noetik. Freiburg, Herd'sche Verlagsbuchh., 1873.

Hahn, O. Zur Axiomatik des logischen Gebietkalkuls. *Arch. f. sys. Phil.*, **15** (1909), pp. 345–47.

*—— Ueber die Koeffizienten einer logischen Gleichung und ihre Beziehungen zur Lehre von den Schlüssen. *Ibid.*, **16** (1910), pp. 149–76.

*Hahn, O., und Neurath, O. Zum Dualismus in der Logik. *Arch. f. sys. Phil.*, **15** (1909), pp. 149–62.

Halsted, G. B. Professor Jevons's criticism of Boole's logical system. *Mind*, **3** (1878), pp. 134–37.

—— Boole's logical method. *J. of Specul. Phil.*, **12** (1878), pp. 81–91.

—— Statement and reduction of the syllogism. *Ibid.*, pp. 418–26.

—— Algorithmic division in logic. *Ibid.*, **13** (1879), pp. 107–12.

—— The modern logic. *Ibid.*, **17** (1883), pp. 210–13.

—— Algebras, spaces, logics. *Pop. Sci. Mo.*, **17** (1880), pp. 516–22.

—— De Morgan as logician. *J. of Specul. Phil.*, **18** (1884), pp. 1–9.

—— Rational Geometry. New York, Wiley, 1907.

HAMILTON, W. Discussions on philosophy. London, Longmans, 1852.

—— Lectures on logic. Blackwood, Edinburgh, 1860.

HAMILTON, W. R. Elements of quaternions. London, Longmans, 1866.

HARLEY, R. Memorial of George Boole. *Brit. Quart. Rev.*, **44** (1866), pp. 141–81.

—— Boole's analysis of logic. *Rep. Brit. Assoc. Adv. Sci.*, **36** (1866), (Sect.) pp. 3–6.

—— Boole's laws of thought. *Ibid.*, **40** (1876), (Sect.) pp. 14–15.

—— Remarks on Mr. Murphy's paper. *Mem. Manchester Lit. and Phil. Soc.*, **23** (1884), pp. 36–40.

HARRIS, J. R. On the syllogism. *Johns Hopkins Univ. Circ.*, **3** (1884), pp. 130–31.

HAUBER, K. F. Scholae logico-mathematicae. Stuttgardiae, 1829.

HEATH, A. E. The geometrical analysis of Grassmann and its connection with Leibniz's characteristic. *Monist*, **27** (1917), pp. 36–56.

HÉRIGONE, P. Cursus mathematicus, nova, brevi, et clara methodo demonstratus per notas reales et universales, citra usum cuiuscunque idiomatis, intellectu faciles. (In both Latin and French.) Paris, 1644.

HERMANT, P., et VAN DE VAELE, A. Les principales théories de la logique contemporaine. Paris, Alcan, 1909.

HICKS, L. E. Euler's circles and adjacent space. *Mind*, n. s. **21** (1912), pp. 410–15.

—— Is inversion a valid inference? *J. Phil., Psych., &c.*, **9** (1912), pp. 65–70.

—— Is inversion a valid inference?—A rejoinder. *Mind*, n. s. **23** (1914), pp. 96–98.

HILBERT, D. Grundlagen der Geometrie. Leipzig, Teubner, 1899.

HILDEBRANDT, T. H. A contribution to the foundations of Fréchet's calcul functionnel. *Amer. Jour. Math.*, **34** (1912), pp. 237–390.

HILLEBRAND, F. Die neuen Theorien der kategorischen Schlüsse. Wien, Hölder, 1891.

HOCKING, W. Two extensions of the use of graphs in elementary logic. *Univ. Calif. Publ. Philos.*, **2** (1909), pp. 31–44.

HODGSON, S. G. The game of logic by Lewis Carroll. London, Macmillan, 1887.

—— Symbolic logic. London, Macmillan, 1896.

HOFFMANN, J. J. Exacte Darstellung aller Urteile und Schlüsse. *Arch. f. sys. Phil.*, **11** (1905), pp. 317–22. *See* Nachtrag, *Ibid.*, **12** (1906), pp. 55–58.

—— Sprachliche Logik und Mathematik. *Arch. f. sys. Phil.*, **19** (1913), pp. 43–49.

*HOLLAND, G. J. VON. Abhandlung über die Mathematik, die allgemeine Zeichenkunst, und die Verschiedenheit der Rechnungsarten. Tübingen, 1764.

*—— Briefe an J. H. Lambert. In *Deutscher Gelehrter Briefwechsel*, **1** (1781).

HOMANS, J. La logique algorithmique. *Rev. Néo-Schol.*, **9**, no. 2.

HONTHEIM, J. Der logische Algorithmus in seinem Wesen, in seiner Anwendung und in seiner philosophischer Bedeutung. Berlin, Dames, 1895.

HOSKINS, L. M. General algebraic solutions in the logic of classes. *Amer. Math. Soc. Bull.*, **15** (1908), pp. 84–85.

HUGHLINGS, I. P. The logic of names: An introduction to Boole's laws of thought. London, Walton, 1869.

HUNTINGTON, E. V. Simplified definition of a group. *Amer. Math. Soc. Bull.*, **8** (1902), pp. 296–300.

—— A second definition of a group. *Ibid.*, pp. 388–91.

†*—— Sets of independent postulates for the algebra of logic. *Trans. Amer. Math. Soc.*, **5** (1904), pp. 288–309.

—— A set of postulates for real algebra. *Ibid.*, **6** (1905), pp. 17–41.

—— The continuum as a type of order. Reprinted from *Annals of Math.* (1905) by the Harvard Univ. Press.

——— A set of independent postulates for cyclic order. *Proc. Nat. Acad. Sci.*, **2** (1916), no. 11.

——— Complete existential theory of the postulates for serial order. *Amer. Math. Soc. Bull.*, **23** (1917), pp. 276–80.

——— Complete existential theory of the postulates for well ordered sets. *Ibid.*, pp. 280–82.

HUNTINGTON, E. V., AND KLINE, J. R.   Sets of independent postulates for betweenness. *Trans. Amer. Math. Soc.*, **18** (1917), pp. 301–25.

HUSSERL, E. G.   Recension, Schröders *Vorlesungen über die Algebra der Logik. Göttingische Gelehrte Anzeige*, 1891, pp. 243–78.

——— Philosophie der Arithmetik, psychologische und logische Untersuchungen. Halle, Pfeffer, 1891.

——— Der Folgerungscalcul und die Inhaltslogik. *Viertelj. f. wiss. Phil.*, **15** (1891), pp. 167–89, 351–56. *See also*, Erwiderung . . ., von A. H. Voigt, also Antwort, *Ibid.*, **17** (1893), pp. 504–11.

——— A. Voigts "elementare Logik" und meine Darstellung zur Logik des logischen Calculs, *Ibid.*, **17** (1893), pp. 111–120.

JÄGER, J. N.   Handbuch der Logik. Wien, Heubner, 1839.

*JEVONS, W. S.   Pure logic, or The logic of quality apart from quantity. London, Stanford, 1864.

——— The substitution of similars, the true principle of reasoning. London, Macmillan, 1869.

——— On the mechanical performance of logical inference. *Phil. Trans. Roy. Soc.* (London), **160** (1870), pp. 497–518.

——— On a general system of numerically definite reasoning. *Mem. Manchester Lit. and Phil. Soc.*, **24** (1870), pp. 330–52.

——— On the inverse, or inductive, logical problem. *Ibid.*, **25** (1871), pp. 119–30.

——— Who discovered the quantification of the predicate? *Contemp. Rev.*, **21** (1873), pp. 821–24.

*——— The principles of science, a treatise on logic and scientific method. Ed. 3. London, Macmillan, 1879.

*——— Studies in deductive logic. London, Macmillan, 1880.

——— Elementary lessons in logic. New ed. London, Macmillan, 1904.

*JOHNSON, W. E.   The logical calculus. *Mind*, n. s. **1** (1892), pp. 3–30, 235–50, 340–57.

*——— Sur la théorie des équations logique. In *Bibl. Cong. int. de Phil.*, Paris, 1900, **3**, pp. 185–99.

JONES, E. E. C.   Mr. Russell's objections to Frege's analysis of propositions. *Mind*, n. s. **19** (1910), pp. 379–87.

——— A new "law of thought" and its implications. *Ibid.*, **20** (1911), pp. 41–53.

JOURDAIN, P. E. B.   De infinito in mathematica. *Rev. de Mathém.* (Turin), **8** (1905), pp. 121 ff.

——— Transfinite numbers and the principles of mathematics. *Monist*, **20** (1910), pp. 93–118.

†——— Development of theories of mathematical logic and the principles of mathematics. *Quar. J. of pure and appl. Math.*, **41** (1910), pp. 324–52, **43** (1912), pp. 219–314, **44** (1912), pp. 113–25.

——— Some modern advances in logic. *Monist*, **21** (1911), pp. 564–66.

——— The philosophy of Mr. B*rtr*nd R*ss*ll. *Ibid.*, **21** (1911), pp. 481–508, **26** (1916), pp. 24–62.

——— Mr. Bertrand Russell's first work on the principles of mathematics. *Ibid.*, **22** (1912), pp. 149–58.

——— The logical work of Leibniz. *Ibid.*, **26** (1916), pp. 504–23.

KAULICH, W.   Handbuch der Logik. Prag, Lehmann, 1869.

KEMPE, A. B.   Memoir on the theory of mathematical form.   *Phil. Trans. Roy. Soc.* (London), **177** (1886), pp. 1–90.   *See also*, Note, *Proc. Royal Soc.* (London), **42** (1887), pp. 193–96.

*——— On the relation between the logical theory of classes and the geometrical theory of points.   *Proc. London Math. Soc.*, **21** (1890), pp. 147–82.

——— The subject matter of exact thought.   *Nature*, **43** (1890), pp. 156–62.

KEYSER, C.   Some outstanding problems for philosophy.   *J. of Phil., Psych., &c.*, **2** (1905), pp. 207–13.

——— The thesis of modern logistic.   *Science*, **30** (1909), pp. 949–63.

KIRCHER, A.   Ars magna sciendi, in XII libros digesta.   Amsterdam, 1669.

KÖNIG, J.   Neue Grundlagen der Logik, Arithmetik und Mengenlehre.   Hrsg. v. König. Leipzig, Veit, 1914.

KORSELT, A.   Bemerkung zur Algebra der Logik.   *Math. Annalen*, **44** (1894), pp. 156–57.

——— Die Logik der Geometrie.   *Jahresber. d. Math. Ver.* (Leipzig), **17** (1908), pp. 98–112.

——— Was ist Mathematik?   *Arch. f. Math.* (Leipzig), **21** (1913), pp. 371–73.

KOYRÉ, A.   Sur les nombres de M. Russell.   *Rev. de Mét. et de Mor.*, **20** (1912), pp. 722–24.

KRAUSE, K. C. F.   Abriss des Systemes des Logik als philosophische Wissenschaft. Göttingen, Dieterich, 1828.

KREIBIG, J. K.   Ueber die Paradoxen in der Logik Bolzanos.   *Viertelj. f. wiss. Phil.*, **28** (1904), pp. 375–92.

KRIENELKE, K.   J. H. Lambert's Philosophie der Mathematik.   Berlin, Mayer, 1905.

KVET, F. B.   Leibnizens Logik, nach den Quellen dargestellt.   Prag, Tempsky, 1857.

LADD, CHRISTINE.   *See* Ladd-Franklin.

†*LADD-FRANKLIN, C.   On the algebra of logic.   In *Studies in Logic* by Johns Hopkins University, pp. 17–71.

——— On some characteristics of symbolic logic.   *Amer. J. of Psych.*, **2** (1889), pp. 543–67.

——— Some proposed reforms in common logic.   *Mind*, **15** (1890), pp. 75–85.

——— Dr. Hillebrand's syllogistic.   *Mind*, n. s. **1** (1892), pp. 527–30.

——— The reduction to absurdity of the ordinary treatment of the syllogism.   *Science*, **13** (1901), pp. 574–76.

——— Implication and existence in logic.   *Phil. Rev.*, **21** (1912), pp. 641–65.

——— The antilogism—an emendation.   *J. of Phil., Psych., &c.*, **10** (1913), pp. 49–50.

——— Articles on *Syllogism* and *Proposition* in Baldwin's *Dict. of Phil. and Psych.*

LALANDE, L.   Le mouvement logique.   *Rev. Phil.*, **63** (1907), pp. 256–88.

LAMBERT, J. H.   Neues Organon.   2 vols.   Leipzig, Wendler, 1764.

*——— De universaliori calculi idea, disquisitio.   *Nova Acta Eruditorum*, 1765, pp. 441 ff.

——— Anlage zur Architectonic.   Riga, Hartknoch, 1771.

*——— Logische und philosophische Abhandlungen; hrsg. v. J. Bernouilli.   2 vols. Berlin, Bernouilli, 1782–87.

*J. H. Lamberts Deutscher Gelehrter Briefwechsel; hrsg. v. Bernouilli.   4 vols.   Berlin, Bernouilli, 1781–84.

LANGE, F. A.   Logische Studien.   Iserlohn, Baedeker, 1877.

LANGE, I. C.   Inventum novi quadrati logici universalis in trianguli quoque formam commode redacti.   Giessen, Müller, 1714.

——— Neucleus logicae Weisianae.   Giessen, Müller, 1712.

*LEIBNIZ, G. W.   Philosophische Schriften, hrsg. v. C. I. Gerhardt.   7 vols.   Berlin, Weidmannsche Buchh., 1887.

*——— Opuscules et fragments inédits . . . ; extraits de manuscrits de la Bibliothèque royale de Hanovre, par L. Couturat.   Paris, Alcan, 1903.

Leibnitiana, Elementa philosophiae arcanae, De summa rerum.   Ed. Ivan Jagodinsky. Kazan, Imp. Univ., 1913.

LEWIS, C. I.   Implication and the algebra of logic.   *Mind*, n. s. 21 (1912), pp. 522–31.

—— Interesting theorems in symbolic logic.   *J. of Phil., Psych., &c.*, 10 (1913), pp. 239–42.

—— A new algebra of implications and some consequences.   *Ibid.*, pp. 428–38.

—— The calculus of strict implication.   *Mind*, n. s. 23 (1914), pp. 240–47.

—— The matrix algebra for implications.   *J. of Phil., Psych., &c.*, 11 (1914), pp. 589–600.

—— A too-brief set of postulates for the algebra of logic.   *Ibid.*, 12 (1915), pp. 523–25.

—— Types of order and the system.   (Among *Papers in honor of Josiah Royce on his Sixtieth Birthday.*)   *Phil. Rev.*, pp. 407–19, May 1916.

—— The issues concerning material implication.   *J. of Phil., Psych., &c.*, 14 (1917), pp. 350–56.

LIARD, L.   Un nouveau système de logique formelle, M. Stanley Jevons.   *Rev. Phil.*, 3 (1877), pp. 277–93.

—— La logique algebrique de Boole.   *Ibid.*, 4 (1877), pp. 285–317.

†—— Les logiciens anglais contemporains.   Ed. 5.   Paris, Alcan, 1907.

LICHTENFELS, J.   Lehrbuch der Logik.   Wien, Heubner, 1842.

LIPPS, G. F.   Untersuchung über die Grundlagen der Mathematik.   *Phil. Studien*, 14 (1898), pp. 157–241.

Logicae Compendium.   [Anonymous.]   Glasgow, 1764.

LORIA, G.   La logique mathématique avant Leibniz.   *Bull. des sci. Mathém.*, 18 (1894), pp. 107–12.

LOURIÉ, S.   Die Prinzipien der Wahrscheinlichkeitsrechnung, eine logische Untersuchung des disjunktiven Urteils.   Tübingen, Mohr, 1910.

LÖWENHEIM, L.   Ueber das Auflösungsproblem in logischen Klassenkalkul.   *Sitzber. math. Gesell.* (Berlin), 7 (1908), pp. 89–94.

*—— Auflösung von Gleichungen im logischen Gebietekalkul.   *Math. Annalen*, 68 (1910), pp. 169–207.

*—— Ueber Transformationen im Gebietkalkul.   *Ibid.*, 73 (1913), pp. 245–72.

*—— Potenzen im Relativkalkul und Potenzen allgemeiner endlicher Transformationen.   *Sitzber. math. Gesell.* (Berlin), 12 (1913), pp. 65–71.

*—— Ueber eine Erweiterung des Gebietekalkuls, welche auch die gewöhnliche Algebra umfasst.   *Arch. f. sys. Phil.*, 21 (1915), pp. 137–48.

LÜROTH, J.   Aus der Algebra der Relative, nach dem 3. Bd. von E. Schröders Vorlesungen über die Algebra der Logik.   *Jahresber. d. Deutsch. Math.-Ver.*, 13 (1904), pp. 73–111.

MAASS, J. G. E.   Grundriss der reinen Mathematik.   Halle, Ruff, 1796.

—— Grundriss der Logik.   Halle, Ruff, 1807.

MACCOLL, H.   Symbolical or abbreviated language with an application to mathematical probability.   *Math. Questions*, 28 (1877), pp. 20–23, 100.

*—— The calculus of equivalent statements.   (Seven papers and a note.)   *Proc. London Math. Soc.*, 9 (1877), pp. 9–20; *ibid.*, pp. 177–86; 10 (1878), pp. 16–28; 11 (1880), pp. 113–21; 28 (1896), pp. 156–83; 28 (1897), pp. 555–79; 29 (1897), pp. 98–109; Note, 30 (1898), pp. 330–32.

*—— Symbolical reasoning.   (Eight papers.)   *Mind*, 5 (1880), pp. 45–60; n. s. 6 (1897), pp. 403–510; n. s. 9 (1900), pp. 75–84, n. s. 11 (1902), pp. 352–68; n. s. 12 (1903), pp. 355–64; n. s. 14 (1905), pp. 74–81; *ibid.*, pp. 390–97; n. s. 15 (1906), pp. 504–18.

—— On the growth and use of symbolical language.   *Mem. Manchester Lit. and Phil. Soc.*, 27 (1881), pp. 225–48.

—— Implicational and equational logic.   *Phil. Mag.*, ser. 5, 11 (1881), pp. 40–43.

—— Question for logicians.   *Mind*, n. s. 9 (1900), p. 144, 288, 432.)

———— Logique tabulaire. *Rev. de Mét. et de Mor.*, **10** (1902), pp. 213–17.

———— La logique symbolique et ses applications. *Bibl. du Cong. Int. de Phil.*, *Paris 1900*, **3**, pp. 135–83.

———— La logique symbolique. *Enseign. Mathém.* (Paris), **6** (1904), pp. 372–76.

*———— Symbolic Logic and its applications. London, Longmans, 1906.

———— Symbolic logic: A reply. *Mind*, n. s. **16** (1907), pp. 470–73.

———— Linguistic misunderstanding. *Mind*, n. s. **19** (1910), pp. 186–99, 337–55.

———— Problems, in *Math. Questions* **29** (1878), pp. 66–68; **33** (1880), p. 113; **35** (1881), p. 29; **36** (1881), pp. 50, 55, 72.

*MacFarlane, A. Principles of the algebra of logic. Edinburgh, Douglas, 1879.

———— On a calculus of relationship (algebra of relationship). *Proc. Roy. Soc. Edinburgh*, **10** (1879), pp. 224–32; **11** (1880), pp. 5–13; **11** (1881), pp. 162–73.

———— An analysis of relationship. *Phil. Mag.*, ser. 5, **11** (1881), pp. 436–46.

———— Analysis of relationships, of consanguinity and affinity. 18 pp. London, Harrison, 1882.

———— Analysis of relationships applied to various problems. *J. of Anthrop. Inst.* (London), 1882.

———— The logical spectrum. *Phil. Mag.*, ser. 5, **19** (1885), pp. 286–90.

———— Principles of the algebra of physics. *Proc. Amer. Assoc. Adv. Sci.*, **40** (1891), pp. 65–117.

———— On exact analysis as the basis of language. *Trans. Texas Acad. of Sci.*, Feb. 1892, pp. 5–10.

———— The fundamental principles of algebra. *Proc. Amer. Assoc. Adv. Sci.*, **48** (1899), pp. 21–51.

———— Les idées et principes du calcul géométrique. *Bibl. du Cong. Int. de Phil.*, *Paris 1900*, **3**, pp. 405–23.

———— Problems, in *Math. Questions* **32** (1879), pp. 17–19, 74–77, 90; **35** (1881), pp. 103–04; **36** (1881), pp. 27–28, 78–81.

Maimon, S. Versuch einer neuen Logik. Berlin, Felisch, 1798.

Mally, E. Zur Gegenstandstheorie des Messens. In Meinongs *Untersuchungen zur Gegenstandstheorie und Psychologie.* Leipzig, Barth, 1904.

———— Gegenstandstheoretische Grundlagen der Logik und Logistik. Ergänzungsheft zu 148. Bd. *Zeitsch. f. Phil.* (1912).

Mannoury, G. Methodologisches und Philosophisches zur Elementär-Mathematik. Haarlem, Visser, 1910.

Marquand, A. A machine for producing syllogistic variations, and A note on an eight-term logical machine. In *Studies in Logic* by Johns Hopkins Univ., pp. 12–16.

———— A new logical machine. *Proc. Amer. Acad. Arts and Sci.*, **21** (1885), pp. 303–07.

Medolaghi, P. La logica matematica ed il calcolo delle probabilità. *Boll. Ass. Ital. incr. scienza attuari* (Milan), **18** (1907), pp. 20–40.

———— Intorno al calcolo formale delle probibilità. *Gior. Matem.*, **45** (1907), pp. 192–200.

Mich, J. Grundriss der Logik. Wien, Buchholz, 1871.

Mineo, C. Logica e matematica. *Riv. Ital. di Filos.*, **3** (1911), pp. 49–70.

Mitchell, O. H. On the algebra of logic. *Johns Hopkins Univ. Circ.*, **1** (1879–82), p. 208, May 1882.

*———— On a new algebra of logic. In *Studies in Logic* by Johns Hopkins Univ., pp. 22–106.

———— Note on Venn's review of *Studies in Logic.* . . . *Mind*, **9** (1884), pp. 321–22.

Montague, W. P. The meaning of identity, similarity and non-entity: a criticism of Mr. Russell's logical puzzles. *J. of Phil., Psych., &c.*, **3** (1906), pp. 127–31.

Moore, E. H. A definition of abstract groups. *Trans. Amer. Math. Soc.*, **3** (1902), pp. 485–92.

—— On the foundations of mathematics. *Amer. Math. Soc. Bull.*, **9** (1903), pp. 402–24.

—— Introduction to a form of general analysis. *New Haven Math. Colloquium (1910)*; Yale Univ. Press, 1910; pp. 1–150.

MÜLLER, E. *See also* Schröder, E.

—— Ueber die Algebra der Logik: I. Die Grundlagen des Gebietekalkuls; II. Das Eliminationsproblem und die Syllogistik. *Programm des Gymnasiums Tauberbischofsheim, 1900.*

—— Ueber die Algebra der Logik und über die hinterlassene algebraische-logische Schriften von Ernst Schröder. *Ber. int. Kong. Phil., Heidelberg 1908*, **3**, pp. 686–91.

MURPHY, J. J.   Relation of logic to language. *Belfast Nat. Hist. and Phil. Soc.*, Feb. 1875.

—— Fundamental logic. *Mind*, **2** (1877), pp. 47–55.

—— On an extension of ordinary logic, connecting it with the logic of relatives. *Mem. Manchester Lit. and Phil. Soc.*, **27** (1879), pp. 90–101.

—— On the addition and multiplication of logical relatives. *Ibid.*, **27** (1881), pp. 201–24.

—— On the transformations of a logical proposition containing a single relative term. *Ibid.*, **28** (1882), pp. 132–38.

—— A new system of logical notation. *Ibid.*, **32** (1888), pp. 22–32.

—— A new symbolic treatment of the old logic. *Ibid.*, **34** (1891), pp. 201–15.

NAGY, A.   Sulla rappresentazione grafica delle quantità logiche. *Rend. Accad. Lincei*, **6** (1890), pp. 373–78.

—— Fondamenti del calcolo logico. *Gior. Matem.*, **28** (1890), pp. 1–35.

—— I teoremi funzionali nel calcolo logico. *Riv. di Matem.* (Turin), **2** (1892), pp. 177–79.

*—— Principî di logica, esposti secondo le dottrine moderne. Torino, Loescher, 1892.

—— Ueber Beziehungen zwischen logischen Grössen. *Monatshefte f. Math. u. Phys.*, **4** (1893), pp. 147–53.

*—— Ueber das Jevons-Clifford'sche Problem. *Ibid.*, **5** (1894), pp. 331–45.

NASSÒ, M.   Alcuni teoremi di arithmetica. *Rev. de Mathém.* (Turin), **7** (1900), pp. 42–55.

NATORP, P.   Zu den logischen Grundlagen der neueren Mathematik. *Arch. f. sys. Phil.*, **7** (1901), pp. 177–209, 372–438.

NEURATH, O.   *See also* Hahn and Neurath.

—— Eindeutigkeit und Kommutativität des logischen Produkte *a b*. *Arch. f. sys. Phil.*, **15** (1909), pp. 342–44.

—— Ernst Schröders Beweis des 12. Theorems. Für die identischen Operationen gilt das "Kommutationsgesetz"? *Ibid.*, pp. 104–06.

—— Definitionsgleichheit und symbolische Gleichheit. *Ibid.*, **16** (1910), pp. 142–44.

NICOLI, P. F.   Il metodo delle matematiche e l'insegnamento elementare della logica. *Riv. Ital. di Filos.*, **11** (1908), pp. 355–63.

NEWLIN, W. J.   A new logical diagram. *J. of Phil., Psych., &c.*, **3** (1906), pp. 539–45.

PADOA, A.   Conférences sur la logique mathématique. Univ. nouvelle de Bruxelles, 1898.

—— Algebra elementare logicamente esposta. Conferenze tenuto nella R. Univ. di Pavia, 1899, pp. 35 ff.

—— Essai d'une théorie algébrique des nombres entiers, précédé d'une introduction logique à une théorie déductive quelconque. *Bibl. du Cong. Int. de Phil., Paris 1900*, **3**, pp. 309–65.

—— Théorie des nombres entiers absolus. *Rev. de Mathém.* (Turin), **7** (1900), pp. 1–41.

—— Numeri interi relativi. (Translation of "Essai d'une théorie . . .".) *Rev. di Mathém.* (Turin), **7** (1900), pp. 73–84.

—— Logica matematica e matematica elementare. *Atti del II. Congr. dei Professori di Matem., Livorno 1902*, pp. 186–200.

—— Le problème nr. 2 de M. David Hilbert. *Enseign. Mathém.*, **5** (1903), pp. 85–91.

—— Che cos'è una relazione? *Atti Accad. Sci.* (Turin), **41** (1905–06), pp. 1084–92.

—— Ideografia logica. Ateneo Veneto, 1906.

—— Sul teorema Cantor-Bernstein-Peano. *Period. Matem.* (Livorno), **22** (1906), pp. 23–28.

†—— La logique déductive dans sa dernière phase de developpement. *Rev. de Mét. et de Mor.*, **19** (1911), pp. 828–83; **20** (1912), pp. 48–67, 207–31.

†—— La logique déductive dans sa dernière phase de developpement. Paris, Gauthier-Villars, 1912.

—— Des conséquences d'un changement d'idées primitives dans une théorie deductive quelconque. *Rev. de Mét. et de Mor.*, **24** (1917), pp. 315–25.

PASCH, M.   Vorlesungen über neuere Geometrie. Leipzig, Teubner, 1882.

PEACOCK, G.   Report on recent progress and present state of certain branches of analysis. *Rep. Brit. Assoc. Adv. Sci.*, **3** (1883), pp. 185–352.

—— On symbolical algebra and its applications to the geometry of position. (Vol. 2 of *A treatise on algebra.*) Cambridge, Deighton, 1845.

PEANO, G.   Calcolo geometrico secondo l'Ausdehnungslehre di H. Grassmann, preceduto dalle operazioni della logica deduttiva Torino, Bocca, 1888.

—— Arithmetices principia, nova methodo exposita. Torino, Bocca, 1889.

—— Sur la définition de la limite d'une function; exercise de logique mathématique. *Amer. J. of Math.*, **17** (1894), pp. 37–68.

—— Sui fondamenti della geometria. *Riv. di Matem.* (Turin), **4** (1894), pp. 51–90.

†*—— Notations de logique mathématique; introduction au Formulaire de Mathématique. Torino, Bocca, 1894.

—— Saggio di calcolo geometrico. *Atti Accad. Torino*, **31** (1896), pp. 3–26.

—— Studii in logica matematica. *Ibid.*, **32** (1897), pp. 3–21.

—— Les définitions mathématique. *Bibl. du Cong. Int. de Phil., Paris 1900*, **3**, pp. 279–88.

—— Arithmetica generale e algebra elementare. Torino, Paravia, 1902.

—— La geometria basata sulle idee di punto e di distanza. *Atti Acad. Torino*, **38** (1902), pp. 6–10.

—— Super theorema de Cantor-Bernstein. *Rev. de Mathém.* (Turin), **8** (1906).

*PEANO, G., redacteur.   Formulaire de Mathématiques. Tome I, 1895; II, 1897; III, 1901; IV, 1902; V, 1908. Torino, Bocca, 1895–1908.

In addition to Peano, the chief contributor, the other contributors were MM. Arbicone, Bellazzi, Boggio, Burali-Forti, Cantoni, Castellano, Ciamberlini, Giudice, Fano, Padoa, Vacca, Vivianti, *et al.* The successive volumes are comparable to new, revised and enlarged editions. Tome V is written in the proposed international language, Interlingua.

PEIRCE, B.   Linear associative algebras. New edition, with notes and addenda by C. S. Peirce. *Amer. J. of Math.*, **4** (1881), pp. 97–229.

PEIRCE, C. S.   Complete bibliography, by M. R. Cohen, see *J. of Phil., Psych., &c.*, **13** (1916), pp. 733–37.

*PEIRCE, C. S.   On an improvement in Boole's calculus of logic. *Proc. Amer. Acad. Arts and Sci.*, **7** (1867), pp. 250–61.

—— Upon the logic of mathematics. *Ibid.*, pp. 402–12.

*—— Description of a notation for the logic of relatives. *Mem. Amer. Acad. Arts and Sci.*, **9** (1870), pp. 317–78.

—— On the application of logical analysis to multiple algebra. *Proc. Amer. Acad. Arts and Sci.*, **10** (1875), pp. 392–94.

———— Note on Grassmann's "Calculus of Extension". *Ibid.*, **13** (1877), pp. 115–16.
*———— On the algebra of logic. *Amer. J. of Math.*, **3** (1880), pp. 15–57.
———— On the logic of number. *Ibid.*, **4** (1881), pp. 85–95.
———— On the algebra of relatives. 6 pp., 1882. Separately published without indication of the publisher.
———— On the relative forms of quaternions. *Johns Hopkins Univ. Circ.*, Feb. 1882, p. 179.
———— A theory of probable inference. In *Studies in Logic* by Johns Hopkins Univ., pp. 126–82.
†*———— The logic of relatives. *Ibid.*, pp. 187–203.
*———— On the algebra of logic; a contribution to the philosophy of notation. *Amer. J. of Math.*, **7** (1885), pp. 180–202.
———— The critic of arguments: Exact thinking, *Open Court*, **6** (1892), pp. 3391–94; The reader is introduced to relatives, *Ibid.*, pp. 3415–19.
———— Recension, Schröder's *Vorlesungen*, Bd. III: The regenerated logic, *Monist*, **7** (1896), pp. 19–40; The logic of relatives, *Ibid.*, (1897), pp. 161–217.
PESLOUAN, C. L. DE. Sur les fondements de l'arithmetique et autres questions connexes. *Rev. Phil.*, **10** (1907), pp. 372–97, 489–509, 568–92, **11** (1907), pp. 182–206.
———— Les systèmes logique et la logistique. Paris, Rivière, 1909.
PIERI, M. Sur la géométrie envisageé comme un système purement logique. *Bibl. du Cong. Int. de Phil.*, *Paris 1900*, **3**, pp. 367–404.
———— Sur la compatibilité des axiomes de l'arithmetique. *Rev. de Mét. et de Mor.*, **14** (1906), pp. 196–207.
———— Sopra una definizione aritmetica degli irrazionali. *Accad. Gioenia di Catania*, 1906.
———— Uno sguardo al nuovo indirizzo logico-matematico delle scienza deduttive. Discorso letto inaugurandosi l'anno accademico 1906–07 nella R. Univ. di Catania.
PLOUCQUET, G. Fundamenta philosophiae speculativae. Tübingen, Cotta, 1759.
*———— Untersuchung und Abänderung der logicalischen Constructionen des Herrn Professor Lambert. Tübingen, Cotta, 1765.
*———— Sammlung der Schriften welche den logischen Calcul Herrn Professor Ploucquet's betreffen. Frankfurt, 1766.
*———— Institutiones philosophiae theoreticae sive de arte cogitandi. Tübingen, 1772.
*———— Elementa philosophiae contemplativae, sive de scientia ratiocinandi. Stuttgart, 1778.
POINCARÉ, H. Les mathématiques et la logique. *Rev. de Mét. et de Mor.*, **13** (1905), pp. 816–35, **14** (1906), pp. 17–34, 294–317.
———— A propòs de la logistique. *Ibid.*, **14** (1906), pp. 866–68.
———— La logistique de l'infini. *Ibid.*, **17** (1909), pp. 461–82.
———— The new logics. *Monist*, **22** (1912), pp. 243–56.
———— The latest effort of the logisticians. *Ibid.*, pp. 524–39.
POKORNY, I. Neuer Grundriss der Logik. Wien, Graeser, 1878.
PORETSKY, P. On the subject of mathematical-logic. (In Russian.) *Bull. Phys.-Math. Soc. Kazan*, 1881.
———— First principles of mathematical-logic. (In Russian.) *Ibid.*, 1883.
———— Logical equations, methods of solution, and inverse method of mathematical-logic. (In Russian.) *Ibid.*, 1884.
———— Solution of the general problem of the theory of probabilities by means of mathematical-logic. (In Russian.) *Ibid.*, 1887.
———— On the monograph of M. Volcov, *Le calcul logique*. (In Russian.) *Ibid.*, 1889.
———— La loi de racines en logique. *Rev. de Mathém.* (Turin), **6** (1896), pp. 5–8.
†*———— Sept lois fondamentales de la théorie des égalités logiques. *Bull. Phys.-Math. Soc. Kazan*, 1898.

———— Exposé élémentaire de la théorie des égalités logique à deux termes *a* and *b*. *Rev. de Mét. et de Mor.*, **8** (1900), pp. 169–88.

*———— Quelques lois ultérieures de la théorie des égalités logiques. *Bull. Phys.-Math. Soc. Kazan*, 1900–01.

———— Théorie des égalités logiques à trois termes, *a*, *b*, and *c*. *Bibl. du Cong. Int. de Phil.*, Paris 1900, **3**, pp. 201–33.

*———— Théorie des non-égalités logiques. *Bull. Phys.-Math. Soc. Kazan*, 1903.

*———— Théorie conjointe des égalités et des non-égalités logiques. *Ibid.*, 1908.

(The four most important papers by Poretsky—those indicated by *—are reprinted and issued separately by the Imperial Univ. of Kazan.)

PRANTL, K. v.   Geschichte der Logik im Abendlände. 4 vols. Leipzig, Hirzel, 1855–70.

PROCHÁZKA, I. J.   Gesetzbuch für das Denken.   Wien, Gerold, 1842.

REIMARUS, H. S.   Vernunftlehre. Hamburg, Bohn, 1790.

REYES Y PRÓSPER, V.   Christina Ladd-Franklin: Matemática americana y su influencia en la lógica simbólica.   *Progr. Matem.* (Zaragoza), **1** (1891), no. 12.

———— Ernesto Schroeder: Sus merecimientos ante la lógica, su propaganda lógico-mathematica, sus obras.   *Ibid.*, **2** (1892), no. 14.

REYMOND, A.   Logique et mathématiques: Essai historique critique sur le nombre infini. Paris, Alcan, 1908.

———— Note sur le théorème d'existence des nombres entiers, et sur la définition logistique du zéro.   *Rev. de Mét. et de Mor.*, **17** (1909), pp. 237–39.

RIEBER, C. H.   Is inversion a valid inference?   *Mind*, n. s. **22** (1913), pp. 258–59.

RIEHL, A.   Die englische Logik der Gegenwart, mit besonderer Berücksichtigung von W. S. Jevons.   *Viertelj. f. wiss. Phil.*, **1** (1877), pp. 150–80.

RIQUIER, C.   Des axiomes mathématiques.   *Rev. de Mét. et de Mor.*, **3** (1895), pp. 269–84.

ROSS, G. R. F.   Inversion and the diagrammatic representation of negative terms.   *Mind*, n. s. **22** (1913), pp. 254–57.

*ROYCE, J.   The relations of the principles of logic to the foundations of geometry.   *Trans. Amer. Math. Soc.*, **6** (1905), pp. 353–415.

*———— Prinzipien der Logik.   *In* Ruges *Encyc. d. philosoph. Wiss.*, *Bd. I, Logik*, pp. 61–136.

*———— ———— Principles of Logic; translated by B. E. Meyer, pp. 67–135.

———— An extension of the algebra of logic.   *J. of Phil., Psych., &c.*, **10** (1913), pp. 617–33. (*See* correction, p. 672.)

RUSSELL, B. A. W.   *See also* Whitehead and Russell.

———— The logic of geometry.   *Mind*, n. s. **5** (1896), pp. 1–23.

———— On the relations of number and quantity.   *Mind*, n. s. **6** (1897), pp. 326–41.

———— An essay on the foundations of geometry. Cambridge Univ. Press, 1897.

———— Sur la logique des relations. . . .   *Rev. de Mathém.* (Turin), **7** (1901), pp. 115–148.

———— On the notion of order.   *Mind*, n. s. **10** (1901), pp. 30–51.

———— Théorie générale des séries bien ordonnées.   *Rev. de Mathém.* (Turin), **8** (1902), pp. 12–43.

†*———— Principles of mathematics: I. Camb. Univ. Press, 1903. No more volumes published.

———— On denoting.   *Mind*, n. s. **14** (1905), pp. 479–93. *See also* Notes by MacColl, Russell, and Shearman, *Ibid.*, pp. 295, 398, 401, 578.

———— Sur la relation des mathématiques à la logistique (avec une note de M. Whitehead).   *Rev. de Mét. et de Mor.*, **13** (1905), pp. 906–17.

*———— The theory of implication.   *Amer. J. of Math.*, **28** (1906), pp. 159–202.

———— Les paradoxes de la logique.   *Rev. de Mét. et de Mor.*, **14** (1906), pp. 627–50.

———— On some difficulties in the theory of transfinite numbers and order types.   *Proc. London Math. Soc.*, ser. 2, **4** (1906), pp. 29–53.

*——— Mathematical logic as based on the theory of types. *Amer. J. of Math.*, **30** (1908), pp. 222–62.

——— La théorie des types logiques. *Rev. de Mét. et de Mor.*, **18** (1910), pp. 263–301.

——— L'importance philosophique de logistique. *Ibid.*, **19** (1911), pp. 281–91.

——— Réponse à M. Koyré. *Ibid.*, **20** (1912), pp. 725–26.

——— The philosophical importance of mathematical logic. *Monist*, **23** (1913), pp. 481–93.

RUSSELL, F. C.   Hints for the elucidation of Peirce's logical work. *Monist*, **18** (1908), pp. 406–15.

SCHADEN, E. A. VON.   System der positiven Logik. Erlangen, Palm, 1841.

SCHEFFLER, H.   Die Naturgesetze und ihr Zusammenhang mit den Prinzipien der abstrakten Wissenschaften. Leipzig, Foerster, 1876–80. See especially Part 3.

SCHLÖTEL, W.   Kleine Bausteine zu einem Denkmale. Freiburg i. B., 1876.

SCHMIDT, K.   Studies in the structure of logical systems: The separation of problems. *J. of Phil., Psych., &c.*, **9** (1912), pp. 197–204. The deductive system form. *Ibid.*, pp. 317–21. Postulates. *Ibid.*, pp. 431–40. The generating problem. *Ibid.*, **10** (1913), pp. 64–75.

†——— Inversion. *Ibid.*, **9** (1912), pp. 232–34.

SCHNIPPENKÖTTER, J.   Bedeutung der mathematischen Untersuchungen Coutourats für die Logik. *Phil. Jahrb.* (Fulda), **23** (1910), pp. 447–68.

SCHRÖDER, E.   Ueber unendliche viele Algorithmen zur Auflösung der Gleichungen. *Math. Annalen*, **2** (1870), pp. 317–65.

——— Lehrbuch der Arithmetik und Algebra. Leipzig, Teubner, 1873.

——— Ein auf die Einheitswurzeln bezügliches Theorem der Funktionenlehre. *Zeitsch. f. Math. u. Phys.*, **22** (1877), pp. 183–90.

†*——— Der Operationskreis des Logikkalkuls. Leipzig, Teubner, 1877.

——— Ueber den Operationskreis (Note). *Math. Annalen*, **12** (1877), pp. 481–84.

——— Recension, Freges *Begriffsschrift*. *Zeitsch. f. Math. u. Phys.*, **25** (1880), Historisch-literarisch Abt., pp. 81–94.

——— On the most commodious and comprehensive calculus: Exposition of a logical principle, as disclosed by the algebra of logic but overlooked by the ancient logicians. *Rep. Brit. Assoc. Adv. Sci.*, **53** (1883), (Sect.) pp. 411–12.

——— Ueber das Eliminationsproblem im identischen Kalkul. *Tageblatt der Naturforscherversammlung zu Strassburg*, 1885, pp. 353–54.

——— Ueber Algorithmen und Kalkuln. *Arch. f. Math. u. Phys.*, 1887, pp. 225–78.

†*———' Vorlesungen über die Algebra der Logik (exakte Logik), Leipzig, Teubner; 1. Bd., 1890; 2. Bd. 1. Abth., 1891; 3. Bd., 1895; 2. Bd. 2. Abth., hrsg. v. E. Müller, 1905.

——— Eine Berichtigung zum ersten Band meiner Algebra der Logik. *Math. Annalen*, **36** (1890), p. 602.

——— Ueber das Zeichen. Festrede bei dem Direktoratswechsel an der Technischen Hochschule zu Karlsruhe am 22. November 1890. Karlsruhe, 1890.

——— Ueber die Algebra der binären Relative (Note). *Math. Annalen*, **46** (1895), pp. 144–58.

——— Ueber Pasigraphie, ihren gegenwärtigen Stand und die pasigraphische Bewegung in Italien. *Verh. der 1. int. Math. Kong., Zurich 1898*.

——— ——— On Pasigraphy; its present state and the pasigraphic movement in Italy; translation. *Monist*, **9** (1898), pp. 44–62. (See *corrigenda*, p. 320.)

——— Sur une extension de l'idée d'ordre. *Bibl. du Cong. Int. de Phil., Paris 1900*, **3**, pp. 235–40.

†——— Abriss der Algebra der Logik; hrsg. v. E. Müller. Leipzig, Teubner; 1. Teil, 1909; 2. Teil, 1910. (The third part not yet published.)

SCHWEITZER, A. R.   A theory of geometrical relations. *Amer. J. of Math.*, **31** (1909), pp. 365–410, **35** (1913), pp. 37–56.

——— Concerning linear projective order. *Ibid.*, **34** (1912), pp. 169–76.

——— Les idées directrice de la logique génétique des mathématiques. *Rev. de Mét. et de Mor.*, **22** (1914), pp. 175–97; also published by Univ. of Chicago Press, 1915.

SEGNER, J. A.   Specimen logicae universaliter demonstratae.   Jena, Cröcker, 1740.

SEMLER, C. A.   Versuch über die combinatorische Methode, ein Beitrag zur angewandten Logik und allgemeinen Methodik.   Dresden, Walther, 1811.

SETON, J.   Dialectica.   1611.

†SHAW, J. B.   What is Mathematics?   Review of *Principia Mathematica, vol. I. Amer. Math. Soc. Bull.*, **18** (1912), pp. 386–411.

——— Logistic and reduction of mathematics to logic. *Monist*, **26** (1916), pp. 397–414.

SHEARMAN, A. T.   Some controverted points in symbolic logic. *Proc. Aristot. Soc.*, n. s. **5** (1904–05), pp. 74–105.

——— The development of symbolic logic.   London, Williams, 1906.

——— Mr. MacColl's views on logical existence. *Mind*, n. s. **15** (1906), pp. 143–44.

——— Certainties, impossibilities and variables (reply to Mr. MacColl). *Mind*, **16** (1907), pp. 315–16.

——— Definition in symbolic logic. *Mind*, **19** (1910), pp. 387–89.

†——— The scope of formal logic.   London, Univ. Press, 1911.

*SHEFFER, H. M.   A set of five independent postulates for Boolean algebras, with application to logical constants. *Trans. Amer. Math. Soc.*, **14** (1913), pp. 481–88.

SIGWART, H. C. W.   Handbuch zu Vorlesungen über die Logik.   Ed. 3.   Tübingen, Osiander, 1835.

SOLLY, T.   A syllabus of logic.   Cambridge, Deighton, 1839.

SPOTTISWOODE, W.   Remarks on some recent generalizations of algebra. *Proc. London Math. Soc.*, **4** (1871), pp. 147–64.

STAMM, E.   On the theory of relations and operations.   (In Polish.) *Prace mat.-fiz. Warszawa*, **21** (1919), pp. 42–54.

——— What is and what should be Mathematics.   (In Polish.) *Wiad. mat. Warszawa*, **14** (1910), pp. 189–96.

——— Principles of the algebra of logic.   (In Polish.) *Ibid.*, **15** (1911), pp. 1–87.

STERZINGER, O.   Logik und Naturphilosophie der Wahrscheinlichkeitslehre; ein umfassender Lösungsversuch.   Leipzig, Xenien Verlag., 1911.

STÖKL, A.   Lehrbuch der Logik.   8 Aufl., neuarbeitet v. Dr. G. Wohlmuth.   Mainz, Kirchheim, 1905.

STÖHR, A.   Logik im psychologisierender Darstellung.   Wien, Deuticke, 1910.

STOLZ, O.   Vorlesungen über allgemeine Arithmetik, nach den neueren Ansichten bearbeitet.   2 vols.   Leipzig, Teubner, 1885–86.

STRACHEY, O.   Mr. Russell and some recent criticisms of his views. *Mind*, n. s. **24** (1915), pp. 16–28.

THOMSON, W.   Outline of the necessary laws of thought.   (From the 4th London ed.)   New York, Sheldon, 1860.

TÖNNIES, I. H.   De logicae scientiae ad exemplar arithmeticae instituenda ratione.   1752.

TRENDELENBURG, F. A.   Logische Untersuchungen.   Ed. 3.   Leipzig, Hirzel, 1862.

TRUAN-BORSCHE, M.   Die ersten Schritte zur Entwicklung der logischen und mathematischen Begriffe.   Langensalza, Beyer, 1912.

TWESTEN, A. D. C.   Die Logik, insbesondere die Analytik.   Schleswig, Taubst-Inst., 1825.

VAILATI, G.   Un teorema di logica matematica. *Riv. di Matem.* (Turin), **1** (1891), pp. 103 ff.

——— Le proprietà fondamentali delle operazioni della logica deduttiva, studiate dal punto di vista d'una teoria generale delle operazioni. *Ibid.*, pp. 127 ff.

——— Sui principî fondamentali della geometria della retta. *Ibid.*, **2** (1892), pp. 71 ff.

——— Dipendenza fra le proprietà delle relazioni. *Ibid.*, pp. 161 ff.

——— La logique mathématique et sa nouvelle phase de développement dans les écrits de M. J. Peano. *Rev. de Mét. et de Mor.*, **7** (1899), pp. 86–102.

VATER, J. S. Pasigraphie und Antipasigraphie; oder Ueber die neueste Erfindung einer allgemeinen Schriftsprache für alle Völker, und von Wolkens, Leibnitzens, Wilkins und Kalmars pasigraphischen Ideen. . . . Leipzig, 1799.

VEBLEN, O. A system of axioms for geometry. *Trans. Amer. Math. Soc.*, **5** (1904), pp. 343–84.

——— The foundations of geometry. In Young's *Monographs on Topics of Modern Math.*, pp. 1–51.

VENN, J. Consistency and real inference. *Mind*, **1** (1876), pp. 43–52.

——— Boole's logical system. *Ibid.*, pp. 479–91.

——— On the various notations adopted for expressing the common propositions of logic. *Proc. Camb. Phil. Soc.*, **4** (1880), pp. 35–46.

——— On the diagrammatic and mechanical representations of propositions and reasoning. *Phil. Mag.*, ser. 5, **10** (1880), pp. 1–15.

——— On the forms of logical proposition. *Mind*, **5** (1880), pp. 336–49.

——— On the employment of geometrical diagrams for the sensible representation of logical propositions. *Proc. Camb. Phil. Soc.*, **4** (1880), pp. 35–46.

†*——— Symbolic logic. Ed. 2. London, Macmillan, 1894.

——— ——— *Princeton Rev.*, Sept. 1883, pp. 247–67.

——— Notice of Castillon's *Sur un nouvel algorithme logique*. *Mind*, **6** (1881), pp. 447–48.

Catalogue of a collection of books on logic presented to the library by John Venn. . . . *Univ. Library Bull.* Extra series. Cambridge, 1889.

VICTORIN, A. Neue natürliche Darstellung der Logik. Wien, Schaumburg, 1835.

VOIGT, A. Die Auflösung von Urtheilssystemen . . . in der Algebra der Logik. Leipzig, 1890.

——— Was ist Logik? *Viertelj. f. wiss. Phil.*, **16** (1892), pp. 289–332.

VOSS, A. Ueber das Wesen der Mathematik. Leipzig, Teubner, 1908.

WAGNER, L. H. Grundriss der reinen und allgemeinen Logik. Hof., Grau, 1806.

WARRAIN, G. Les principes des mathématiques de M. Couturat. *Rev. de Phil.*, **8** (1906), pp. 517–29, 658–73.

WERNER, H. Ein Beitrag zur Lehre logischer Substitutionen. *Arch. f. sys. Phil.*, **18** (1912), pp. 431–44.

†*WHITEHEAD, A. N. A treatise of universal algebra. Camb. Univ. Press, 1898.

†*——— Memoir on the algebra of symbolic logic. *Amer. J. of Math.*, **23** (1901), pp. 139–65, 297–316.

*——— On cardinal numbers. *Ibid.*, **24** (1902), pp. 367–94.

*——— The logic of relations, logical substitution groups, and cardinal numbers. *Ibid.*, **25** (1903), pp. 157–78.

*——— Theorems on cardinal numbers. *Ibid.*, **26** (1904), pp. 31–32.

*——— On mathematical conceptions of the material world. *Phil. Trans. Roy. Soc.* (London), ser. A, **205** (1906), pp. 465–525.

——— The axioms of projective geometry. Camb. Univ. Press, 1906.

——— The axioms of descriptive geometry. Camb. Univ. Press, 1907.

——— Introduction logique à la géométrie. *Rev. de Mét. et de Mor.*, **15** (1907), pp. 34–39.

——— La théorie relationniste de l'espace. *Ibid.*, **23** (1916), pp. 423–54.

†*WHITEHEAD, A. N., and RUSSELL, B. Principia Mathematica. Vol. 1, 1910; vol. 2, 1912; vol. 3, 1913. Camb. Univ. Press.

WIENER, N. Studies in synthetic logic. *Proc. Camb. Phil. Soc.*, **18** (1914), Part 1, pp. 14–28.

——— A simplification of the logic of relatives. *Ibid.*, **17** (1914), pt. 5, pp. 387–90.

*——— Certain formal invariances in Boolian algebras. *Trans. Amer. Math. Soc.*, **18** (1917), pp. 65–72.

WILBRAHAM, H.   On the theory of chances developed in Professor Boole's *Laws of Thought*. *Phil. Mag.*, ser. 4, **7** (1854), pp. 465–76.

WILKINS, J.   Essay toward a real character and philosophical language. London, 1668.

——— Mercury, or the secret and swift messenger. Ed. 2. London, 1694.

WILSON, E. B.   Logic and the continuum. *Amer. Math. Soc. Bull.*, **14** (1908), pp. 432–43.

——— Symbolic logic. *Ibid.*, pp. 341–44.

WINTER, M.   Métaphysique et logique mathématique. *Rev. de Mét. et de Mor.*, **13** (1905), pp. 589–619.

——— Application de l'algèbre de logique à une controverse juridique. *Ibid.*, **14** (1906), pp. 617–25.

——— Sur l'introduction logique à la théorie des foncotins. *Ibid.*, **15** (1907), pp. 186–216.

——— Les principes du calcul fonctionnel. *Ibid.*, **21** (1913), pp. 462–510.

WOLF, A.   Existential import of categorical predication. Camb. Univ. Press, 1905.

WUNDT, W.   Logik. Ed. 3, 3 vols. Stuttgart, Enke, 1906–08. Refer especially to vol. 1.

YOUNG, G. P.   Remarks on Professor Boole's mathematical theory of the *Laws of Thought*. *Canad. Jour.*, **10** (1865), pp. 161–82.

YOUNG, J. W.   Lectures on the fundamental concepts of algebra and geometry. New York, Macmillan, 1911.

YULE, G. U.   On the theory of the consistence of logical class-frequencies and its geometrical representation. *Phil. Trans. Roy. Soc.* (London), ser. A, **197** (1901), pp. 91–133.

——— An introduction to the theory of statistics. Ed. 2. London, Griffin, 1912.

INDEX

(References here given are in addition to, not incusive of, those readily suggested by the Table of Contents.)

Absorption, law of, 74.
Absurd, *see* Impossible.
Addition, definition of arithmetical by Peirce, 81 ff.; relative addition, 91, 95, 275 ff. *See also* Sum.
Alphabet, logical, 74.
Aristotle, 231.
Bayne, A., 36.
Bentham, G., 36.
Bernoulli, J., 18.
Bernstein, B., 119.
Boole, G., 3, 4, 31, 78–79, 118, 137, 207, 211, 212, 217; Jevons on system of, 72; system of, compared with Peirce's, 80 ff.; his general problem, 162.
Calculus, 4, 6, 8. *See also* Classes, Propositions, Propositional functions, Relations.
Cantor, G., 4, 5.
Carroll, Lewis, *see* Hodgson, S. G.
Castillon, G. F., 4, 18, 32–35.
Classes, conception of, 261; application of Boole-Schröder Algebra to, 121–22.
Coefficients, in Boole's system, 59–63; in the Boole-Schröder Algebra, 137 ff.
Consistency, relation of, in Mrs. Ladd-Franklin's system, 109.
Contained in (the relation ⊂), 13, 16, 47, 65, 118–19, 262, 270; Peirce on the meaning of, 83–84, 96.
Contradictory propositions, 189; as treated by De Morgan, 40, Jevons, 76–77.
Contrary propositions, 189; as treated by Jevons, 76–77.
Converse, propositions, 191; Converse relations, 46, 74, 91, 273-74.
Dalgarno, G., 5.
Dedekind, R., 4, 5, 114.
del Ré, A., 119.
DeMorgan, A., 4, 5, 79, 209; DeMorgan's Theorem, 125, 237, 283.
Descriptions, 290.
Distribution of terms, 43.
Division, in Lambert's system, 21 ff.; in Holland's, 30 ff.; in Boole's, 61 ff.; in Peirce's, 81 ff.
Duality, law of, in terminology of Boole, 58, in Boole-Schröder Algebra, 126.

Either......or, meaning of, 213.
Elective symbols, 52.
Elimination, in Boole's system, 59–60, 64; in Jevons's, 75–76; in the Boole-Schröder Algebra, 153 ff., 194.
ε-relation, 16, 261-62, 270.
Equivalence, in the Boole-Schröder Algebra, 120; of classes, 262; of relations, 270.
Euler's diagrams, 176.
Existence, 12, 14, 186–88.
Exponents, in the logic of relatives, 87 ff.
Extension, Chap. I, Sects. II and III, *passim;* in Leibniz's system, 13–14; Boole's logic based on, 52; classes in, 184–86; relations in, 219; propositions in, 230–31. *See also* Intension.
Formal implication, *see* Implication.
Formulaire de Mathématiques, vii, 5, 7, 115–16, 278, 280–81.
Fractions, *see* Division.
Frege, G., 4, 5, 50, 114–15, 273.
Functions, as developed by Boole, 58, 82; in the Boole-Schröder Algebra, 125, 133 ff. *See also* Propositional Functions.
Geometry, 10.
Grassmann, H., 4.
Grassmann, R., 107–08.
Hamilton, Sir W., 4, 36–37.
Hamilton, W. R., 4.
Hilbert, D., 5.
Hodgson, S. G., his diagrams, 180 ff.
Holland, G. J. von, 18, 29–32.
Huntington, E. V., 119.
Ideographic language, 2, 6–8.
Implication, no symbol for, in Boole's system, 65; material, 84–85, 214–15, 231; formal, 243; four types of, 259. *See also* Contained in.
Impossible, 32. *See also* Consistency.
Inclusion, *see* Contained in.
Inconsistent triad, 195-97.
Indeterminate, *see* Undetermined.
Index law, 54.
Individual, *see* ε-relation.
Induction, *see* Mathematical induction.
Inference, 57–58, Chap. III, Sects. II and III, *passim;* immediate, 14, 33, 39, 41, 77, 190 ff.

Intension, 8, 13 ff., Chap I, Sects. II and III, *passim*, 73.
Jevons, W. S., 4, 118, 149, 205
Kempe, A. B., 198.
Kircher, A., 5.
Ladd-Franklin, Mrs. C., 78, 108–10; 118, 195, 205, 211, 231.
Lambert, J. H., 4, 18–29, 32, 204.
Leibniz, G. W., 3, 4, 79.
Logical product, *see* Product.
Logical sum, *see* Sum.
Logistic, viii, 5–7, 11.
Lully, R., 5.
MacColl, H., 4, 108, 119.
Mathematical induction, 29, 131, 236.
Multiplication, arithmetical, defined by Peirce, 101–02; relative multiplication, 86ff., 275 ff. See also Product.
Necessary, 17.
Negative, in the Boole-Schröder Algebra, 119, 124; terms, 38, 53, 73; classes, 121, 185, 263; relations, 46, 220, 271; propositions, 14–15, 25–26, 30–31, 32–33, 40, 57, 108, 188–89, 213.
Null-class, 185–90. *See also* 0.
Null-proposition, *see* 0.
Null-relation, *see* 0.
Number, 80, 101.
1, *see* Universe of discourse; *see also* under 0.
Order, logical, 3.
Peano, G., 50, 115. *See also Formulaire de Mathématiques.*
Peirce, C. S., 4, 261, 279.
Plato, 4.
Ploucquet, C., 4, 18.
Π and Σ operators, 79, 97 ff., 140, 234.
Pieri, M., 5.
Poretsky, P., 114, 145–46, 163–66, 200.
Possible, 15. *See aso* Impossible.
Primitive concepts, in Leibniz, 7.
Primitive ideas and propositions, of *Principia Mathematica*, 282, 287–88.
Principia Mathematica, vii, 5, 7, 8, 102, 116, 222, 261, 277, 279, 281.
Probability, Boole's treatment of, 67 ff.; Peirce's treatment of, 105–06.
Product, in Leibniz's system, 12 ff.; in Lambert's, 19; in Boole's, 52; in Peirce's, 81; in the Boole-Schröder Algebra, 119; of classes, 120, 185, 262; of regions in space, 175; of relations, 86 ff., 219, 271, 275; of two functions, 143. *See also* Multiplication and Π and Σ operators.
Propositional functions, 94, 113; meaning of, 232-33; range of significance of, 233, 242, 254; in *Principia Mathematica*, 287.
Quantification of the predicate, 19, 24, 36, 38, ff., 56. *See also* Undetermined coefficient.

Quaternions, 4; Peirce's logical, 103 ff.
Reductio ad absurdum, 166–67.
Regions in a pane, application of the Boole-Schröder Algebra to, 120–21, 175.
Relations, as treated by Lambert, 28–29, by DeMorgan, 37, 45 ff., by Peirce, 85 ff., 102–05, by Schröder, 111 ff.; Peirce's paper on logic of, 100; meaning of, in extension, 219, 269; calculus of, compared with calculus of classes, 271; converse, 91, 273–74, 276; powers of, 29, 277; domain, converse domain, and field of, 277–78.
Relative terms, 277–78; in DeMorgan's system, 45 ff.; Peirce's treatment of, 85ff.; Schröder's treatment of, 111 ff. *See also* Relations.
Royce, J., viii, 195.
Schröder, E., vii, 4, 5, 78, 110 ff., 211, 246, 261, 279.
Science, exact, 7.
Segner, J. A., 18.
Self-contradictory, *see* Impossible.
Sheffer, H. M., 119.
Σ operator, *see* Π and Σ operators.
Solly, 7, 29, 36.
Solutions, in Boole's system, 60–63; in Jevons's, 76–77; in Peirce's, 98–100; by means of diagrams, 77, 181 ff.; of some logical problems, 201–12, 215–19. *See also Equations* and *Inequations* in Table of Contents.
Square of opposition, 190.
Subcontrary propositions, 190.
Substitution of similars, in Jevons, 75.
Subtraction, arithmetical, treated by Peirce, 80–81; in Leibniz's system, 17–18; in Lambert's, 19; in Castillon's, 32; in Boole's, 53; in Peirce's, 81 ff.
Sum, in Leibniz's system, 16 ff.; in Lambert's, 19; in Castillon's, 32 ff.; in Boole's, 52–53; in Jevons's, 73; in Pierce's, 81–82; in Schröder's, 111; in the Boole-Schröder Algebra, 119; of classes, 121, 185, 263; of propositions, 213; of relations, 271; of two functions, 143; of propositional functions, 94; strict logical, 291. *See also* Addition.
Syllogisms, in Lambert's system, 26 ff.; in Holland's, 31–32; in Castillon's, 34; in DeMorgan's, 41, 49 ff.; in Boole's, 57–58; in Jevons's, 75; in Mrs. Ladd-Franklin's, 109–10, 195–97; Pierce's principle of, 85; application of the Boole-Schröder Algebra to, 181–82, 193–95; in *Barbara*, 245; conditional, 197; limitation of, 1, 198–201.
Thomson, W., 36.

Tönnies, I. H., 18.
Truth value of propositions, 227, 230.
Two-valued Algebra, defects of, as a calculus of propositions, 281.
Undetermined class, in Holland's system, 30; in Castillon's, 32. *See also* Undetermined coefficient.
Undetermined coefficient, in Leibniz's system, 15; in Lambert's, 24 ff.; in Boole's, 50–51; in Jevons's, 75; in Peirce's, 82; in the Boole-Schröder Algebra, 186.
Universe of discourse, 37; diagrams of, 177 ff. *See also* refs. under 0.
Variables, 3, 232 ff.; Peirce on, 93; in *Principia Mathematica*, 289.

Venn, J., vii, 18, 201, 203, 211; diagrams, 77, 176 ff.
Whitehead, A. N., vii, 118. *See also Principia Mathematica.*
Wilkins, J., 5.
0: in Boole's system, 52 ff.; in Jevons's, 73–74; in Peirce's, 82; in Schröder's, 111; in the Boole-Schröder Algebra, 119; in the Calculus of classes, 121, 185 ff., 263; in the system of regions in a plane, 181; in the calculus of propositions, 213–14, 223 ff.; in the calculus of relations, 218–19, 271; Boole's algebra is an algebra of 0 and 1, 52.

SOME DOVER SCIENCE BOOKS

SOME DOVER SCIENCE BOOKS

WHAT IS SCIENCE?,
Norman Campbell
This excellent introduction explains scientific method, role of mathematics, types of scientific laws. Contents: 2 aspects of science, science & nature, laws of science, discovery of laws, explanation of laws, measurement & numerical laws, applications of science. 192pp. 5⅜ x 8.   Paperbound $1.25

FADS AND FALLACIES IN THE NAME OF SCIENCE,
Martin Gardner
Examines various cults, quack systems, frauds, delusions which at various times have masqueraded as science. Accounts of hollow-earth fanatics like Symmes; Velikovsky and wandering planets; Hoerbiger; Bellamy and the theory of multiple moons; Charles Fort; dowsing, pseudoscientific methods for finding water, ores, oil. Sections on naturopathy, iridiagnosis, zone therapy, food fads, etc. Analytical accounts of Wilhelm Reich and orgone sex energy; L. Ron Hubbard and Dianetics; A. Korzybski and General Semantics; many others. Brought up to date to include Bridey Murphy, others. Not just a collection of anecdotes, but a fair, reasoned appraisal of eccentric theory. Formerly titled *In the Name of Science.* Preface. Index. x + 384pp. 5⅜ x 8.
Paperbound $1.85

PHYSICS, THE PIONEER SCIENCE,
L. W. Taylor
First thorough text to place all important physical phenomena in cultural-historical framework; remains best work of its kind. Exposition of physical laws, theories developed chronologically, with great historical, illustrative experiments diagrammed, described, worked out mathematically. Excellent physics text for self-study as well as class work. Vol. 1: Heat, Sound: motion, acceleration, gravitation, conservation of energy, heat engines, rotation, heat, mechanical energy, etc. 211 illus. 407pp. 5⅜ x 8. Vol. 2: Light, Electricity: images, lenses, prisms, magnetism, Ohm's law, dynamos, telegraph, quantum theory, decline of mechanical view of nature, etc. Bibliography. 13 table appendix. Index. 551 illus. 2 color plates. 508pp. 5⅜ x 8.
Vol. 1 Paperbound $2.25, Vol. 2 Paperbound $2.25,
The set $4.50

THE EVOLUTION OF SCIENTIFIC THOUGHT FROM NEWTON TO EINSTEIN,
A. d'Abro
Einstein's special and general theories of relativity, with their historical implications, are analyzed in non-technical terms. Excellent accounts of the contributions of Newton, Riemann, Weyl, Planck, Eddington, Maxwell, Lorentz and others are treated in terms of space and time, equations of electromagnetics, finiteness of the universe, methodology of science. 21 diagrams. 482pp. 5⅜ x 8.
Paperbound $2.50

CHANCE, LUCK AND STATISTICS: THE SCIENCE OF CHANCE,
Horace C. Levinson
Theory of probability and science of statistics in simple, non-technical language. Part I deals with theory of probability, covering odd superstitions in regard to "luck," the meaning of betting odds, the law of mathematical expectation, gambling, and applications in poker, roulette, lotteries, dice, bridge, and other games of chance. Part II discusses the misuse of statistics, the concept of statistical probabilities, normal and skew frequency distributions, and statistics applied to various fields—birth rates, stock speculation, insurance rates, advertising, etc. "Presented in an easy humorous style which I consider the best kind of expository writing," Prof. A. C. Cohen, Industry Quality Control. Enlarged revised edition. Formerly titled *The Science of Chance*. Preface and two new appendices by the author. Index. xiv + 365pp. 5⅜ x 8.　Paperbound $2.00

BASIC ELECTRONICS,
prepared by the U.S. Navy Training Publications Center
A thorough and comprehensive manual on the fundamentals of electronics. Written clearly, it is equally useful for self-study or course work for those with a knowledge of the principles of basic electricity. Partial contents: Operating Principles of the Electron Tube; Introduction to Transistors; Power Supplies for Electronic Equipment; Tuned Circuits; Electron-Tube Amplifiers; Audio Power Amplifiers; Oscillators; Transmitters; Transmission Lines; Antennas and Propagation; Introduction to Computers; and related topics. Appendix. Index. Hundreds of illustrations and diagrams. vi + 471pp. 6½ x 9¼.
Paperbound $2.75

BASIC THEORY AND APPLICATION OF TRANSISTORS,
prepared by the U.S. Department of the Army
An introductory manual prepared for an army training program. One of the finest available surveys of theory and application of transistor design and operation. Minimal knowledge of physics and theory of electron tubes required. Suitable for textbook use, course supplement, or home study. Chapters: Introduction; fundamental theory of transistors; transistor amplifier fundamentals; parameters, equivalent circuits, and characteristic curves; bias stabilization; transistor analysis and comparison using characteristic curves and charts; audio amplifiers; tuned amplifiers; wide-band amplifiers; oscillators; pulse and switching circuits; modulation, mixing, and demodulation; and additional semiconductor devices. Unabridged, corrected edition. 240 schematic drawings, photographs, wiring diagrams, etc. 2 Appendices. Glossary. Index. 263pp. 6½ x 9¼.　Paperbound $1.25

GUIDE TO THE LITERATURE OF MATHEMATICS AND PHYSICS,
N. G. Parke III
Over 5000 entries included under approximately 120 major subject headings of selected most important books, monographs, periodicals, articles in English, plus important works in German, French, Italian, Spanish, Russian (many recently available works). Covers every branch of physics, math, related engineering. Includes author, title, edition, publisher, place, date, number of volumes, number of pages. A 40-page introduction on the basic problems of research and study provides useful information on the organization and use of libraries, the psychology of learning, etc. This reference work will save you hours of time. 2nd revised edition. Indices of authors, subjects, 464pp. 5⅜ x 8.
Paperbound $2.75

THE RISE OF THE NEW PHYSICS (formerly THE DECLINE OF MECHANISM), *A. d'Abro*
This authoritative and comprehensive 2-volume exposition is unique in scientific publishing. Written for intelligent readers not familiar with higher mathematics, it is the only thorough explanation in non-technical language of modern mathematical-physical theory. Combining both history and exposition, it ranges from classical Newtonian concepts up through the electronic theories of Dirac and Heisenberg, the statistical mechanics of Fermi, and Einstein's relativity theories. "A must for anyone doing serious study in the physical sciences," *J. of Franklin Inst.* 97 illustrations. 991pp. 2 volumes.

Vol. 1 Paperbound $2.25, Vol. 2 Paperbound $2.25,
The set $4.50

THE STRANGE STORY OF THE QUANTUM, AN ACCOUNT FOR THE GENERAL READER OF THE GROWTH OF IDEAS UNDERLYING OUR PRESENT ATOMIC KNOWLEDGE, *B. Hoffmann*
Presents lucidly and expertly, with barest amount of mathematics, the problems and theories which led to modern quantum physics. Dr. Hoffmann begins with the closing years of the 19th century, when certain trifling discrepancies were noticed, and with illuminating analogies and examples takes you through the brilliant concepts of Planck, Einstein, Pauli, de Broglie, Bohr, Schroedinger, Heisenberg, Dirac, Sommerfeld, Feynman, etc. This edition includes a new, long postscript carrying the story through 1958. "Of the books attempting an account of the history and contents of our modern atomic physics which have come to my attention, this is the best," H. Margenau, Yale University, in *American Journal of Physics.* 32 tables and line illustrations. Index. 275pp. 5⅜ x 8.

Paperbound $1.75

GREAT IDEAS AND THEORIES OF MODERN COSMOLOGY, *Jagjit Singh*
The theories of Jeans, Eddington, Milne, Kant, Bondi, Gold, Newton, Einstein, Gamow, Hoyle, Dirac, Kuiper, Hubble, Weizsäcker and many others on such cosmological questions as the origin of the universe, space and time, planet formation, "continuous creation," the birth, life, and death of the stars, the origin of the galaxies, etc. By the author of the popular *Great Ideas of Modern Mathematics.* A gifted popularizer of science, he makes the most difficult abstractions crystal-clear even to the most non-mathematical reader. Index. xii + 276pp. 5⅜ x 8½.

Paperbound $2.00

GREAT IDEAS OF MODERN MATHEMATICS: THEIR NATURE AND USE, *Jagjit Singh*
Reader with only high school math will understand main mathematical ideas of modern physics, astronomy, genetics, psychology, evolution, etc., better than many who use them as tools, but comprehend little of their basic structure. Author uses his wide knowledge of non-mathematical fields in brilliant exposition of differential equations, matrices, group theory, logic, statistics, problems of mathematical foundations, imaginary numbers, vectors, etc. Original publications, 2 appendices. 2 indexes. 65 illustr. 322pp. 5⅜ x 8.   Paperbound $2.00

THE MATHEMATICS OF GREAT AMATEURS, *Julian L. Coolidge*
Great discoveries made by poets, theologians, philosophers, artists and other non-mathematicians: Omar Khayyam, Leonardo da Vinci, Albrecht Dürer, John Napier, Pascal, Diderot, Bolzano, etc. Surprising accounts of what can result from a non-professional preoccupation with the oldest of sciences. 56 figures. viii + 211pp. 5⅜ x 8½.   Paperbound $1.50

COLLEGE ALGEBRA, *H. B. Fine*

Standard college text that gives a systematic and deductive structure to algebra; comprehensive, connected, with emphasis on theory. Discusses the commutative, associative, and distributive laws of number in unusual detail, and goes on with undetermined coefficients, quadratic equations, progressions, logarithms, permutations, probability, power series, and much more. Still most valuable elementary-intermediate text on the science and structure of algebra. Index. 1560 problems, all with answers. x + 631pp. 5⅜ x 8. Paperbound $2.75

HIGHER MATHEMATICS FOR STUDENTS OF CHEMISTRY AND PHYSICS, *J. W. Mellor*

Not abstract, but practical, building its problems out of familiar laboratory material, this covers differential calculus, coordinate, analytical geometry, functions, integral calculus, infinite series, numerical equations, differential equations, Fourier's theorem, probability, theory of errors, calculus of variations, determinants. "If the reader is not familiar with this book, it will repay him to examine it," *Chem. & Engineering News.* 800 problems. 189 figures. Bibliography. xxi + 641pp. 5⅜ x 8. Paperbound $2.50

TRIGONOMETRY REFRESHER FOR TECHNICAL MEN, *A. A. Klaf*

A modern question and answer text on plane and spherical trigonometry. Part I covers plane trigonometry: angles, quadrants, trigonometrical functions, graphical representation, interpolation, equations, logarithms, solution of triangles, slide rules, etc. Part II discusses applications to navigation, surveying, elasticity, architecture, and engineering. Small angles, periodic functions, vectors, polar coordinates, De Moivre's theorem, fully covered. Part III is devoted to spherical trigonometry and the solution of spherical triangles, with applications to terrestrial and astronomical problems. Special time-savers for numerical calculation. 913 questions answered for you! 1738 problems; answers to odd numbers. 494 figures. 14 pages of functions, formulae. Index. x + 629pp. 5⅜ x 8. Paperbound $2.00

CALCULUS REFRESHER FOR TECHNICAL MEN, *A. A. Klaf*

Not an ordinary textbook but a unique refresher for engineers, technicians, and students. An examination of the most important aspects of differential and integral calculus by means of 756 key questions. Part I covers simple differential calculus: constants, variables, functions, increments, derivatives, logarithms, curvature, etc. Part II treats fundamental concepts of integration: inspection, substitution, transformation, reduction, areas and volumes, mean value, successive and partial integration, double and triple integration. Stresses practical aspects! A 50 page section gives applications to civil and nautical engineering, electricity, stress and strain, elasticity, industrial engineering, and similar fields. 756 questions answered. 556 problems; solutions to odd numbers. 36 pages of constants, formulae. Index. v + 431pp. 5⅜ x 8. Paperbound $2.00

INTRODUCTION TO THE THEORY OF GROUPS OF FINITE ORDER, *R. Carmichael*

Examines fundamental theorems and their application. Beginning with sets, systems, permutations, etc., it progresses in easy stages through important types of groups: Abelian, prime power, permutation, etc. Except 1 chapter where matrices are desirable, no higher math needed. 783 exercises, problems. Index. xvi + 447pp. 5⅜ x 8. Paperbound $3.00

FIVE VOLUME "THEORY OF FUNCTIONS" SET BY KONRAD KNOPP

This five-volume set, prepared by Konrad Knopp, provides a complete and readily followed account of theory of functions. Proofs are given concisely, yet without sacrifice of completeness or rigor. These volumes are used as texts by such universities as M.I.T., University of Chicago, N. Y. City College, and many others. "Excellent introduction . . . remarkably readable, concise, clear, rigorous," *Journal of the American Statistical Association*.

ELEMENTS OF THE THEORY OF FUNCTIONS,
Konrad Knopp
This book provides the student with background for further volumes in this set, or texts on a similar level. Partial contents: foundations, system of complex numbers and the Gaussian plane of numbers, Riemann sphere of numbers, mapping by linear functions, normal forms, the logarithm, the cyclometric functions and binomial series. "Not only for the young student, but also for the student who knows all about what is in it," *Mathematical Journal*. Bibliography. Index. 140pp. 5⅜ x 8.   Paperbound $1.50

THEORY OF FUNCTIONS, PART I,
Konrad Knopp
With volume II, this book provides coverage of basic concepts and theorems. Partial contents: numbers and points, functions of a complex variable, integral of a continuous function, Cauchy's integral theorem, Cauchy's integral formulae, series with variable terms, expansion of analytic functions in power series, analytic continuation and complete definition of analytic functions, entire transcendental functions, Laurent expansion, types of singularities. Bibliography. Index. vii + 146pp. 5⅜ x 8.   Paperbound $1.35

THEORY OF FUNCTIONS, PART II,
Konrad Knopp
Application and further development of general theory, special topics. Single valued functions. Entire, Weierstrass, Meromorphic functions. Riemann surfaces. Algebraic functions. Analytical configuration, Riemann surface. Bibliography. Index. x + 150pp. 5⅜ x 8.   Paperbound $1.35

PROBLEM BOOK IN THE THEORY OF FUNCTIONS, VOLUME 1.
Konrad Knopp
Problems in elementary theory, for use with Knopp's *Theory of Functions*, or any other text, arranged according to increasing difficulty. Fundamental concepts, sequences of numbers and infinite series, complex variable, integral theorems, development in series, conformal mapping. 182 problems. Answers. viii + 126pp. 5⅜ x 8.   Paperbound $1.35

PROBLEM BOOK IN THE THEORY OF FUNCTIONS, VOLUME 2,
Konrad Knopp
Advanced theory of functions, to be used either with Knopp's *Theory of Functions*, or any other comparable text. Singularities, entire & meromorphic functions, periodic, analytic, continuation, multiple-valued functions, Riemann surfaces, conformal mapping. Includes a section of additional elementary problems. "The difficult task of selecting from the immense material of the modern theory of functions the problems just within the reach of the beginner is here masterfully accomplished," *Am. Math. Soc.* Answers. 138pp. 5⅜ x 8.
Paperbound $1.50

NUMERICAL SOLUTIONS OF DIFFERENTIAL EQUATIONS,
H. Levy & E. A. Baggott
Comprehensive collection of methods for solving ordinary differential equations of first and higher order. All must pass 2 requirements: easy to grasp and practical, more rapid than school methods. Partial contents: graphical integration of differential equations, graphical methods for detailed solution. Numerical solution. Simultaneous equations and equations of 2nd and higher orders. "Should be in the hands of all in research in applied mathematics, teaching," *Nature.* 21 figures. viii + 238pp. 5⅜ x 8. Paperbound $1.85

ELEMENTARY STATISTICS, WITH APPLICATIONS IN MEDICINE AND THE BIOLOGICAL SCIENCES, *F. E. Croxton*
A sound introduction to statistics for anyone in the physical sciences, assuming no prior acquaintance and requiring only a modest knowledge of math. All basic formulas carefully explained and illustrated; all necessary reference tables included. From basic terms and concepts, the study proceeds to frequency distribution, linear, non-linear, and multiple correlation, skewness, kurtosis, etc. A large section deals with reliability and significance of statistical methods. Containing concrete examples from medicine and biology, this book will prove unusually helpful to workers in those fields who increasingly must evaluate, check, and interpret statistics. Formerly titled "Elementary Statistics with Applications in Medicine." 101 charts. 57 tables. 14 appendices. Index. vi + 376pp. 5⅜ x 8. Paperbound $2.00

INTRODUCTION TO SYMBOLIC LOGIC,
S. Langer
No special knowledge of math required — probably the clearest book ever written on symbolic logic, suitable for the layman, general scientist, and philosopher. You start with simple symbols and advance to a knowledge of the Boole-Schroeder and Russell-Whitehead systems. Forms, logical structure, classes, the calculus of propositions, logic of the syllogism, etc. are all covered. "One of the clearest and simplest introductions," *Mathematics Gazette.* Second enlarged, revised edition. 368pp. 5⅜ x 8. Paperbound $2.00

A SHORT ACCOUNT OF THE HISTORY OF MATHEMATICS,
W. W. R. Ball
Most readable non-technical history of mathematics treats lives, discoveries of every important figure from Egyptian, Phoenician, mathematicians to late 19th century. Discusses schools of Ionia, Pythagoras, Athens, Cyzicus, Alexandria, Byzantium, systems of numeration; primitive arithmetic; Middle Ages, Renaissance, including Arabs, Bacon, Regiomontanus, Tartaglia, Cardan, Stevinus, Galileo, Kepler; modern mathematics of Descartes, Pascal, Wallis, Huygens, Newton, Leibnitz, d'Alembert, Euler, Lambert, Laplace, Legendre, Gauss, Hermite, Weierstrass, scores more. Index. 25 figures. 546pp. 5⅜ x 8. Paperbound $2.25

INTRODUCTION TO NONLINEAR DIFFERENTIAL AND INTEGRAL EQUATIONS,
Harold T. Davis
Aspects of the problem of nonlinear equations, transformations that lead to equations solvable by classical means, results in special cases, and useful generalizations. Thorough, but easily followed by mathematically sophisticated reader who knows little about non-linear equations. 137 problems for student to solve. xv + 566pp. 5⅜ x 8½. Paperbound $2.00

An Introduction to the Geometry of N Dimensions,
D. H. Y. Sommerville
An introduction presupposing no prior knowledge of the field, the only book in English devoted exclusively to higher dimensional geometry. Discusses fundamental ideas of incidence, parallelism, perpendicularity, angles between linear space; enumerative geometry; analytical geometry from projective and metric points of view; polytopes; elementary ideas in analysis situs; content of hyper-spacial figures. Bibliography. Index. 60 diagrams. 196pp. 5⅜ x 8.
Paperbound $1.50

Elementary Concepts of Topology, P. Alexandroff
First English translation of the famous brief introduction to topology for the beginner or for the mathematician not undertaking extensive study. This unusually useful intuitive approach deals primarily with the concepts of complex, cycle, and homology, and is wholly consistent with current investigations. Ranges from basic concepts of set-theoretic topology to the concept of Betti groups. "Glowing example of harmony between intuition and thought," David Hilbert. Translated by A. E. Farley. Introduction by D. Hilbert. Index. 25 figures. 73pp. 5⅜ x 8.
Paperbound $1.00

Elements of Non-Euclidean Geometry,
D. M. Y. Sommerville
Unique in proceeding step-by-step, in the manner of traditional geometry. Enables the student with only a good knowledge of high school algebra and geometry to grasp elementary hyperbolic, elliptic, analytic non-Euclidean geometries; space curvature and its philosophical implications; theory of radical axes; homothetic centres and systems of circles; parataxy and parallelism; absolute measure; Gauss' proof of the defect area theorem; geodesic representation; much more, all with exceptional clarity. 126 problems at chapter endings provide progressive practice and familiarity. 133 figures. Index. xvi + 274pp. 5⅜ x 8.
Paperbound $2.00

Introduction to the Theory of Numbers, L. E. Dickson
Thorough, comprehensive approach with adequate coverage of classical literature, an introductory volume beginners can follow. Chapters on divisibility, congruences, quadratic residues & reciprocity. Diophantine equations, etc. Full treatment of binary quadratic forms without usual restriction to integral coefficients. Covers infinitude of primes, least residues. Fermat's theorem. Euler's phi function, Legendre's symbol, Gauss's lemma, automorphs, reduced forms, recent theorems of Thue & Siegel, many more. Much material not readily available elsewhere. 239 problems. Index. I figure. viii + 183pp. 5⅜ x 8.
Paperbound $1.75

Mathematical Tables and Formulas,
compiled by Robert D. Carmichael and Edwin R. Smith
Valuable collection for students, etc. Contains all tables necessary in college algebra and trigonometry, such as five-place common logarithms, logarithmic sines and tangents of small angles, logarithmic trigonometric functions, natural trigonometric functions, four-place antilogarithms, tables for changing from sexagesimal to circular and from circular to sexagesimal measure of angles, etc. Also many tables and formulas not ordinarily accessible, including powers, roots, and reciprocals, exponential and hyperbolic functions, ten-place logarithms of prime numbers, and formulas and theorems from analytical and elementary geometry and from calculus. Explanatory introduction. viii + 269pp. 5⅜ x 8½.
Paperbound $1.25

A SOURCE BOOK IN MATHEMATICS,
D. E. Smith
Great discoveries in math, from Renaissance to end of 19th century, in English translation. Read announcements by Dedekind, Gauss, Delamain, Pascal, Fermat, Newton, Abel, Lobachevsky, Bolyai, Riemann, De Moivre, Legendre, Laplace, others of discoveries about imaginary numbers, number congruence, slide rule, equations, symbolism, cubic algebraic equations, non-Euclidean forms of geometry, calculus, function theory, quaternions, etc. Succinct selections from 125 different treatises, articles, most unavailable elsewhere in English. Each article preceded by biographical introduction. Vol. I: Fields of Number, Algebra. Index. 32 illus. 338pp. 5⅜ x 8. Vol. II: Fields of Geometry, Probability, Calculus, Functions, Quaternions. 83 illus. 432pp. 5⅜ x 8.
Vol. 1 Paperbound $2.00, Vol. 2 Paperbound $2.00,
The set $4.00

FOUNDATIONS OF PHYSICS,
R. B. Lindsay & H. Margenau
Excellent bridge between semi-popular works & technical treatises. A discussion of methods of physical description, construction of theory; valuable for physicist with elementary calculus who is interested in ideas that give meaning to data, tools of modern physics. Contents include symbolism; mathematical equations; space & time foundations of mechanics; probability; physics & continua; electron theory; special & general relativity; quantum mechanics; causality. "Thorough and yet not overdetailed. Unreservedly recommended," *Nature* (London). Unabridged, corrected edition. List of recommended readings. 35 illustrations. xi + 537pp. 5⅜ x 8.   Paperbound $3.00

FUNDAMENTAL FORMULAS OF PHYSICS,
ed. by D. H. Menzel
High useful, full, inexpensive reference and study text, ranging from simple to highly sophisticated operations. Mathematics integrated into text—each chapter stands as short textbook of field represented. Vol. 1: Statistics, Physical Constants, Special Theory of Relativity, Hydrodynamics, Aerodynamics, Boundary Value Problems in Math, Physics, Viscosity, Electromagnetic Theory, etc. Vol. 2: Sound, Acoustics, Geometrical Optics, Electron Optics, High-Energy Phenomena, Magnetism, Biophysics, much more. Index. Total of 800pp. 5⅜ x 8.
Vol. 1 Paperbound $2.25, Vol. 2 Paperbound $2.25,
The set $4.50

THEORETICAL PHYSICS,
A. S. Kompaneyets
One of the very few thorough studies of the subject in this price range. Provides advanced students with a comprehensive theoretical background. Especially strong on recent experimentation and developments in quantum theory. Contents: Mechanics (Generalized Coordinates, Lagrange's Equation, Collision of Particles, etc.), Electrodynamics (Vector Analysis, Maxwell's equations, Transmission of Signals, Theory of Relativity, etc.), Quantum Mechanics (the Inadequacy of Classical Mechanics, the Wave Equation, Motion in a Central Field, Quantum Theory of Radiation, Quantum Theories of Dispersion and Scattering, etc.), and Statistical Physics (Equilibrium Distribution of Molecules in an Ideal Gas, Boltzmann Statistics, Bose and Fermi Distribution. Thermodynamic Quantities, etc.). Revised to 1961. Translated by George Yankovsky, authorized by Kompaneyets. 137 exercises. 56 figures. 529pp. 5⅜ x 8½.
Paperbound $2.50

MATHEMATICAL PHYSICS, *D. H. Menzel*
Thorough one-volume treatment of the mathematical techniques vital for classical mechanics, electromagnetic theory, quantum theory, and relativity. Written by the Harvard Professor of Astrophysics for junior, senior, and graduate courses, it gives clear explanations of all those aspects of function theory, vectors, matrices, dyadics, tensors, partial differential equations, etc., necessary for the understanding of the various physical theories. Electron theory, relativity, and other topics seldom presented appear here in considerable detail. Scores of definition, conversion factors, dimensional constants, etc. "More detailed than normal for an advanced text . . . excellent set of sections on Dyadics, Matrices, and Tensors," *Journal of the Franklin Institute.* Index. 193 problems, with answers. x + 412pp. 5⅜ x 8.   Paperbound $2.50

THE THEORY OF SOUND, *Lord Rayleigh*
Most vibrating systems likely to be encountered in practice can be tackled successfully by the methods set forth by the great Nobel laureate, Lord Rayleigh. Complete coverage of experimental, mathematical aspects of sound theory. Partial contents: Harmonic motions, vibrating systems in general, lateral vibrations of bars, curved plates or shells, applications of Laplace's functions to acoustical problems, fluid friction, plane vortex-sheet, vibrations of solid bodies, etc. This is the first inexpensive edition of this great reference and study work. Bibliography, Historical introduction by R. B. Lindsay. Total of 1040pp. 97 figures. 5⅜ x 8.   Vol. 1 Paperbound $2.50, Vol. 2 Paperbound $2.50,
                                                                                    The set $5.00

HYDRODYNAMICS, *Horace Lamb*
Internationally famous complete coverage of standard reference work on dynamics of liquids & gases. Fundamental theorems, equations, methods, solutions, background, for classical hydrodynamics. Chapters include Equations of Motion, Integration of Equations in Special Gases, Irrotational Motion, Motion of Liquid in 2 Dimensions, Motion of Solids through Liquid-Dynamical Theory, Vortex Motion, Tidal Waves, Surface Waves, Waves of Expansion, Viscosity, Rotating Masses of Liquids. Excellently planned, arranged; clear, lucid presentation. 6th enlarged, revised edition. Index. Over 900 footnotes, mostly bibliographical. 119 figures. xv + 738pp. 6⅛ x 9¼.   Paperbound $4.00

DYNAMICAL THEORY OF GASES, *James Jeans*
Divided into mathematical and physical chapters for the convenience of those not expert in mathematics, this volume discusses the mathematical theory of gas in a steady state, thermodynamics, Boltzmann and Maxwell, kinetic theory, quantum theory, exponentials, etc. 4th enlarged edition, with new material on quantum theory, quantum dynamics, etc. Indexes. 28 figures. 444pp. 6⅛ x 9¼.
                                                                         Paperbound $2.75

THERMODYNAMICS, *Enrico Fermi*
Unabridged reproduction of 1937 edition. Elementary in treatment; remarkable for clarity, organization. Requires no knowledge of advanced math beyond calculus, only familiarity with fundamentals of thermometry, calorimetry. Partial Contents: Thermodynamic systems; First & Second laws of thermodynamics; Entropy; Thermodynamic potentials: phase rule, reversible electric cell; Gaseous reactions: van't Hoff reaction box, principle of LeChatelier; Thermodynamics of dilute solutions: osmotic & vapor pressures, boiling & freezing points; Entropy constant. Index. 25 problems. 24 illustrations. x + 160pp. 5⅜ x 8.   Paperbound $1.75

DIFFERENTIAL EQUATIONS,
F. R. Moulton
A detailed, rigorous exposition of all the non-elementary processes of solving ordinary differential equations. Several chapters devoted to the treatment of practical problems, especially those of a physical nature, which are far more advanced than problems usually given as illustrations. Includes analytic differential equations; variations of a parameter; integrals of differential equations; analytic implicit functions; problems of elliptic motion; sine-amplitude functions; deviation of formal bodies; Cauchy-Lipschitz process; linear differential equations with periodic coefficients; differential equations in infinitely many variations; much more. Historical notes. 10 figures. 222 problems. Index. xv + 395pp. 5⅜ x 8.   Paperbound $2.00

PARTIAL DIFFERENTIAL EQUATIONS OF MATHEMATICAL PHYSICS,
A. G. Webster
A keystone work in the library of every mature physicist, engineer, researcher. Valuable sections on elasticity, compression theory, potential theory, theory of sound, heat conduction, wave propagation, vibration theory. Contents include: deduction of differential equations, vibrations, normal functions, Fourier's series, Cauchy's method, boundary problems, method of Riemann-Volterra, spherical, cylindrical, ellipsoidal harmonics, applications, etc. 97 figures. vii + 440pp. 5⅜ x 8.   Paperbound $2.25

THE CONTINUUM AND OTHER TYPES OF SERIAL ORDER,
E. V. Huntington
This famous book gives a systematic elementary account of the modern theory of the continuum as a type of serial order. Based on the Cantor-Dedekind ordinal theory, which requires no technical knowledge of higher mathematics, it offers an easily followed analysis of ordered classes, discrete and dense series, continuous series, Cantor's transfinite numbers. 2nd edition. Index. viii + 82pp. 5⅜ v 8.   Paperbound $1.00

CONTRIBUTIONS TO THE FOUNDING OF THE THEORY OF TRANSFINITE NUMBERS, *Georg Cantor*
These papers founded a new branch of mathematics. The famous articles of 1895-7 are translated, with an 82-page introduction by P. E. B. Jourdain dealing with Cantor, the background of his discoveries, their results, future possibilities. Bibliography. Index. Notes. ix + 211pp. 5⅜ x 8.   Paperbound $1.35

ADVANCED EUCLIDEAN GEOMETRY,
R. A. Johnson
For years the standard textbook on advanced Euclidean geometry, requires only high school geometry and trigonometry. Explores in unusual detail and gives proofs of hundreds of relatively recent theorems and corollaries, many formerly available only in widely scattered journals. Covers tangent circles, the theorem of Miquel, symmedian point, pedal triangles and circles, the Brocard configuration, and much more. Formerly "Modern Geometry." Index. 107 diagrams. xiii + 319pp. 5⅜ x 8.   Paperbound $1.65

Prices subject to change without notice.

Available at your book dealer or write for free catalogue to Dept. Adsci, Dover Publications, Inc., 180 Varick St., N.Y., N.Y. 10014. Dover publishes more than 150 books each year on science, elementary and advanced mathematics, biology, music, art, literary history, social sciences and other areas.